Arthurian Legends

Valarie Jones

Arthurian Legends

The Land of Arthur:
its heroes and heroines

by
Marie Trevelyan

SIENA

This edition published and distributed by Parragon, 1998

Parragon
13 Whiteladies Road
Clifton
Bristol
BS8 1PB

First published 1895 as *The Land of Arthur*

ISBN 0 75252 683 9

A copy of the British Library Cataloguing-in-Publication Data
is available from the British Library.

Printed and bound in the EC

Dedicated

TO

THE IMMORTAL MEMORY

OF

LLEWELYN AP GRUFFYDD,

LAST NATIVE PRINCE OF WALES,

WHO

HEROICALLY DEFENDED

NATIONAL HONOUR, PRIVILEGE, AND LIBERTY,

AND

FACED A CRUEL DOOM AND TRAGIC DEATH|
RATHER THAN DESERT HIS
COUNTRY'S CAUSE.

A

PREFACE

AMONG the numerous heroes of Britain King Arthur stands pre-eminent and unrivalled. As the central figure of European romance and chivalry, he appears to all the civilised world in his highest dignity. He is the ideal and fervent protector of Christendom, and the leader of a mystic fraternity whose lofty attributes are honour, fidelity, and all courtly graces.

History and tradition describe him as a warrior whose series of victories are unsurpassed in splendour, and whose forces have the reputation of being the most heroic in the world.

In song and story the achievements of Arthur and his knights are surrounded with the brilliance of the French Troubadours, the quaint diction of the "Morte d'Arthur," the glowing imagery of Spenser, and the magic power of Tennyson.

But although Arthur's deeds have stirred the

hearts of people of all nationalities for nearly twelve centuries, in his own land his influence is most potently felt.

In the folk-lore of Wales, the Silurian hero and monarch takes a most prominent position, but under curiously varied aspects.

He is gigantic while resting on his bed, called Gwely Arthur, among the Carmarthenshire Vans, or, when from the summit of Pen Arthur he throws the great quoit known as the Coiten Arthur in the river Sawdde, a mile below the black mountains of Breconshire. He is the mighty potentate upon whose empire the sun shall never set, when he goes forth to lead his forces against the "heathens" and "pagans" who endeavour to oppose the knights of Christendom, and he becomes the mysterious wanderer into the land of the Hereafter, wherefrom his countrymen through long centuries eagerly expected him to return.

He appears as a sleeping warrior and an enchanted knight with his comrades in the cave of Craig-y-Dinas, where he waits for the great day of battle between the Black Eagle and the Golden Eagle, after which Arthur will return, and war shall be no more.

He is seen in the form of a raven hovering over old haunts of his pleasure and pain, wherefore the people of Siluria and Cornwall even now refuse to kill that bird, lest in doing so they would "destroy Arthur."

In the silence of the night his symbols are seen in the heavens, sharing distinction with Caer Gwyddion, the Milky Way, and Caer Arianrod, the constellation *Corona Septentrionalis*, or the Northern Crown. Arthur in Welsh is synonymous with *Ursa Major;* the constellation *Lyra* is known to the Celts as the *Telyn*, or harp of Arthur, and the stars called by the English country-people "Charles's Wain" are known to the old folk of Wales as Arthur's Plough.

Places and objects bearing his name abound in Wales and Cornwall, and evidences of his heroic and regal qualifications exist in the Cadair Arthur, and the great amphitheatre, which is called Arthur's Round Table, at Caerlleon-upon-Usk.

Second only to Arthur is Merlin the Seer, whose name, enshrined in the history, folk-lore, traditions, and superstitions of Wales, is still as fresh and vigorous as ever.

In the north it is wedded to Dinas Emrys in Eryri, as the scene of his first prophecy; in the south it survives in the town of Carmarthen—the Caer or City of Myrddin or Merlin; in England it is inseparable from the building of *Gwaith Emrys*, or Stonehenge, while it is cherished among our Bréton relatives in connection with the dim forest of Brécéliande.

Around the names of Arthur and Merlin romance and tradition have woven their silver mists, through which the real is strongly defined beside the ideal; but there are other celebrated heroes whose names and deeds, surrounded by stern fact, have had only slight recognition.

Caractacus, whose military skill, and Carausius, whose naval prowess were the wonder and admiration of the Romans; Princess Eurgain, the pioneer of British education; Hywel Dda, the law-maker; Llewelyn the Great, who united Wales—all these and more are names sacred to the Welsh.

The struggles of Llewelyn ap Gruffydd with Edward Plantagenet, and Owain Glyndwr's revolt against Henry of Lancaster's unjust " Ordinances," vie with those of Sir William Wallace, the patriotic Scottish hero, who opposed the English monarch and suffered martyrdom for similar causes.

It is the fault of the Welsh that the English are not more familiar with the heroes of Wales.

When the Welsh entered the " valley of the shadow of death," after Owain Glyndwr's defeat, they became apparently oblivious of all but their sorrows, and from the dawn of the sixteenth to the end of the eighteenth century, splendid but in some instances ponderous histories of the Principality were written. The majority of these, though invaluable to the literary researcher, are of no service to the active reader of to-day, who desires much information in small space.

Many of the histories are in the vernacular, and therefore unintelligible to English-speaking students and interested Saxons, who find themselves destitute of a useful and entertaining work giving simple outlines of Wales and its history.

I have humbly endeavoured within the bounds of this small volume to supply the want, and if it will give those for whom it is intended as much interest as the necessary research in order to write the work has given me, I shall be satisfied.

My original intention was to divide the book into historical sections, each of which would include its own particular heroes; but, in view of attracting the general reader, I have arranged the work in correct chronological order, without attempting to encroach upon the charmed realm of the historian.

In selecting a title, the name of King Arthur, as being most popularly known, was aptly suggested. According to the ancient chronicles of Wales, the Elegy of Llywarch Hên, and the old Romances, Arthur was styled the " Emperor," and therefore takes rank as king of kings. Quaint old Malory, in his "Morte d'Arthur," says he was crowned "Emperour with creme as it bylongeth to so hyhe astate."

As in the case of my former works, " Glimpses of Welsh Life and Character," and "From Snowdon to the Sea," my publisher, Mr. John Hogg, suggested for this book a national cover design, which, through the courtesy of Mr. Everard Green, has been prepared from one of the most valuable volumes in the Heralds' College, and is certified as follows :—

"I hereby certify that the Banner of King Arthur has been copied from the book entitled ' Prince Arthur,' in the archives of the Heralds' College, London, and has been examined therewith by me, this 17th day of July, A.D. 1895.

"(Signed)   EVERARD GREEN,
"*Rouge Dragon.*"

On this occasion I have dedicated my book as a souvenir to the memory of one of the greatest heroes Wales ever produced—"Llewelyn Ein Llyw Olaf!" "Llewelyn our Last Helm!"

MARIE TREVELYAN.

1895.

LIST OF AUTHORITIES CONSULTED

In writing this book the following Authorities have been consulted :—

"The Myvyrian Archæology."
Jones's "History of Breconshire."
"*Giraldus Cambrensis*."
Mr. G. T. Clark's "Land of Morgan."
"The *Liber Landavensis*."
"*Archæologia Cambrensis*."
Davies' "Celtic Researches."
"*The Cambro-Britain*," 1818 to 1829.
Davies' "Mythology of the Druids."
Warrington's "History of Wales."
Ancient Welsh Chronicles.
Bohn's "Six Chronicles."
Probert's "Ancient Welsh Laws."
Williams's "Cymry."
The late Lady Charlotte Guest's (Schreiber) "Mabinogion."
"*Origines Sacræ*."
"Tracts on the British Church."
Tacitus.
The Iolo MSS.
Rees's "Essay on the Welsh Saints."
Fenton's "History of Pembrokeshire."
Malory's "*Morte d'Arthur*."
Stephen's "Literature of the Cymry."
Geoffrey of Monmouth.
Turner's "Anglo-Saxons."
"*The Brut*."
Caradoc of Llancarvan.
Pennant's "Tour in Wales."
Leland's "Itinerary" and "Latin Collectina."
Thierry's "History of the Norman Conquest."
Ordericus Vitalis, the Saxon monk and historian.
Sixteenth century pamphlets.
Matthew of Paris.
Hakluyt's "Voyages."
Sir Thomas Herbert's "Travels."

Powell's "Historie of Cambria."
Rymer's "*Foedera*."
Roger of Wendover.
Matthew of Westminster.
Ariosto's "*Orlando Furioso*."
"*Annales Cambriæ*."
Stukeley on Stonehenge.
The Mostyn MSS.
The Old Welsh "Greal," 1805.
Florence of Worcester.
Cotton's "*Historia Anglicana*."
Piers Langtoft's "Rhyming Chronicles."
"*Annales Menevenses.*"
Harleian Collection of MSS.
The late Professor Skene's "Ancient Books of Wales."
Halle the historian.
"The Archæology of Wales."
Fuller's "Worthies."
"*The Cambrian Register*."
Churchyard's "Worthiness of Wales."
Hollinshed's Chronicles.
"*Cambria Depicta*."
Ellis's "Original Letters, 1404."
The "*Vita Sancti Iltuti*."
William of Malmesbury.
The "*Vita Sancti Cadoci*."
Henry of Huntingdon.
The Hengwret MSS.
Sir George Peckham's Pamphlet on the Discoveries in Newfoundland of Sir Humphrey Gilbert.
Southey's "Madoc."
A "History of Wales," with an Appendix in English and Latin The volume consists of 398 pages, and appears to have been written early in the reign of King Charles the First, and the author refers to the "learned Dr. Heylyn." It lacks both original cover and title-page, and I have so far failed to identify the book.

It may here be mentioned that I gratefully acknowledge the kindness of Illtyd Bond Nicholl, Esq., F.S.A.; J.P., and Mrs. G. W. Nicholl, of The Ham, Glamorganshire, for having placed the valuable collection of books in their library unreservedly at my service. I am also indebted to Owain Morgan, Esq., B.B.D. (Morien), the enthusiastic Welsh journalist and *litterateur*, for much information relating to ancient British history.

CONTENTS

Contents

Arthurian Legends

CHAPTER I

THE ISLAND OF GREEN HILLS

SILVER-GREEN icebergs gliding slowly through the desolate seas had long passed southward, and terrible throes of a great geological convulsion completed the separation of the continent of Europe from Great Britain, leaving a beautiful "Island of green hills," populated only by bears and bisons, strangely uncouth water-beasts, and other gruesome monsters, of which many legends survive.

In those dateless days, through scenes that can only be portrayed by magic touches of a vivid imagination, a long nomadic procession toiled steadily onward from the golden glory of the "Summer Country" to the cold and lonely regions of the north. Across the weird and wild Sarmatian steppes; among the dark and dense forests, the gloomy ravines, and noisome marshes of Germany, then along the dreary stretches of the Baltic shores, these primitive people wan-

dered until they reached the " Hazy Sea " that
formed a barrier between them and the " Honey
Island." Some of these wanderers settled in
Bretagne, but others followed their great chieftain, Hu Gadarn, or Hugh the Mighty, who
with vocal song led his nomads into the unex-
plored country which to-day is one of the most
important nations in the world.

Hu Gadarn stands forth in Welsh history as
the first and foremost of its early heroes. In the
Triads and legends of Wales he is described as
the leader of nomad hordes, the hero of many
adventures, the guardian of a nation's infancy,
the law-giver of stern-souled people ; and when,
rich with mundane honours, his followers laid
him to rest in his primitive barrow, he was
translated to the dignity of a Celtic deity. As
a leader, he is described as " having originally
conducted the nation of the Cymry into the Isle
of Britain." In his capacity of law-giver " Hu
the Mighty first formed mote and retinue for the
nation of the Cymry." He promoted the interests of his nomadic tribes, and introduced law
and order among them. Again, it is said that he
" first applied vocal song to the preserving of
memory and record," and Taliesin, writing in the
sixth century, describes him as the " dispenser
of good, the proprietor and rightful claimant of
Britain." As a patron of the arts of peace, he
appears as the promoter of agriculture, who

"first showed the method of ploughing land to the nation of the Cymry, when they were in the country of the summer, before their coming into the Isle of Britain."

In the Triads, Hu is described as one of the "Three Pillars of the race of the Island of Britain;" as leader of one of the "Three Benevolent Tribes . . . for he would not have lands by fighting and contention, but of equity and in peace." He is recognised as one of the "Three Great Regulators" of Britain; one of the "Three Benefactors of the race of the Cymry;" one of the "Primary Sages" of his adopted land; and second only to Gwyddon Ganhebon, as one of the "Three Elementary Masters of Poetry," and Hu is recognised as the "first who adopted poetry to the preservation of record and memorials."

Later on, the deified Hu, with the Sacred Ox as his symbol, appears accompanied by his goddess Ceridwen, whose symbols were a cow and a boat. Hu represented the Sun, and Ceridwen the Moon, and the orbs respectively of day and night were surrounded by satellites and subordinate deities, known as the three Bull Demons of Britain. These were the Ellyl Gwidawl, or demon of the whirlpool; the Ellyl Llyr Merini, or demon of the sea; and the Ellyl Gurthmwl Wledig, or demon of the earth.

In his most awe-inspiring dignity, Hu stands

as the central figure in the great historical scenes
of the Triads, beginning with the Deluge, and
merging into the religious festivals connected
with Bardism. The sanctuary of Hu the Mighty
was supposed to be in Ynys Enlli, the Island in
the Current, to which the Saxons subsequently
gave the name of Bardsey. In that sacred
island the shrined Ked, or Ark, rested, and within
the precincts of the Druidical temple there, fes-
tive rites in honour of the deified nomad were
held with solemn and splendid ceremony.

Aneurin, the Celtic poet, thus describes these
rites :—" In the festival on the Eve of May, they
celebrate the praise of the Holy Ones, in the
presence of the purifying fire which was made to
ascend on high. On Tuesday they wear their
dark garments. On Wednesday they purified
their fair attire. On Thursday they duly performed their due rites. On Friday the victims
were conducted around the circle. On Saturday
their united exertions were displayed without
the circular dome. On Sunday the men with
red blades were conducted round the circle ; and
on Monday the banquet was served."

Hu Gadarn's name is recorded in connection
with the "Three chief master-works of the Island
of Britain," which included the " drawing of the
Avanc to land out of the lake, by the branching
oxen . . . so that the lake burst no more."

Ancient Welsh mythology attributes the final

cause of the Deluge to the Black Beaver, who, having broken the dyke that supported the Great Lake, sank into the depths of the abyss, and, in order to prevent further damages from the same source, Hugh the Mighty, with the assistance of his own oxen, called the Ychain Banawg, extricated the Avanc, or beaver, which represented the ark of the diluvian patriarch.

The result of their effort was that one of the celebrated oxen died as soon as the task was completed; and the other, grieving for its companion, wandered to Llan Dewi Brevi, in Cardiganshire, where, dismally moaning, it died of a broken heart. In former times, a huge branching horn, said to be one of those of Hu's oxen, used to be exhibited in that quiet Cardigan village.

Before the primitive Druids of Britain shed their life's blood for their homes and altars, their faith and freedom, the symbolical rites of Bardism included a religious, dramatic, and realistic spectacle, which represented the Avanc being drawn from the lake.

It was a gorgeous and imposing ceremony.

On May morning vast crowds assembled near the shores of any of the lakes of Wales where it was usual for these representations to be given; while two sacred oxen, with large and "branching horns," drew the shrine from a small island through shallow waters to dry land.

Then the grand scene was enacted.

Through the mists of the May morning, the sacred oxen, with dilated eyes and nostrils, snorted under their burden, and, with heavy plunges, ascended to the shore of the lake, where crowds waited their coming. Like wraiths beside the dark shadows of the purple mountains and the silvery strand of the lake, white-robed choristers congregated and chanted the Cainc-y-Ychain Banawg, a song descriptive of the chained oxen and the rattling of their fetters.

After a brief pause the procession was formed.

At the head of it appeared the Chief Bard, bearing his magic wand of divination. He was followed by one hundred and fifty bards, each playing a harp. Then came the shrine of Ceridwen, the sacred boat or ark, borne aloft by the priests, and preceded by three important dignitaries. The first of these was the hierophant, representing the Creator ; the torch-bearer, representing the Sun, and the herald, who, as the special envoy of the goddess, symbolised the Moon.

A strange and motley crowd brought up the rear of that curious procession.

Wild dancers, whose heads were wreathed with ivy or covered with "cornute caps," made weird circles as they went along, and singers, singing in mystical cadences, announced the Avanc or Ark. Rude musicians, blowing on crooked horns or clashing double pateras, and war-men, beating their swords against their shields, wended their way to the sacred temple, and took up the proper positions therein.

The great earth rampart that surrounded the temple was crowded with petty princes and the chief members of various tribes and families, with their standard-bearers and shield-holders, and below them the general public congregated in numberless groups to watch the winding course of the religious procession from the lake to the druidical grove.

One of the followers of Hu was Aedd Mawr, whose son Prydain established monarchy in Britain, which was called in honour of its first king, Ynys Prydain. In the Triads, Prydain is described as one of the " Three Pillars of the race of the Island of Britain," and he "first established regal government" in this country. In another Triad his name appears as one of the "Three Regulators" of the law, and one of the "Three Happy Controllers . . . suppressing the dragon tyranny. This was a tyranny of pillage and contempt of equity that sprang up in the Island." In the Iolo MSS. he is mentioned as being a "potent, wise, and merciful king, and sole monarch of the Island. He introduced many sciences and much knowledge to the Cimbric nation; and lived eighty-seven years after he was made king."

In some of the chronicles, Dyvnwal Moelmud, the celebrated law-maker, is described as being the son of Prydain, but in the Welsh "Chronicles of the Kings" it is recorded that he was the son of Cludno Earl of Cornwall. He lived in the year 441 B.C., and was a "wise, powerful, and praiseworthy king, who made a survey of the island, its mountains, its rivers, its forests, and its chief harbours. He also erected on the banks of the Severn a city, and it was called Caer Odor, because the small river which runs through the town is called Odor Nant-y-Badd ; and this town is called to this day, in both languages, Brysto, now called Bristol." In the Triads he is mentioned as being one of the "Three Pillars of the Island of Britain," and was the first who "discriminated the laws and ordinances, customs and privileges of the land and of the nation."

Geoffrey of Monmouth, describing this monarch, says : "When he had made an entire reduction of the whole island, he prepared for himself a crown of gold, and restored the kingdom to its ancient state. This prince established what the Britons call the Moelmutine laws, which are among the English to this day. In these, among other things, of which St. Gildas wrote a long time after, he enacted that the temples of the gods, as also cities, should have the privilege of giving sanctuary and protection to any fugitive or criminal that should flee to them from the enemy. He likewise enacted that the ways leading to these temples and cities, as also husbandmen's ploughs, should be allowed the same privileges; so that in his day the murders and cruelties committed by robbers were prevented, and everybody passed safe, without any violence offered to him."

The laws of Dyvnwal Moelmud, known as the Moelmutine laws, were adopted by the Saxons, among whom they became as celebrated as in Wales. In the Triads of Law and Equity enacted by this monarch the following excellent maxims are included:—

"The three privileges and protections of a social state—Security of life and person; security of possession and dwelling; security of national right.

"Three things that confirm the social state—Effectual security of property; just punishment when it is due; and mercy tempering justice where the occasion requires it in equity.

"Three elements of law are — Knowledge, national right, and conscientiousness.

"Three ornaments of a social state—The learned scholar, the ingenious artist, and the just judge.

"Three proofs of a judge—Knowledge of the law; knowledge of the customs which the law does not supersede; and knowledge of its times, and the business thereto belonging.

"Three things which a judge ought always to study—Equity habitually; mercy conscientiously; and knowledge profoundly and accurately."

This early legislator displayed extraordinary

wisdom and liberality in his capacity as a law-maker, and in Probert's "Welsh Laws" the following decrees of Moelmud appear :—" There are three common rights of the neighbouring country and bordering kingdom—a large river, a high road, and a place of meeting for religious adoration ; and these are under the protection of God and His tranquillity so long as those who frequent them do not unsheath their arms against those whom they meet. He that offends in this respect, whether he may be a citizen or a stranger, shall be visited with the fine of murder, upon application to the lord of the district. There are three privileged persons of the family, who are exempt from manual labour, work, and office—the infant, the aged, and the family teacher, for these are not to bear arms, attend to the horn, nor cultivate the soil. There are three things which strengthen the tranquillity of the neighbouring country, emanating from union and national right. There are three leading objects of the neighbouring country—common and perfect defence, equal protection of the arts and sciences, and the cherishing of domestication and peaceable customs. There are three family arts—agriculture, or the cultivation of the soil, the management of a dairy, and the art of weaving. And it is the duty of the chief of the tribe to insist that they are duly taught, and to avouch for their being so in the court, in the sacred place, and in every assembly for religious adoration." In addition, it is stated that "every Cambrian, being a landed proprietor, must keep and support a wife." In the chronological records of Wales, Dyvnwal Moelmud is called one of the "three wise kings of Britain; and he established a national and municipal government at Caerlleon upon Usk, the capital of all Britain, granting it a right of barter in all the other cities of the Island." In the Chronicles of the Ancient British Kings this monarch is thus described:— "*Dyfnwal Moelmud* (B.C. 441).—Dyfnwal ab Cloden, Duke of Cornwall, made all Brittain one monarch, which before was divided between five Kings or Dukes, hee buylded a cittee at the sid of a little rivere called Odornant-y-Baedd, this cittee is called in both languages Bristowe."

Dyvnwal Moelmud reigned for forty years, and was buried in the city of Trinovantum.

Belinus appears as one of the first to whom the right of sovereignty brought uneasiness. Upon the death of his father, Dyvnwal, the kingdom was divided between Belinus or Beli, and his brother, Brennus or Bran. Beli was crowned king of Loegria and Wales, and Bran, subject to his brother, succeeded to all the kingdom north of the Humber. By-and-by Brennus sought the aid of the King of Norway against Belinus, and the latter, during his brother's absence, took possession of the whole kingdom.

Romance adds a magic yet mournful touch to the scenes of this period. Brennus, returning with his bride, a fair Norwegian princess, encountered Guithlac, the Danish king, who, without much ado, and assisted by a storm which lasted nearly a week, seized the bride. Evil befell the Danish king and his charming prize, for both were wrecked on the shores of North Britain, and became prisoners of Belinus. Ill-fated Brennus demanded his bride and his kingdom, and accordingly took up arms for the restoration of both, but, being defeated, escaped in a solitary ship to Gaul.

Belinus, in consideration of the payment of an annual tribute, released and dismissed the King of Denmark and the Norwegian princess, and devoted himself to the enforcement of the Moelmutine laws and the advancement of his people.

In his reign two very important causeways were made, "with stone and mortar," one from Menevia to Hamo's Port, and the other from Cornwall to Caithness.

Later on, Brennus, after much wandering in Gaul, where he experienced many sorrows, married the daughter of the Prince of Burgundy, and, with his father-in-law's assistance, invaded Britain. Belinus, in warlike array, and at the head of a large army, went forth to meet his brother, but, just as the armies were about to join in battle, Conwenna, the aged mother of the rival kings, heroically and fearlessly, though in danger of death, rushed through the lines and effected a reconciliation between the brothers, who immediately formed a league of peace and friendship.

Conwenna, Queen of Britain, and widow of the celebrated Welsh law - maker, Dyvnwal Moelmud, thus appears as the first of the early heroines of Welsh history. With the exception of this brave mediation between the rival brothers, nothing is known of Conwenna, but her name survives in Celtic lore as having effected a great change in the history of Europe. Through her intercession and affectionate appeals to Belinus, Brennus was reinstated in his patrimony, and the two triumphant brothers subsequently destroyed the power of Gaul, and, passing on through Italy, compelled Rome to pay them tribute. Later on Brennus appears as the conquerer of Rome, while Belinus, after many victories, returned to Britain and devoted his life to the welfare of his kingdom. His name lives in the active present as the builder of that wonderful structure, the site of which is known to this day as Billingsgate, corrupted from Belin's Gate.

The following record appears in an ancient Welsh MS. :—" *Beli* (B.C. 401).—Belyn, the sone of Dyfnwal, was kinge of all Brittain, and his Brother Brenny was made Emperor in the East. . . . He made a cittee at the sid of the Rivere of Uske, where an Ould Castle of Llyon the Great was, and called the same cittee Caer Llyon ar Wyrge, and this was the principal cittee of all Brithayne, and the head cittee, and hitt was all the Rialte of all Brittaine, the 7 liberal arts, the Round Table, and the head Arch Bishoppricke of the 3 Archbishopprickes, and she was called the Seconde Rome, because of her fairness, myrthe, strength, and riches, and he buylded Wattling Street in London."

It is curious to note in passing that about this period a woman appears as a law-maker. In the list of Ancient British Kings the following particulars are recorded :—" *Cybylyn ap Gwrgant* was Kinge of all Brittaine (B.C. 356), and his *Queene Marcia made the most part of the laws*, which is as it used to be in this land of Brittaine. He buylded a cittee at the side of the sea, and called hitt Caer Byris, and now in English, it is called Dorchester." Of this monarch, quaint old Hardnyge writes :—

" The justest man, and truest in his days,
    Who had to wife dame Mertia the fair,
    A woman worthy of immortal praise,
    Who for this realm found many goodly lays,
    And wholesome statutes to her husband brought ;
    Her, many deemed to have been of the fays,
    As was Egeria, that Numa taught ;
Those yet of her be Mertian laws both named and thought."

CHAPTER II

LLUDD, THE BUILDER OF LONDON, AND OTHER EARLY MONARCHS

THE name of Lludd is thus mentioned in the records of the British Monarchs:—
"This Lludd renewed the cittie of London, and called hitt aftere his owne name Ludston, in British Caer Lludd, and now bye translation of speache hitt is called London."

English historical records describe King Lludd as a semi-mythical character, who is supposed to have fortified and beautified Trinovantum, but, in support of the reality of his existence, his burial-place has been known through all generations even to the present day as the historical Ludgate.

The *Brut* and Geoffrey of Monmouth state that he surrounded with stately walls the ancient city of Troy-novant, or New Troy, afterwards known as Trinovantum, and changed its name to the Caer or City of Lludd, which was altered by the

later British to Porthlud, and by the Saxons to
Ludesgate.

In the "Mabinogion" he is represented as
having "rebuilt the walls of London, and encom-
passed it about with numberless towers. And
after that he bade the citizens build houses
therein, such as no houses in the kingdom could
equal. . . . And he dwelt therein most part of
the year." During his reign it is said that "Three
plagues fell on the Island of Britain." The first
was the coming of the Corainans, whose knowledge was so great that "there was no discourse
upon the face of the Island, however low it might
be spoken, but what, if the wind met it, it was
known to them." The second plague was "a
shriek which came on every May-Eve, on every
hearth in the Island of Britain. And this went
through people's hearts, and so scared them . . ."
that old men and women, young men and
maidens, were paralysed with fear. The third
plague was, "that however much of provisions
and food might be prepared in the king's courts,
were there even so much as a year's provision, . . .
none of it could ever be found, except what was
consumed in the first night. . . ."

King Lludd and his brother Llevelys then
conferred together for the purpose of obtaining
a remedy to overcome these untoward calamities.
In order that the wind and the Coranians should
not know what the brothers said, Llevelys in-

vented "a long horn . . . made of brass,"
through which "they discoursed." Then Llevelys
gave as a cure for the first plague some insects to
bruise in water, and while the decoction would
poison the Coranians, it would not harm the
British. The second plague was caused by
dragons, the remedy for which was, after many
preliminaries, to "bury them in a kistvaen, in
the strongest place . . . " in the Island of Britain.
They were to be hidden in the earth, "and so long
as they shall bide in that strong place, no plague
shall come to the Island of Britain from elsewhere." The third plague was caused by "a
mighty man of magic, who takes thy meat and
thy drink, and . . . he through illusions and
charms, causes every one to sleep." Lludd was
warned of this, and advised to keep "a cauldron
of cold water by" his side, into which, when
"oppressed with sleep," he was to plunge. One
night in the third watch Lludd heard "many
surpassing fascinations and various songs. And
drowsiness urged him to sleep. Upon this, lest
he should be hindered from his purpose, and be
overcome by sleep, he went often into the water."
By-and-bye a man clad in armour appeared.
Thereupon King Lludd proceeded to try the
stranger's "skill in arms" and prowess, with the
result that the British monarch, after a "fierce
encounter," was victorious. And, it is said, "he
threw the plague to the earth . . . from thence-

forth until the end of his life, in prosperous peace did Lludd the son of Beli rule the Island of Britain."

Five centuries later the Dragon Myth is revived, with the subsequent discovery of Merlin the Seer and man of mystery.

Caswallon, also known as Cassibellaunus, or Cassivelaunus, succeeded his brother Ludd. In one of the old Welsh Chronicles he is described as the fourteenth British king:—"Cadwallawn ab Bely (B.C. 47), brother unto Llud, was Kinge of all Brittain, and he fought with Julius Cesar, Emperoure of Rome, and this Cadwallawn made the great feast in London, wherein were killed xx thousand of oxen, and other fatted beasts, and xl thousand of sheep, and lx thousand of geese and capons, and two times so much of all manner of other fowls, bothe wylde and tame, and this was one of the 3 most greatest feasts which ever was made in Greatt Britain."

Cassivelaunus, one of the war-kings of Britain, was chosen to oppose the invasion of Julius Cæsar. He is one of the most celebrated characters in early Welsh history. Linking the distant and primitive past of Britain with the advent of Roman power and influence, Caswallon stands forth as the scion of a race that owed its greatness, heroism, and fearlessness of death to the training of the Druids, those noble professors of a primitive though calumniated faith, for which many suffered persecution and martyrdom.

This celebrated war-king made stern resistance against Julius Cæsar, who expected it was only necessary to demand tribute in order to gain it. The great Roman invader's messages were treated with indignant remonstrances and sturdy refusals, which caused Cæsar in person to enforce his demand. An inglorious defeat, and the loss of his renowned sword, the "Crocea Mors," sent Cæsar, with his shattered and spiritless forces, back into Gaul.

Two years later, Cæsar again renewed his attempt to conquer the "Island of Green Hills," and not until a quarrel arose between Caswallon and his nephew were the Romans successful in their efforts.

All through the scenes of warfare and national struggle to repel the invader, Caswallon appears as the stern and determined patriot of his land and people, until they were eventually betrayed by Avarwy, the son of Ludd, into the hands of the Romans.

In some of the ancient histories of Wales it is stated that Avarwy, the son of Ludd, gave the Romans the fatal counsel permitting them to have place for the "point of their horses' hoofs in the cove of Min-y-Glas, in the isle of Daned; and gave them that space, and not more; receiving treasure of gold and silver from the Cæsarians year by year. And, in consequence thereof, the men of this island were compelled to pay yearly, as a tribute to the men of Rome, three thousand of silver, until the time of Owain, son of Maxen Wledig, who refused that tribute. Wherefore that man, Avarwy ab Ludd, was consigned to everlasting disgrace and disenfranchisement, with his progeny, who could not be otherwise than in the condition of slaves."

According to the national chronicles of Wales, Caswallon commanded an army of about sixty-two thousand men against Julius Cæsar, who, attracted by the wonderful charms of Flûr, the daughter of Mygnach Gorr, made his first incursion into Britain. In the Triads, Caswallon is described as one of the "Three Makers of Golden Shoes of the Isle of Britain," and his strange adventures are thus recorded:—"Caswallawn, the son of Beli, when he went as far as Gascony to obtain Flûr, the daughter of Mygnach Gorr, who had been carried thither to Cæsar the Emperor, by one Mwrchan the Thief, king of that country, and friend of Julius Cæsar, and Caswallawn brought her back to the Isle of Britain." The expedition led by Caswallon to rescue Flûr, the beautiful, and restore her to her father, was successful. Flûr was regained, and six thousand of Cæsar's soldiers were slain. This brave achievement obtained for Caswallon rank among the "Three Faithful Lovers of

Britain." He was also called the "Amorous Gallant," because, disguised as the maker of pretty golden shoes, he discovered the whereabouts of Flûr, and then returned to conduct his men into Gascony. This army, after rescuing Flûr, did not return with their war-king, but remained in Gaul, and consequently obtained and shared the name of one of the "Three Emigrant Hosts of Britain." Caswallon, in common with nearly all great generals, had a celebrated horse called Meinlas. This monarch was succeeded by Tenefan, Teneuvan, or Tenuantims, whose coinage bears the name Tasciovanus.

Cynfelyn, or Cunobelnuis, the "brave sovereign," immortalised by Shakespeare as Cymbeline, is described in the records of the ancient British kings thus:—"*Cynfelyn ab Tenefan* (B.C. 4) was the right Kinge of all Brittan, and, in his time, was our Saviour Lorde Jesus Christ borne of our most Blessed ladie St. Mary the Virgine."

Cynfelyn appears as a tributary Briton in Shakespeare's drama, in which the hero exclaims—

> "Publish we this peace
> To all our subjects. Set we forward: let
> A Roman and a British ensign wave
> Friendly together: so through Lud's-town march:
> And in the temple of Great Jupiter
> Our peace will ratify: seal it with feasts
> Set on there;—never was a war did cease
> Ere bloody hands were washed, with such a peace."

C

After the death of Cynfelyn, his eldest son,
Gwydyr, who succeeded as king, immediately
revolted, and heroically refused to continue
tributary to the Romans. Ultimately he was
completely subjugated, and, according to Geoffrey
of Monmouth, fell a victim to the treachery of
one Hamo, a Roman, who is said to be the
name-giver of Southampton.

When Gwairyd ab Cynfelyn succeeded his
brother, Britain had fallen beneath the triumphant power of Roman sway. Gwairyd, or, as he
is known to Saxon readers, Gweyrydd, gained renown for his justice and wisdom, and, according to
the Triads, his obstinate steadfastness of purpose
became a household word. In the " Chronicles
of the Kings " he is thus described :—" *Gwairyd
ab Cynfelyn* (A.D. 17) . . . was kinge of all
Brittain, and, in his tyme, was our Lord Jesus
Christ christened whene he was 30 years oulde,
and also in this kinge's tyme our Saviour
suffered death upon the tree crosse whene he
was somewhat about 32 yeares of age. . . .
This kinge married Gwenwissa, in the Brittish
tongue, and in Latin Gennissa, the daughter of
Cæsar (Claudius), Emperor of Rome, and buylded
a cittee at the side of the rivere of Sevarne, where
they were married, and that cittee in the Brittish
tongue is called Caerloyne. . . ."

The reign of Gwairyd or Gweyrydd brings
this record down to the dawn of the Christian

era, when the ancient and primitive faith of the Druids, abolished as a political institution, gradually developed into Christianised Bardism.

It was the policy of the Roman powers to suppress, and, if possible, totally exterminate, nationality by blotting out the past, destroying natural rights, and crushing out with the forces of hard, prosaic fact all hoary and hallowed traditions connected with Britain. To weaken the power of the Druids and Bards, the Romans sternly interdicted the religious rites of the Britons, and stigmatised with intense indignation the barbarity of human sacrifices.

In our days of toleration and mercy, and just, but gentler treatment of crime and criminals, the sacrificial rites of the Druids appear grossly cruel. Yet, judged by calm and fair consideration, the mode of death subservient to the science of divination was no more severe than later methods of life-taking, after which the bodies of the executed were handed over to the dissector for the advancement of medical science.

With the Druids execution was a religious act in order to surround outraged justice with warning terrors, amid which the victim bled on an altar. With the pagans, with all civilised nations, and the wide realm of Christendom, the condemned paid the penalty of religious intolerance or criminal law by means of slow consuming fires, fearful tortures of rack and wheel, merciless mutilation and barbarity.   In more enlightened centuries woeful sufferings have been inflicted by skilful headsmen and hangmen in the presence of sickening crowds, whose morbid delight was to behold the malefactor on the scaffold, and afterwards listen to farcical inquests and burial services over victims of a legalised form of murder.

To the Druids, as a matter of course, the imperial invaders attributed the continual conspiracies, insurrections, and revolts, the leaders of which made sturdy resistance against the enemies of their lives and liberties, and for that reason the Romans sternly denounced the religious rites and sacrifices of the ancient Britons.   They speedily persecuted the honoured priests of a Bardic system which breathed a primitive, and in some respects a more sincere and faithful, "peace on earth and goodwill to men" than is generally to be found as the world grows older; and although stories of ruthless massacres may be to a great extent exaggerated, many a noble-hearted and heroic Druid in death found a martyr's crown, and truly of them it can be said, "The memory of the just is blessed."

The stern measures vindictively enforced by Roman power caused the leading Druids to seek new and more secure places of sanctuary for the preservation of their faith.   Some fled to Ireland, Scotland, the Isle of Man, the lesser isles surrounding Britain, and even to Norway, where, slowly but surely, the old theology and science of the Britons passed away. Ordinary believers in Druidism, who remained in their own homes and localities, outwardly conformed to the Roman edicts, but inwardly clung with a deeper fervency to their national religion, and, possessing a rich language which was unintelligible to the oppressors, they were able to preserve their doctrines, poems, and traditional records intact.

During this bitter persecution the Druids are supposed to have formed a Bardic college in the marches of Scotland, where the solemn festivals were held which devout adherents of the national faith attended. Thus the tenets of Druidism survived the suppression of Druidical power, and the ancient faith was cherished in remote districts of Britain where Roman influence was not much felt.

With the last of the earliest heroes of British history, the old faith of the Druids had partially given way to the religious rites and ceremonies of the Romans, and when Ostorius Scapula was sent to Britain, the hitherto passive inhabitants of Wales arose in a rebellion, the result of which was the introduction of Christianity to Clas Merddin, or the "Island of Green Hills."

CHAPTER III

THE STORY OF CARACTACUS

HEN Aulus Plautius led his legions west-ward against the men of Essyllwg—a name corrupted by the Romans to the Silures—he was met by one of the bravest and most intrepid races he had yet encountered. Their commander was no less a person than the cele-brated Caradwg, the son of Bran, better known by his Latinised name of Caractacus, who for nine years heroically struggled against the enemy. In the Silures the invaders found unquailing hearts and heroic fortitude, and it was not until A.D. 50, when Plautius was succeeded in the command by Publius Ostorius Scapula, that the Silures were finally conquered, and their brave chieftain was led into captivity.

Caractacus, one of the most celebrated of the British generals or war-kings, held so high a place in the esteem of his countrymen that it is stated in the Triads, "The men of Britain, from

the prince to the slave, became his followers in
their country's need against the progress of the
foe and of destruction, and wheresoever he went
in war, all the men of the island went in his train,
and none desired to remain at home."

It is strange that a prince, a general, and the
greatest hero Wales has ever produced should
have had so little recognition in the ancient
chronicles of his country.   With the exception of
brief notices in the Triads there are few accounts
of him, but Tacitus has vigorously given him un-
grudging praise, which, coming from the side of
the enemy, is one of the highest tributes.

In Williams's " Cymry " the selection of Caractacus as general of the British forces is thus
described :—" In a convention of the country,
and neighbouring country, under all the limits
of the nation of the Cymry, Caradog, the son of
Bran, was invested with the martial sovereignty
of all the Isle of Britain, that he might oppose the
invasion of the Romans.   All the Britons, from
king to vassal, enlisted under his banner at the
call of the country against foe and depredation."

Having successfully defended himself for nine
years against the Romans, Caractacus found that
he had to urge his forces with fresh vigour to
meet the new commander, Ostorius Scapula.
In many a weary but well-won battle, in many a
fierce fray, the men of Essyllwg, led by their brave
general, had fought against the Romans under

Aulus Plautius and his subordinate commanders, and when the worst came, neither the smooth promises nor the sharp threats of the enemy deluded or terrorised them. Yet they knew now that the Romans meant to vanquish them, as they had conquered the less heroic tribes, which gladly accepted peace rather than degradation, and death or exile, with imprisonment, torture, and martyrdom.

Finding the power of the Romans greatly strengthened, Caractacus saw that it was necessary to decide the fate of Siluria by a single battle. To some this appeared an unwise policy, but the difficulties of his position were daily increasing; the resources upon which he had to depend were gradually being lessened, and, in taking the course he did, he only acted as any other brave general would have under similar circumstances.

Caractacus quitted Siluria, or South Wales, for North Wales, the land of the Ordovices, and there selected his own ground, the precise locality of which is much disputed. From the description given by Tacitus, the site chosen for the great and eventful battle proves the unswerving excellence of this noble hero's judgment. Tacitus writes thus :—" He posted himself on a spot to which the approaches were as advantageous to his own troops as they were perplexing to us. He then threw up, on the more accessible parts of the highest hills, a rampart of stones, below and in front of which was a river difficult to ford. Picked men showed themselves before the ramparts." Brandon Camp and Coxal Knoll, in Shropshire; Cefn Carnedd, in Montgomeryshire; and Breidden Hill, on the banks of the Severn between Shrewsbury and Welshpool, are named by the various antiquarians who still agree to differ as to the exact spot.

The great British general did not merely satisfy himself by means of discipline and the advantageous arrangement of his forces, but, with the fierce and intense fervour of natural heroism, he went rapidly from rank to rank, inspiring his men with courage equal to the occasion, reminding them that on the day's events liberty and slavery were evenly poised, and either was ready to descend, bringing on the one hand the rapture of victory, and the sweet, wild joys of continued freedom, or the miserable disgrace of defeat and the wormwood and gall of bondage. The great leader, with all the eloquent powers of a rich language and its proverbial "hwyl" at his command, appealed to the emotions of his bravehearted war-men. His rhetoric resembled the wild mountain torrents of Wales, when, swollen by raging storms, the waters roll thundering downward, casting all obstacles before them. In burning words he spoke of the stinging darts and lashes of oppression; of the grovelling humiliation

engendered by disgrace ; of the galling yoke of
tyranny, and the cruel pangs caused by dishonour.
He told them, too, of their wives and daughters,
whose beauty was their bane, and whose pure
and stainless fame had been tarnished or irrevo-
cably destroyed by ruthless strangers, while held
in bondage with fetters of gold in the marble
mansions of Roman generals. He reminded them
that the Romans, though powerful and mighty,
were not invincible. Great Cæsar, with all his
tact and stratagem, had been driven back, and
may not the ancient fire of British valour be rekindled with such force that the Romans, quailing
before it, would eventually surrender the sea-girt
island to its peace-loving people and brave warriors ? The earnest appeal immediately reached
the hearts of the Britons, and with one stentorian
voice, in grand and solemn acclaim, the whole
army, in the " face of the sun and the eye of
light," responded, promising " never to yield to
weapons or to wounds."

Brilliant was the sunrise of the morrow. The
river below the British ramparts glittered with
golden sunrays, and the broad meadow-lands
sparkled with silvery dewdrops. Beyond and
above the river, grim precipices appeared to be
shielding dark secrets of warfare, and the gloomy
overhanging mountains stretched away into the
purple distance like gigantic war-men ranged for
the fray.

The Romans stood aghast before the formidable barriers. Their commanders for once quailed when they reached the apparently inaccessible steeps and deeply flowing river. Probably for the first time in the history of the Roman invasion of Britain the common soldiers had to urge their general to lead the attack. At first the national cause was highly favoured, and the legions were repulsed with great slaughter. For a time the Britons triumphantly resisted and actively repelled the enemy, but when fresh troops arrived to support their slain or wounded comrades and replace those that had fallen in battle, the science of military superiority superseded native courage and fortitude. In close combat the lightly-clothed Britons were unequal to the armour-clad Romans, and soon the grand old hosts of Caractacus began to waver.

When the sun slowly sank beyond the western mountains the Britons were conscious of defeat, and as the purple twilight crept stealthily through the dim glens, rugged ravines, and along the lonely pasture-lands of Wales, the warriors of Britain gave way.

In vain were the gallant retinues of many brave leaders; in vain were the eloquent and enthusiastic speeches of Britain's chosen chieftain; in vain the valour that was supposed to be capable of storming any position.

Night, with its crescent moon and silver stars,

found the imperial army in possession of the British camp, with the wife, daughters, and relatives of the great British prince and general prisoners-at-war. Caractacus fled to his relative, Cartismandua, queen of the Brigantes, with whom he intended remaining until the dawn of better and more hopeful days. But the treacherous queen gave up her brave warrior-kinsman to the Romans, who loaded him with chains and sent him as a prisoner and exile to " make a Roman holiday."

With broken battle-axe and fettered hands, Caractacus appears even a greater and more heroic character than when a free and resolute warrior. Adversity, the truest test of genuine worth and unflinching fortitude, truly enhanced the noble qualities of heart and head for which that celebrated British leader has become a nation's admiration and lofty example. His fame as an intrepid warrior and resolute defender of national freedom had preceded him to Rome, where the whole population awaited his coming with intense and almost morbid interest. The warrior, who commanded an army totally unacquainted with military science, against Roman hosts for nine years, was at once the object of idle speculation and intelligent curiosity. His name and deeds had long been familiar to the Romans who remained at home, where they eagerly awaited and received tidings from the

invaders, who found in Caractacus their most
obstinate and persistent opponent. To see the
wonderful and princely chieftain, commander,
and captive in person was a rare event even in
a city long accustomed to triumphal processions,
bringing in the spoils and prisoners of war and
costly tributes from earth and ocean. The circumstance was made the occasion of a general
holiday, shared alike by patrician and plebeian,
who for the time set aside other pleasures and
daily commerce in order to see the wonderful
British warrior and prisoner. In Hoare's "Giraldus" the following account is given of the scene
in Rome on the day of the celebrated captive's
entry:—"The Prætorian cohorts were under arms
in the field before the camp. First came the
king's dependents and retinue, with the trap-
pings, collars, and other trophies he had won in
foreign wars; next came his brothers, his wife
and daughter; and last himself appeared before
the assembled multitude. The rest gave way to
their terrors. Caractacus, neither by a down-
cast expression nor plaintive words, appealed to
compassion. When he came in front of the
throne (on which the emperor was seated) he
spoke to this effect:—

"'If to the nobility of my birth and the
splendour of exalted station I had united the
virtues of moderation (policy and tact), Rome
had beheld me not in captivity, but a royal

visitor and friend. The alliance of a prince descended from an illustrious line of ancestors, a prince whose sway extended over many nations, would not have been unworthy of your choice. A reverse of fortune is now the lot of Caractacus. The event to you is glorious, and to me humiliating. I had arms, and men, and horses; I had wealth in abundance. Can you wonder I was unwilling to lose them? The ambition of Rome aspires to universal dominion, and must mankind, in consequence, stretch their necks to the yoke? I stood at bay for years. Had I acted otherwise, where, on your part, had been the glory of conquest, and where, on mine, the honour of a brave resistance? I am now in your power. If you are bent on vengeance, execute your purpose: the bloody scene will soon be over, and the name of Caractacus will sink into oblivion. Preserve my life, and I shall be to the latest posterity a monument of Roman clemency.'"

It is stated by Tacitus that the dignified attitude of Caractacus before Claudius Cæsar and the Empress Agrippina caused the emperor to pardon the distinguished British captive, who, however, appears to have been detained in military custody, which is to say, chained by the arm to a soldier of the Imperial Guard, but allowed to go freely about the city thus accompanied. It is known that St. Paul spent two

years about the period A.D. 59–60 in Rome, and
it is highly probable he then met Caractacus,
and a warm friendship between the great Apostle
and the Cambro - British commander was the
result.   How very grand it is to picture the
veteran of Christianity and the veteran of the
Cymry—both heroes in their respective lines—
discussing together in the Roman Capitol !

CHAPTER IV

PRINCESS EURGAIN, THE PIONEER OF BRITISH EDUCATION

IN connection with the name of Ilid is that of Eurgain, who is described as the "first female saint of the Island of Britain." This distinguished Welsh princess is described in the ancient records as having founded a church and a college that afterwards became very celebrated as the first university in Britain. Martial, in his Epigrams, addresses Pudens the Roman, whom he congratulates upon his marriage with the British princess, Claudia Rufina. In the Second Epistle of Paul to Timothy, kindly messages and greetings are sent from "Pudens, Linus, and Claudia" to his friend. Both Protestant and Roman Catholic writers agree in the belief that this lady was Eurgain, the daughter of Caractacus, who assumed the name of Claudia. At the time when Caractacus and his young family were taken captives before Claudius

Cæsar and the Empress Agrippina, Aulus Plautius, the first Roman Governor of Britain, had
been recalled, and Ostorius Scapula was sent in
his stead. The wife of Aulus Plautius was known
as Pomponia Græcina, but her real surname was
Rufina. It is considered probable that Claudius
became so greatly interested in the noble British
captive and his family as to give the name Claudia
to Eurgain, the daughter of Caractacus. The
British princess, then a child of tender years, was
placed under the care of Pomponia, who, having
been accustomed to the Britons, was regarded as
being the best guardian for the purpose. For
that reason, doubtless, Eurgain came to be known
at Rome as Claudia Rufina. Tacitus states that
when Aulus Plautius returned from Britain to
Rome, his wife, Pomponia Græcina, was accused
of " foreign superstition," and upon being examined according to ancient legal customs by her
father, in the presence of her husband and members of the family on both sides, the noble lady
was declared to be innocent of the charges brought
against her. The " superstition" was supposed
to be Christianity, to which, as a matter of course,
Eurgain was in time converted by her guardian,
Pomponia. Later on Claudia, or Eurgain, became
the wife of Pudens, a member of one of the
highest Roman patrician families, and her brother
Cyllin embraced the Christian faith under the
baptismal name of Linus.

D

In the "Genealogies of the Saints" it is stated that "Caractacus, king of Morganwg (Siluria or Glamorgan), who, after being carried captive to Rome, was, together with his daughter Eurgen, converted to the Christian faith by St. Ilid, a man of Israel; which Ilid came from Rome to this Island with Caractacus and Eurgen, and they were the first that converted the Cymry to Christianity. And Eurgen formed a college of twelve saints, . . . and after that it became an exceeding eminent monastery."

Among the names of those who founded churches and choirs in Glamorgan, that of Claudia, or Eurgain, stands first on the list, and appears thus :—"Eygen (by some called Eurgain), sister in the faith to Saint Ilid, who was also called Joseph of Arimathea. She founded the church and college of Caer Urgon, called by some Caer Worgorn, and now Llanilltyd, from the name of Illtyd, knight and saint."

It may here be explained that the terms Côr, Chorea, and Bangor mean a circle, a college, or higher circle and college including also a choir, for which the early Christian Church was justly celebrated. The primitive Côr or Bangor developed into a university, the most renowned of which was the Côr or Bangor, founded by the British princess at the old Caer or city of Eurgain, afterwards corrupted to Caer or Côrworgan. The site of this ancient city and university is

now known as Llantwit Major, in the Vale of Glamorgan, where numerous relics precious to antiquarians still remain as memorials of the former
importance of the town. From this ancient
institution, which was the only seat of learning
and instruction in Britain, the Christian religion
extended all over the country. Some authorities
state that Mawan, who came with Ilid and Cyndav from Rome with the family of Caractacus, was
the first principal of the college at Caerworgan.

The Côr or Bangor Eurgain continued in
a flourishing condition, until a raid was made
upon it by Irish pirates, who carried away
therefrom a beautiful youth and scholar, afterwards known as St. Patrick. In the later half
of the fourth century, probably about A.D. 385,
Theodosius, the father of the emperor of that
name, was sent by Valentinian to restore order in
Britain. According to some authorities, this distinguished general, who in A.D. 388 succeeded
in defeating "Maxen Wledig," or Maximus the
Cruel, restored and re-established the primitive
British institution founded by Princess Eurgain,
and gave it the name of Côr Tewdws, or the
College of Theodosius, its second patron. An
ardent modern Welsh antiquarian, who claims to
be descended from the Silurian kings, contends
that the College of Eurgain was restored by
Tewdrig, or Theodore, king of Glamorgan, and
thus came to be known as the Côr Tewdrig.

Early in the fifth century this college again
suffered at the hands of the piratical hordes that
ravaged the shores of Siluria, but in A.D. 430,
when Germanus, Bishop of Auxerre, and Lupus,
Bishop of Troyes, came to controvert the Pelagian
heresy in Britain, Iltyd, the Breton knight, was
persuaded to undertake a religious life, immediately after which he was appointed principal of
the Côr Tewdws, subsequently known as the Côr
Iltutus, or Bangor Iltyd. This college, under the
guidance of Iltyd, developed into a celebrated
university, the reputation of which spread all
over Europe. From every part of Britain and
the opposite continent pupils flocked to it, and
its fame was so great that it became the *Alma
Mater* of renowned scholars and teachers. The
students of this fifth century university included
St. David, Dubricius, Bishop of Caerleon, Teilo,
Gildas the historian, St. Maglorius, St. Paul de
Léon, Paulinus or Paul Hên, Paternus, Taliesin
and Talhairan the bards, Samson, Archbishop of
Dôl, in Brittany; Elphin, the son of Gwyddno,
and others well known in Welsh history. The
Bangor Iltyd had two thousand four hundred
members, and was in the fifth century the largest
and most flourishing university in Britain. It is
worthy of note that the university which succeeded
the primitive school of Eurgain, the College of St.
Dubricius at Henllan on the Wye, and the College
of Cadoceus, or Cattwg the Wise, at Llancarvan,

Glamorganshire, were in existence and of wide renown nearly four hundred years before Alfred the Great established the University of Oxford. It is still more interesting to know that when Alfred the Saxon desired to give his newly founded, or perhaps, to be more correct, his re-founded University of Oxford a good beginning, he sent for three of the most learned men in the kingdom to assist him. One of these was the Benedictine monk of St. David's, beloved in Wales as Geraint Bard Glâs, or the Blue Bard and Celtic minstrel, afterwards known as Asser Menevensis, the historian and author of "The Life of Alfred."

History is silent as to whether Eurgain, or Claudia, married a second time, or whether Pudens, on his return with his wife to the land of her birth, was created lord of Caersarllog; but this much is certain—the first patroness of education and promoter of the Christian religion was a Welsh princess, whose name truly deserves higher recognition than it obtains.

From the days of Brân and Eurgain the Christian religion steadily but slowly progressed until the reign of King Lucius, who is thus described : —" Lleirwg, the son of Coel, who was the son of Cyllin, surnamed Lleuver Mawr . . . who bestowed the privilege of country, and nation and judgment, and validity of oath, upon those who should be of the faith of Christ."

Lleufer Mawr, or the "Great Luminary," was
in succeeding ages better known by his Latin
name, Lucius, who confirmed the rights of teachers
of the Gospel to equal immunities with those
enjoyed by the Druids, which, according to
Williams's "Cymry," were "five acres of land
free; exemption from personal attendance in
war; permission to pass unmolested from one
district to another in time of war, as well as in
peace; support and maintenance wherever they
went; exemption from land tax; and a contri-
bution from every plough in the district in which
they were authorised teachers." "Validity of
oath" referred to the substitution of an oath
on the Decalogue for the old Druid oath. The
ancient Christian form of oath in Wales was on
the "Ten Commandments, the Gospel of St. John,
and the Blessed Cross." Lucius established the
Archbishopric of Llandaff, which was "the first
in the Isle of Britain." This was between A.D.
173 and A.D. 189. In the Calendar of the Church
of Rome the following appears :—"St. Eleutherius, Pope and martyr, Rome, at the request of
King Lucius, sent St. Fugatius and St. Damianus
into Britain, June 1, 179, or October 9, 182."
The dates refer to the day on which the festival
of the saint occurs and the year in which Eleutherius is supposed to have died. The name of
Fugatius, or Ffagan, survives to this day in St.
Fagan's, and that of Damianus or Dyfan exists in

Merthyr Dyfan, where the latter saint suffered martyrdom—both places being parishes in the Vale of Glamorgan.

In the ancient record of the British kings Lucius is thus described:—" *Lles ab Cael* . . . (A.D. 181) was a wise and godlie kinge, and said that he would that his end should be better than his begininge, and he caused the rest of the kingdome of Brittayne to be cristened, they which had not received the Christiane faith before of Josephe of Aramathia, or of his deciples, and this kinge sent them to the Pope or Bishopp of Rome, for two preachers, whose names in the British tongue were Dyfan and Fagan, and in Latene, Dunianus and Faganus, who instructed the Brittones in the Catholicke faith, and from thence until nowe of late, the Brittones continue altogethere with one accord in the same faith without anye alteration or changinge of religion for the space of 1400 years or thereabout."

CHAPTER V

IN THE DAWN OF CHRISTIANITY

THE captivity of Caractacus is so closely allied with the introduction of Christianity into Britain that it will be necessary here to bring under notice a digest of the ancient records of Wales, before sketching out the career of Brân the Blessed, who is regarded as the first veteran, convert, and patron of the Christian religion in Wales.

Stillingfleet states that Godeau, in his life of St. Paul, calculates the Apostle to have spent eight years in the journeys he made, including those to "the utmost bounds of the west." This was after liberation from his second imprisonment, which, according to Massutius, came to a close in A.D. 60. Godeau, Massutius, and Stillingfleet knew nothing of the Cambro-British national historical records preserved in the Cymric language, and possibly neither could the Welsh compilers know anything about the statements of those authorities. In startling and most interesting confirmation of Godeau's statement, it is recorded in ancient Welsh MSS. that King Brân the Blessed, the father of Caractacus, spent seven years in Rome as a hostage for his son. This was apparently from A.D. 60 to A.D. 67. St. Paul was beheaded at the close of the last-named year, and Nero was assassinated in June A.D. 68. The very fact that Brân remained as a hostage seven years for his illustrious son proves Caractacus to have passed the seven years out of the jurisdiction of the Imperial Government, and everything appears to indicate those seven years, or at least a portion of them, were spent in South Wales with St. Paul. It is also supposed that the great Apostle and the celebrated general both hurried back to Rome when St. Paul heard of the terrible persecutions of the Christians which Nero had instigated.

The facts appear to resolve themselves in the following order :—

I. St. Paul and Caractacus were liberated in A.D. 60, but the British prince, though free in Rome, was not permitted to leave that city. St. Paul had, it is supposed, become highly interested in the British captive's account of the Druids, and Caractacus, by inducing the Roman authorities to accept his own father, Brân, as a hostage, as a guarantee that the prince would not join his old army in Britain, was allowed to accompany the Apostle to Siluria, where they spent the whole or part of the next seven years.

II. Immediately after the death of Nero in June 68, all the British captives returned home, and settled down for the remainder of their lives in Siluria.

In concluding this account of the brave British general, it may be remarked that some Welsh authorities believe the Eubulus mentioned in the Second Epistle of Paul to Timothy, chap. iii., ver. 21, was Caractacus, who perhaps adopted that Roman name because of its resemblance to the Welsh name *Helbulus*, which signifies " One full of perplexity," thus aptly describing the condition of the Cambro-British hero since he had become a Roman captive.　In the most reliable Welsh annals it is stated that Caractacus spent the last years of his noble life at Aber Gwaredwyr (" Aber of the Rescued"), the ancient name of St. Donat's Castle, in the Vale of Glamorgan.　According to the " Genealogy of Jestyn ap Gwrgan," Caractacus " was the bravest and most renowned of any in the whole world. . . . He vanquished the Romans in many battles ; but was at last overcome through treachery, and carried captive to Rome, whence he returned eventually to Cambria. . . . This Caradog built a palace, after the manner of the Romans, at Abergwerydwyr, called now Llanddunwyd Major, or St. Donat's.　His daughter Eurgain married a Roman chieftain who accompanied her to Cambria. This chieftain had been converted to Christianity, as well as his wife Eurgain, who first introduced the faith among the Cambro-Britons, and sent for Ilid (a native of the land of Israel) from Rome to Britain. This Ilid . . . became the principal teacher of Christianity to the Cambro-Britons, and introduced good order into the choir of Eurgain, which she had established for twelve saints near the place now called Llantwit, but which was burnt by King Edgar. After this arrangement Ilid went to Ynys Afallon (the Isle of Apples), in the Summer Country (Somersetshire), where he died and was buried; and Ina, king of that country, raised a large church over his grave, at the place called now Glasinbyri (Glastonbury), in Welsh Aberglaston."

Brân, the son of Llyr Llediaith, worthily received the title of Bendigeid, or the Blessed, in recognition of his being the first to introduce Christianity into Britain. He is described as one of the "Three Hallowed Princes" of the Island of Britain, and royal representative of "The Nine Holy Families of the Island of Britain, and all of them sprang from the race of the Cymry. I. Brân, the son of Llyr Llediaith; and he was the first; wherefore he was called Brân Vendigaid [Brân the Blessed], and Bendigeidvran." His name is again mentioned as one of the "Three Chief Holy Families of the Island of Britain. . . . First, the family of Brân, the son of Llyr Llediaith; and from this stock comes the family of Caw of North Britain, called Caw Cawlwyd, and Caw of Twrcellyn in Anglesea."

In the "Genealogies and Families of the Saints of the Island of Britain" the following is given:—
"I. The family of Brân, the son of Llyr. Brân, the son of Llyr Llediaith, brought the Christian faith first to this island from Rome, and is therefore called Brân the Blessed, and with him came St. Ilid, an Israelite, who converted many to the Christian faith.

"Eigen, the daughter of [Caradoc] Caractacus, . . . married a chieftain named Sarllog, who was lord of Caersarllog [Old Sarum], and she was the first female saint of the Island of Britain."

In the "Achau Saint Ynys Prydain" it is recorded that "Brân the Blessed, the son of Llyr Llediath, the first of the race of the Cymry who was converted to the faith in Christ; and his family is the most ancient of the Holy Families of the Island of Britain, and his church is in Llandaff.

"Arwystli Hên, a man from Italy; he came with Brân, the son of Llyr, to the Island of Britain to teach the Christian faith.

"St. Ilid, a man of Israel, who came with Brân, the son of Llyr, from Rome to teach the Christian faith to the race of the Cymry.

" Eigen, the daughter of Caradoc, the son of Brân, . . . wife of Sallwg, lord of Garth Mathrin."

One of the Triads gives the following account:— " The three blissful Rulers of the Island of Britain, Bran the Blessed, the son of Llyr Llediaith, who first brought the faith of Christ to the nation of the Cymry from Rome, where he was seven years a hostage for his son Caradawc, whom the Romans made prisoner through the craft, the deceit, and treachery of Aregwedd Fôeddawg [usually supposed to be Cartismandua]."

Brân also takes rank with Prydain, the son of Aedd Mawr, and Dyvnwal Moelmud, as one of the three kings celebrated for their stability and the excellence of their system of government.

In the ancient annals of Wales it is related that Brân's head was buried, according to his desire, under the White Tower of London. The face was turned towards France, in order to be a talisman against any foreign invasion. King Arthur is reported to have disinterred the head, and proudly preferred to keep the island by means of his own strength and without any aid. This is described as " The three Closures and Disclosures of the Island : First the head of Bendigeid Vran ap Llyr, which Owain the son of Maxen Wledig buried under the White Tower in London, and while it was so placed no invasion could be made upon this Island. . . .

Arthur disclosed the head of Bendigeid Vran ap
Llyr, because he chose not to hold the Island
except by his own strength.   And after the
three disclosures came the chief invasions upon
the race of the Cymry."

It is a remarkable coincidence that Stillingfleet in his "Origines Britannicæ," and being
unacquainted with the Triads, should have mentioned the name of Brân in connection with the
introduction of Christianity into Britain.   This
great authority writes :—" It is certain that St.
Paul did make considerable converts at his
coming to Rome, which is the reason of his
mentioning the saints in Cæsar's household ; and
it is not improbable that some of the British
captives, carried over with Caractacus and his
family, might be some of them, who would certainly promote the conversion of their country
by St. Paul."

Great stress has been laid by many reliable
authorities on two ancient British records which,
to a considerable extent, help to verify the time
of St. Paul's journey to Britain.   One is a passage in the works of Gildas, the historian, which
states that the Gospel was preached in the British
Isles in the latter part of the reign of Tiberius ;
and the other is contained in the Triads already
mentioned.

In " Tracts on the British Church " the following account is given :—" It is a remarkable and

very interesting fact that the detention of the British hostages should have been coincident with St. Paul's residence there as a prisoner; and it was not a less favourable coincidence that they should be released from confinement in the same year in which St. Paul was set at liberty. Nothing could be more convenient for St. Paul's mission to the Gentiles than the opportunity which their return must have afforded him of introducing the Gospel into Britain, and nothing more probable than that he should readily embrace such an opportunity."

The names of the four missionaries who accompanied Brân on his return home were Ilid, Cyndav and his son Mawan, both "men of Israel," and Arwystli Hên, a "man of Italy."

In Romans, chap. xvi., ver. 10, there appears the following:—"Salute them which are of Aristobulus' household." In his "Essay on the Welsh Saints," Professor Rees writes:—"In the Silurian Catalogue, Arwystli is said to have been the confessor or spiritual instructor of Brân; and by some modern commentators he is identified with Aristobulus, mentioned in the Epistle to the Romans, xvi. 10. It is, however, remarkable that, according to Greek martyrology, as cited by Archbishop Usher, Aristobulus was ordained by St. Paul as an apostle to the Britons. Cressy also says that St. Aristobulus, a disciple of St. Peter or St. Paul at Rome, was sent as an apostle

to the Britons, and was the first Bishop in Britain;
and that he died at Glastonbury A.D. 99, and
that his commemoration or saint's day was kept
in the Church, March 15."

With reference to the Silurian home of Brân,
and the precise locality where the primitive
missionaries held the first assemblies of British
Christians who met to worship Christ, the ac-
companying note appears in the Iolo MSS. :—
"Llanlid, in Glamorganshire, appears to have
been a retirement of the Silurian princes. . . .
Its ancient name was Caer-Geri. . . . In this
parish there is an old well, never dry, called
Ffynnon-Geri, or Ceri's Well, . . . and at a little
distance a spot of ground called Castell Ceri, or
Ceri's Castle; but no vestiges of habitation are
now known to have existed there, except a flagged
causeway towards the church, through a bordering marsh, discovered, in draining, about sixty
years ago. Close to the church a very large
round tumulus appears, called Y Gaer Gronn, or
circular fortress, on which, within the memory of
persons now living, immense old oaks grew. The
top of this tumulus has been rendered concave,
apparently for warlike defence; but we may
infer that it was originally a Druidic oratory,
for the first Christian churches were built near
such places. The parish wake was, until of late
years, held for several successive days between
this hillock and the adjoining churchyard, com-

mencing on Gwyl-Geri (the Vigil of Ceri), about midsummer. At a short distance is an old farm-house, called from time immemorial Tre-Frau, or Brân's residence. The parish is called Llanilid, or the Church of Ilid; and a contiguous ancient mansion is also called by that name, where, it may be conjectured, Ilid first resided; for he necessarily must have sought the near refuge of his royal patron, Brân, while encountering ancient prejudices in propagating a new creed. Lastly, old fortifications are numerous in the vicinity, and Bryn Caradoc (Caractacus's eminence) stands not far off, rather adjacent to which extensive remains of early encampments appear."

Brân's great-grandfather was Ceri, of whom it is said :—He " was a remarkably wise man, and constructed many ships at the expense of the country and its lords; hence he was called Ceri of the extensive navy, having numerous fleets at sea. He lived at the place called Porth-Kery."

Porthkery is a quiet lonely spot in Glamorganshire, on the shores of the Severn Sea, and westward of the present Barry Docks. The harbour would now be inadequate for the accommodation of a fleet, and its gradual decay has been attributed to sea-floods inundating extensive plains and sweeping away numerous castles on the coast. Sir Edward Mansell, in his MS. history, refers to the decadence of this port. He says :—" They (the Normans) came to land at

E

Porth-Kery, where was then a good haven for ships, before the fall of the clifft there which was in our grandfathers' days."

To return to Brân and the early Christian missionaries. Llanilid, which means the Llan or Church of Ilid—the "Man of Israel" who came to Glamorganshire with his friend and patron, Brân, king of Siluria—is the oldest church in the whole of Great Britain. There the Gospel was first preached five hundred years before St. Augustine stepped foot in Kent. Arwystli, or Aristobulus, one of the seventy disciples, was ordained by St. Paul, and sent into the country of the Britons, who were regarded as " unbelieving, wild and savage men." In Britain this holy and primitive bishop had at first but a poor reception. He was often beaten and dragged along the streets, and frequently reviled and laughed at, but, in spite of all the persecution, he preached Christ, and converted many from Druidism and Paganism to Christianity. Then he founded a church, appointed elders and deacons, and, after many sorrows and great tribulation, he died.

CHAPTER VI

OUR FIRST SAILOR-KING

CARAUSIUS was the first to claim and win for our island the sovereignty of the sea.

This hero and guardian of a nation's naval infancy was born of humble parentage down in St. David's, or Menevia, where, in earliest childhood, his thoughts and longings gained inspiration from the roar of the ocean waves that surged and dashed against the rock-bound shores and gloomy cliffs of wild West Wales. For him the sea held secrets and promised great things, and ever sang of freedom, success, honour, power, and kingcraft. Its curling wavelets beckoned him away—away from the desolate Welsh coast to scenes of piratical excitement and the enthusiasm of sea warfare. Its long, white-crested rollers urged him to follow their hoarsely roaring voices, and become either their willing slave or yielding master. Sometimes, in the darkling

evenings and the purple or fog-laden twilights
of the mysterious long ago, the boy listened to
witching stories from the stern lips of veteran
and bold sea-captains who frequented the British
coasts, and set him yearning to share their
calling. At last, encouraged by those hardy
men who had to stem the wildest tides and
encounter the terrible hordes of sea-rovers and
robbers, the boy was tempted away from the holy
neighbourhood of Menevia to distant Batavia,
then the nursery and naval school of sailors.
There Carausius remained until his education
was completed, when he entered the service, and
received commendation successively from the
Emperors Probus, Carus, and Carinus.

In the reign of Maximinian, when the Saxons
began to make marauding incursions on the
coast of the North Sea, Carausius appeared as
the skilled commander of the fleet stationed at
Boulogne to prevent the ravages of the Teutonic
sea-kings who made their names a terror to
the defenceless and disheartened inhabitants of
Britain. It was in his great sea battles this
distinguished commander gained the wealth and
fame which made him a rival of Diocletian the
Great. While holding this important and arduous
position all the excellent qualities of Carausius
were brought into exercise. But, as it frequently
happens with well-earned reputation, its heroic
possessor found enemies where previously friends

only existed. The Emperor Maximinian, grown
jealous of the great and powerful admiral, sent
orders to put him to death.

Then the skill, foresight, and energy of the
brave commander were put to the test.

He grasped the situation at once; he knew
the value of his services to his imperial masters;
he felt sure his influence over his comrades was
supreme. Then the old dreams of kingcraft
revived, grew strong, and, determined to make
the visions of his youth the reality of his manhood, Carausius, at the head of his whole fleet,
and taking with him the fourth legion, left
Boulogne for Britain. Once there, it was the
easiest possible matter to win his countrymen to
his standard, and, soon after landing, he declared
himself emperor of the island.

Under the title of Marcus Aurelius, Valerius
Carausius, the boy of Menevia and admiral of
Britain, defied Maximinian, and for eight years
reigned as monarch of his native land.

Judging from the coinage and medals of his
reign, his career as an island emperor must have
been almost unequalled for wealth, taste, and
splendour.

Maximinian endeavoured to quell the "rebellion," as it was called, but before the veteran and
experienced adherents of Carausius the Roman
seamen quailed. Some authorities believe that
Maximinian was taken prisoner, but was released

upon condition that Carausius, with the title of emperor, should hold the sovereignty of Britain.

Henceforth this heroic emperor successfully defended his native land against the barbarians of the north, and still found time to carry out magnificent works of public splendour and utility.

Anticipating the future maritime power of Britain, Carausius set his fleet to "rule the waves." From the North Sea to the Bay of Biscay, from the Rhine to the Straits of Gibraltar, he swept the seas, and not a vessel dared approach Britain on any side without his permission.

During the eight years that he wore the imperial purple Carausius was beloved, and yet to a certain extent was feared, by his subjects. The yearnings and longings of his boyhood were realised; the freedom came soon. Success speedily followed; honours were showered upon him, and his power was acknowledged as unrivalled upon the seas. Then came the skill of kingcraft, the dignity and magnificence of imperial sway, the proud pleasure of national approbation, the joy of making his countrymen happy under the control of their native emperor, and then—this great and good wearer of the royal purple became the victim of treason and murder.

In the old dreams of the long ago the brave boy of Menevia never saw the masked face of the assassin lurking behind the throne, or the sharpened and glittering axe concealed among the foldings of the imperial purple. The faith and trust of childhood ripened into the confidence and friendship of manhood, and in Alectus, his chief minister, Carausius found his traitor and assassin.

Alectus, seizing an opportunity at York, murdered his master and assumed the crown, but was speedily dispossessed by Constantius Chlorus Cæsar, and soon afterwards the traitor was slain. Thus, in A.D. 296, Britain once more fell under the yoke of the Romans.

Carausius, whose name will ever live in the annals of his country as the first naval commander who gave prestige to the maritime power of Britain and made the island of his birth the mistress of the seas, fell in the prime of life, before his noble plans were fully matured.

Yet, though long ages have passed away, wherever the British fleet sails proudly along the seas, the honoured memory of Carausius deserves recognition as the founder of Britain's navy in the third century.

According to the "Chronicles of the Ancient British Kings," the following celebrity of our nursery rhymes was contemporary with Carausius:—
"*Coel Godeboy* (*Iarle Caerloyn*), A.D. 295.—Coel Godeboy . . . made two citties or townes (viz.) Caerffawydd and Caer Fyddan, in the British tongue, and in English Hereford and Sissecher

(Chichester), and he had a daughter called Elen, and she married Constance Emperoure of Rome, and in her righte was Kinge of Great Brittain, and she was the mothere of Constanantyne the Great, the first Christian Emperoure, and she founde the Holy Cross, on which our Lord and Saviour Jesus Christ suffered death, for the redemption of all mankind."

Against this Coel, the hero and "merry old soul" of our nursery rhymes, Constantius, the Roman senator, was sent. This monarch was

> "Coyll,
> Who, after long debate, since Lucie's time,
> Was of the Britons first crowned sovereign;
>
> . . . .
>
> Which when the Romans heard, they hither sent
> Constantius, a man of mickle might,
> With whom King Coyll made an agreement,
> And to him gave for wife his daughter bright,
> Fair Helena, the fairest living wight,
> Who in all godly thews and goodly praise
> Did far excell, but was most famous bright
> For skill in music of all in her days
> As well in curious instruments as cunning lays."

Judging from the "fair Helena's" musical attainments, the court of "Old King Cole, the merry old soul," must have been remarkably cheerful, with its "curious instruments" and "cunning lays," and its blithe-hearted "fiddlers three."

As a connecting-link between Carausius and

our renowned King Arthur, the following details appear in the "Chronicles of the Ancient
British Kings":—"*Macsen* (A.D. 384), a Britton
born in Rome, was King of all Brittaine and
Emperoure of all Rome . . . and this Macsen
buylded 3 cittiees (viz.) Caer Sallawg, Caer
Vethyn, and Caer Alyne—in the English tongue
Serousburie (Shrewsbury), Caernarfon and Har-
fordwest—and hee conquered Armorica in France,
called hitt Little Brittaine, and gave it to Conan
Meriadoc, brother to his wife Elen, to holde
under the Kinge of Great Brittaine, and this
Macsen bye the said Elen had 3 sones (that is
to say) Peblig, Constantine, and Owen. This
Peblig was canonised a Saint, and Constantine
was a Prince of Brittaine, and Owen knighted
in the warres, and of this Owen are counted to
descende the head and principal stock of all
Brittaine. And at this tyme were sent from
Great Brittaine to inhabit Little Brittaine, one
hundred thousand of ploughmen and labourers,
and of knights, esquires, and gents, twenty
thousand of maidens of the lower sort or degree,
eleven thousand virgines of the higher sort or
degree, which eleven thousand maidens landed
at Colen (Cologne) in Almayne, and were there
martyred in the behalf or quarrel of the Catholic
faith, and they are called the eleven thousand
martyrs."

With reference to Cystennyn Fendigaid, Constantine the Blessed, or, as he is sometimes described, Cystennyn Llydaw, Constantine of Armorica, the Chronicles contain this record :— " *Cystennyn brawd Aldwr brenin Llydaw* (A.D. 433).—And after that the Romans forsook the tributt of Greate Brittaine because they were weary to defende the lande frome strange rebells which did then warre upon the Brittons, and the Brittons were in dispare what to doe ; they took counsel therein, and at last they went out to Little Brittaine to King Alan, called in the British tongue Aldwr, and desired hyme to have aide and power to resist there enemyes, and this Kinge of Little Brittaine agreed to give them aide and power, and to perform all their request upon condition that they would make his brother Constantine Kinge of Greate Brittaine ; and soe was done accordinglye. This Constantine was the sone of Ludwal, Kinge of Little Brittaine, and he had three sones (viz.) Constantine, Ambros, and Uthyr Pendragon, which were all three in tyme Kinges of Greate Brittaine. Hee Buylded 3 citties (viz.) Caer Umber, Argaerangon, a Chaerwent, in the Brittish tongue ; and in English they are called Warwicke, Uscestovre, and the third Caerwent in both languages, and hee was called Constantine the Defender, and also Holie Constantine."

CHAPTER VII

ARTHUR, THE WARRIOR-KING

WHEN Cystennyn Llydaw's son, called by Gildas, Ambrosius Aurelianus, known to the Britons as Emrys Wledig, was, to the "great grief of Britain," poisoned by a Saxon disguised as a physician, it is said that mysterious signs and omens were seen in the heavens. A star of great magnitude, consisting of a single beam, ending in a large and perfect ball of fire resembling a dragon's head with two more beams, appeared. The single beam was divided into seven smaller rays, and of the two dragon's head beams, one pointed towards Ireland, and the other towards France.

Merlin regarded the omen to be a token of the death of Emrys and Uthyr's accession to the throne. "Mystic Uthyr," fully believing the prophetic omen of the star, had a banner woven on which was worked in regal and splendid colours a dragon's head, after which

he adopted the surname of Pendragon. Later
on, after many battles and much trouble from
mutinous British princes and nobles, Uthyr the
brave fell a victim to the Saxons, who pursued
him to Verulam, and there poisoned the waters
of the well of which he always drank, so that he
died early and unexpectedly. Then Uthyr was
gathered to his fathers, and buried within the
sacred and solemn Circle of Heroes on Salisbury
Plain.

In common league against the Saxons, the
people of Cornwall united with the natives of
South Wales around the standard of the dragon
borne aloft by Uthyr's army, and after the unnatural death of their leader the great men and
warriors of Britain assembled to elect a new
king. According to some of the chroniclers,
Arthur, on his father's death, and "at an early
age, was, by common voice, elected his successor."

Other authorities state that the British princes
and nobles were for some time unable to come
to a decision. Arthur was young—too young,
many of them thought—for a leader of bearded
men and the great pendragonship. Yet the
youth was fair to look upon and brave-hearted,
and the rumour went that he was courteous,
kindly, and gentle. But even in those far days,
which the modern imagination associates with
deeds of daring and stirring events of crafty
invasion and powerful defence, tongues wagged,

fingers were uplifted, and heads were nodded by those who knew ",what was said," as some of the bearded men in the assembly branded young Arthur as "the false son of Gorlois," and not the heir of Uthyr Pendragon.

Then came the test of heirship and royalty, as prophesied by Merlin.

It was Christmas Eve, and those who approached the "place of assembly" beheld a great stone of white granite or marble, upon which some said there was an anvil, while others saw only a curious kind of sheath.

Fast held in that anvil or sheath was a mystic sword, around which, in letters of gold, there was an inscription worded to the effect that he who should, without much effort, remove the implement of warfare was the rightful heir to the throne. It has been said that this stone, with its anvil or sheath, appeared before the high altar of the cathedral church of Caerleon, when preparations for the holy Christmastide were completed and the congregation assembled for the midnight service.

The scene must have been both striking and effective.

In the dim glimmer of the altar lights, many ambitious youths and knights came forward and tried in vain to remove the sword, while interested bystanders looked eagerly on and shadows lurked in the eyes of the evil ones.

Day after day passed, while gossips watched and warriors waited, and those who loved their lost Uthyr yearned for the coming of his son.

On New Year's Day an unknown youth wished to try his prowess. With courteous demeanour and dignified bearing he stepped forward. Under their breath, the vendors of mischief, who recognised the youth, hoarsely hissed, " Arthur, the son of Gorlois."

Undaunted, the boy approached the great stone, and, putting his hand to the sword, drew it from the anvil or sheath, as an iron from the sparks or a blade from the scabbard.

Thus he proved his right to the kingship, as prophesied by Merlin.

In an instant the scoffers were silenced, and the voices of those who muttered "False" were lost in the popular cry of " Arthur, the king!"

Ancient chronicles of the kings record his accession thus:—"*Arthur* (A.D. 546) [it should be A.D. 517] *ap Uthyr Pendragon* ap Constantine was made Kinge of all Brittaine whene hee was butt younge, of xv years of age, butt hee was fair and boulde, and doughtye of bodie, and to meke folke hee was good and curteous, and lardg of spending, and made hyme wonderouslie well beloved amonge all men were it was neede. And when hee began to reigne hee sware that the Saxons never should have peace nor rest till he had driven them out of the lande. He was a

man of excellent prowesse, who, in xv greate
battles against the Saxons, he vanquished them,
and finallie drove the most parte of them out
of this realme; hee subdued Scotland, Ireland
and France, and the most part of all Europe,
and overcame the Emperoure of Rome in battle,
and slewe hyme. Hee made many houses of
religion, monasteries, and priries, and gave large
livings, rents, and revenuouse to them."

Arthur's sovereignty was immediately acknowledged, and Uthyr Pendragon's son and
successor was crowned by Dubricius. Churchyard, in his "Worthiness of Wales," quaintly
describes the memorable coronation in the
following fashion:—"The appoynted tyme of
the solemnitie approching, and all being readie
assembled in the citie of Carlleon, the Archbishop
Dubright was conveighed to the palace with
royal solemnitie, to crowne King Arthur. Dubright, therefore (because the court then lay
within his diocese), furnished himself accordingly
to perfourme and solemnise this charge in his
owne person. The king, being crowned, was
royally brought to the cathedrall church of that
metropoliticall see. On either hand of him,
both the right and the left, did two arch-
bishoppes support him. And fower kings, to
wit, Angusell king of Albania, Cadnall king
of Venedocia, Cader king of Cornewall, and
Sater king of Demetia, went before him, carry-

ing fower golden swords. The companies also
and concourse of sondrie sorts of officers played
before him melodious and heavenly harmonie."
The same authority also says that the queens
of those kings joined the procession, each
carrying a snow-white dove, while "discreet
personages of reverend countenance" bore
"olive boughs in token of their ambassage
from the Roman general, Lucius Tiberius," on
whose behalf they were come to demand of
Arthur the tribute which had been withheld
from the Romans since "the time of Julius
Cæsar!"

From the moment when Dubricius placed the
crown upon the boy king's head to the last sad
scene in Avalon, Arthur fulfilled a wonderful,
and in many respects an almost unparalleled,
destiny.

As the hero of romance and chivalry, he is
unrivalled; as the valorous, intrepid, and successful warrior, his name was, and remains, a
world-word; as the conqueror of giants and lord
of fairy-land, he presides over the dreams and
fancies of childhood; and as an ideal king and
central figure seated beside the Round Table at
"Old Caerleon upon Usk," he enthrals men's
minds, and holds even the prosaic world of to-
day spell-bound under the influence of his
wonderful career.

Accustomed to the quaint and interesting

details of Malory's "Morte d'Arthur" and the
beautifully picturesque descriptions in Tennyson's
"Idylls of the King," it is almost impossible to
associate this monarch's name with the heroism
of a semi-civilised age. Turner, in his "History
of the Anglo-Saxons," writes :—"When all
fictions are removed, and when those incidents
only are retained which the sober criticism of
history sanctions with its approbation, a fame
ample enough to interest the judicious, and to
perpetuate his honourable memory, will still continue to bloom."

The real Arthur was a hero with a character
composed of "stern stuff."

Many wars and much bloodshed, a life of
rugged simplicity and adventure, conflicts
against national enemies and domestic foes,
developed the strength of will which Arthur
inherited from his forefathers into the highest
form of heroism.

His perseverance and determination were
indomitable and proverbial. He could easily
surmount the greatest obstacle, courageously
overcome any difficulty and conquer every foe.
As a stern, unflinching commander he was
dreaded by his enemies, but even the Saxons
knew full well that the great leader of the Celts
was devotedly beloved by his people for his
courage and generosity, his amiability of temper
and real goodness of disposition.

F

Shorn of all the splendid accessories of court
life at Caerlleon; bereft of all the glamour and
mystery connected with his deeds of chivalry,
robbed of all but his great coat-of-mail, his
golden helmet crowned with the figure of a
dragon; his shield, called Priwen or Prydwen,
emblazoned with the portrait of the "blessed
Mary"; his sword Caliburn, or Excalibur, which
had been made in the island of Avallon; his
spear, called Ron-cymminiad; and his dagger,
Carnwennan, he stands forth in the twilight of
semi-barbaric centuries as a fitting model for
heroes of all ages.   It may here be mentioned
that sometimes the old chroniclers give the name
Prydwen to Arthur's ship bearing the figure-head
of "Our Ladye."   Putting his will to the deed,
he carried out his intentions with unswerving
determination and ceaseless energy.   From the
day on which he was chosen as king and
"leader of men" to the hour of his death he
remained faithful to his country, his people,
and his friends.

Immediately upon his accession to the throne
he raised an army, and forthwith marched
against the Saxons.

First he is seen with his unwavering hosts on
the snow-covered fens beside the river Duglas,
wherefrom he drives Colgrin to York; next he is
at the head of fifteen thousand men making a
barricade of felled trees in the dim and mys-

terious forest of Celidon, where he compelled the
Saxons to capitulate ; and later on, still waging
war against the " faithless heathens," he prepares
for the fierce encounter at Bath, where Arthur,
rushing upon the pagans, smites them "hip and
thigh," and compels them to flee before his
mighty forces.   Afterwards he is seen routing
the   Caledonian   " barbarians,"   and   following
them to Loch Lomond, and, according to the
"Brut-Tysilio," besieging them on the " three
hundred and sixty islands " of that wonderful
lake, into which the same number of rivers
flowed, to the delight of a similar number of
eagles who made their abode there.

Next, Arthur rests a while, and holds court and
council at York during the Christmastide, at
this time acting as restorer and reorganiser of
various churches and religious institutions, and
divider of the kingdom according to his wishes.
By this arrangement Urien receives Rheged,
Arawn has Scotland, and Llew, their brother,
gets Lothian ; after which Arthur takes to himself a wife in the person of Gwenhwyvar, the
daughter of Gogyrvan Gawr, the "fairest woman
in Britain," of whom it is written :—" Gwenhwyvar, the wife of Arthur . . . appeared love-
liest at the Offering on the day of the Nativity,
or at the feast of Easter."   In the next summer-
time he fits out his fleet and sails for Ireland,
and compels the kings of Scotland and Orkney

to willingly pay tribute rather than become
acquainted with his exploits.

During the twelve succeeding years he rules
in peace, and his court becomes a scene of splendour, hospitality, and pleasure. Thereto people
of renown flock, some as his guests, and others
whose curiosity is roused partly in love and half
in awe of him.

Once more the martial fire is rekindled, and
Arthur the king has a mind to subdue Europe.
So he begins with Norway and Denmark, and
proceeds to Gaul, taking Gascony, Normandy,
and other provinces. After this he holds thanks-
giving on the feast of Pentecost at Caerlleon,
where he is solemnly recrowned by three arch-
bishops, Dubricius " singing the service "; after
which are processions, tilt and tournament,
hunting, and hawking. On this occasion the
court is "attended by earls and barons of the kingdom, their ladys and children, who din'd at the
royal table with great pomp and eclat ; minstrels
flocking thither from all parts ; justs and tour-
naments being perform'd, and various other kinds
of divertisements, which lasted several days."

In the "Mabinogion" it is stated :—" Caerlleon was the place most easy of access in his
dominions, both by sea and land. And there
were assembled nine crowned kings, who were his
tributaries, and likewise earls and barons. For
they were his invited guests at all the high festi-

vals, unless they were prevented by any great
hindrance. And when he was at Caerlleon, holding his court, thirteen churches were set apart
for mass. And thus were they appointed : one
church for Arthur, and his kings, and his guests ;
and the second for Gwenhwyvar and her ladies ;
and the third for the steward of the household
and the suitors ; and the fourth for the Franks
and the other officers ; and the other nine churches
were for the nine Masters of the Household."
Very quaintly the "Mabinogion" adds that the
day and the night "were spent in abundance of
minstrelsy, and ample gifts of liquor, and a multitude of games. And when it was time for them
to go to sleep they went!"

These festivities last three days, while on the
fourth, ecclesiastical honours are bestowed, pre-
ferments are made, and David, afterwards the
patron saint of Wales, is made Archbishop of
Caerlleon, in succession to St. Dubricius, who,
weary of court life and its gaieties, retires to a
hermitage.

Arthur next bids defiance to Lucius Tiberius
for claiming tribute. Leaving his queen and
kingdom in the care of his nephew Medrawd—
the Modred of Tennyson—he goes to meet Lucius,
and in the valley of Suesia a fierce battle is fought,
and the Roman is slain. Last of all, this noble-
hearted hero of many battles and much mystery
returns home, to discover the treachery of Med-

rawd, the faithlessness of Gwenhwyvar, and the
bitter woes of civil war.   Arthur and Medrawd
meet, and a terrible battle ensues beside the river
Camlan.   There, in A.D. 542, the traitor is slain
and the victor is wounded unto death.   Soon
afterwards the end slowly approaches, and, in the
words of the sweetest singer of this age—

"So like a shattered column lay the king;
　Not like that Arthur who, with lance in rest,
　From spur to plume a star of tournament,
　Shot thro' the lists at Camelot, and charged
　Before the eyes of ladies and of kings."

Thus runs the story of Arthur, the hero and
king.

It is interesting here to note the account given
by Nennius of Arthur.   According to that ancient
chronicler, Arthur's name was a terror, for translated it meant "dreadful bear" or "iron mace"
wielded by the "dreadful son" of Uthyr Pendragon.   The same author gives the celebrated
battles of this famous king in the following order :
—The first was fought at the "mouth of the
river Glem," the locality of which has been
variously fixed at Glen, in Northumberland ;
Glem, in Lincolnshire ; or Glevi, in Devonshire.
Nennius continues thus :—"The second, third,
fourth, and fifth happened at another river, called
the Duglas, in the region named Linnis," which
may mean Dunglas in Scotland, Duglas in Lan-

cashire, or some river in that district of Cornwall known as Lionesse. "The sixth battle was
on the river Bassas; and the seventh in the forest
of Calidon, that is, *Cat Coit Celidon*. . . . His
eighth victory was gained at Gunnion Castle,
where Arthur bore upon his shoulders the image
of the cross of Christ, and of the Blessed Mary,
ever virgin; and the pagans fled on that day,
and many fell, for sore discomfiture was upon
them through the power of our Lord Jesus Christ
and of his blessed mother.   For Arthur went to
Jerusalem, and there made a cross of the magnitude of the saving cross; and it was consecrated
there; and for three days together he fasted,
and watched, and prayed, before the cross of the
Lord, that he might give him, through that
symbol, victory over the pagans, which also happened; and he brought with him the image of
the Blessed Mary, fragments of which are yet
kept with great veneration in Wedale . . . which
signifies 'the Vale of Woe' . . . in the province of Lodonesia, but now in the jurisdiction
of the bishop of St. Andrews of Scotland, six
miles to the west of that once noble and beautiful monastery of Meilros. . . . The ninth was
fought in Caer Legion; the tenth was on the
banks of the Ribroit, or Trathtrewroit; the
eleventh was on the mountain called Agned
Cathregonnon; and the twelfth was at Mount
Badon, in which eight hundred and forty men

fell by the sole attack of Arthur; none but he laid them low." The "Annales Cambriæ" give as the locality of this battle Bannesdown, near Bath, in A.D. 516, and state that in this important conflict "Arthur bore the Cross of our Lord Jesus Christ for three days and three nights on his shoulders; and the Britons were the victors."

The great battle of Bath was fought in A.D. 520, and not in A.D. 516, as recorded by Nennius. This conflict—the site of which is thus described by Camden: "Bannesdown, hanging over the little village of Bathstone, and showing" in his day "its bulwarks and rampire"—is the last on the list of Nennius, but appears third in other records. Of this great victory Taliesin sings:—

> "Woe to the miserable ones
> On account of the battle of Badon!
> Arthur was at the head of the valiant
> With their blood-red blades.
> He revenged on his foes
> The blood of the warriors—
> Warriors who had been the defence
> Of the sovereign of the North!"

Many memorials of the reverence in which the name of Arthur the king and his great renown were held in Britain are still to be found in many parts of the kingdom. The Roman amphitheatre at Caerlleon, and the top of a hill in Denbighshire bear the name of Arthur's Round

Table ; a stone near Newport, in Pembrokeshire, and another near Harlech, are named Arthur's Quoit. In Penrice, Glamorganshire, there is a cromlech called Arthur's Stone ; on the Berwyn Mountains, near Llandrillo, is the Board or Table of Arthur ; near Mold are the Crag and Cairn of Arthur ; at Lougher, in Glamorganshire, is Arthur's Stone ; while Arthur's Castle, Arthur's Seat, Arthur's Hall, Arthur's Troughs, and the Cadair or Chair of Arthur are to be found in the far west of Cornwall and the high north of Edinburgh. In the heavens the constellation Lyra appears to other nations, but in Wales it is called Telyn Arthur, or Arthur's Harp.

It is somewhat curious to pass from Arthur the hero and his warlike exploits to the scenes through which he moved and the Britain of his days as grotesquely described by Procopius, the Byzantine courtier, who wrote :—" In the Northern Ocean, about two hundred stadia from the continent, and right opposite to the mouths of the Rhine, lies the island of Brittia, between Britannia and Thule at the hindermost extremity of Gaul, where it borders on the ocean, and to the north of Spain. Three very numerous nations possess it —the Angili, the Phrissones, and the Brittones, each having a king of its own. . . . Moreover, here in ancient times a long wall, cutting off a great portion of it, was built ; for the soil is not alike on the two sides, the eastern side being

fertile, and the air temperate, and well watered;
but the western side is so different that no one
could live there half an hour; for it abounds in
vipers, and serpents, and wild beasts, and the air
is so unwholesome that none of the natives
venture to cross the wall, the very beasts which
cross it being killed by the pestiferous atmos-
phere. They say also, that the souls of men
departed are always conducted to this island, and
in this manner. On the coasts opposite to Brittia
are many villages inhabited by men engaged in
fishing and agriculture, and subject, but not
tributary, to the Franks. They often pass to the
island for the sake of merchandise; and the con-
ducting of souls thither devolves on them by
turn. When it is any one's turn to undertake
this operation, he retires to rest at dark, and
sleeps till he is summoned; for the conductor of
the souls shakes his door, and indistinct voices
call him; and he, as if constrained, rises and
goes to the shore, where he finds strange vessels
waiting to be rowed over; and entering one, he
sees it sink deeper into the water, even to the
gunwale, with the weight of its passengers, but
he sees them not. Then rowing, he reaches the
island in an hour, although in their own vessels,
with their oars, they can barely reach it in a day
and a night; and being arrived, he sees by the
boat rising out of the water, even to the keel,
that the freight is disembarked; yet still he sees

no one, but only hears a voice calling over the names, and dignities, and hereditary titles of those who have crossed, wives giving the names of their husbands; and being thus released, he immediately returns. And this the men of the district affirm takes place."

CHAPTER VIII

KING ARTHUR'S COURT

URNING from the warrior life of this
renowned monarch to his career as the
hero of court life and the Arthur of
chivalry, he stands surrounded by numerous
knights and fair dames, who appear in interesting array as heroes and heroines of reality and
romance.

There are the "Three knights of battle in
Britain," to whom Arthur is said to have sung—

"These are my three knights of battle;
Mael the tall, and Llyr mighty in arms,
And the pillar of the Cymry, Caradawg."

Beside them stand Gwalchmai, or Sir Gawaine
of romance; Arawn, the wise counsellor; Llywarch Hên, the bard of Argoed; Llawnslot dy
Lac, Sir Lancelot of the Lake; Galath, or Gala-
had, who went in quest of the "San Graal," or
Holy Grail; Peredwr ab Evarwg, or Percivale

of chivalry. There, too, are Cador of Cornwall;
Owain, the son of Urien Rheged; Trystan, Sir
Tristram; and Cai, better known as Sir Kai.
Near them are the guardians of the Graal, Cadawg, Iltyd, and Peredur; and, according to the
Triads, there are the "Three privileged knights
of the court of Arthur—Eithew, son of Gwrgawn;
Coleddawg, son of Gwyn; and Geraint the Tall,
son of Cymmanon the Aged. They were ple-
beians, and the sons of vassals; but their word,
their disposition for honesty, urbanity, gentle-
ness, wisdom, bravery, justice, mercy, and every
praiseworthy quality and science, either in peace
or in war, were so good, that the court of Arthur
and its privileges were free for them."

In the Triads, Gwalchmai, or Gawaine, takes
his place as one of the "Three golden-tongued
knights in the court of Arthur . . . for there
was neither King, nor Earl, nor Lord, to whom
these came, but would listen to them before all
others; and whatever request they made, it
would be granted them, whether willingly or
unwillingly; and thence they were called the
Golden-Tongued."

Gwalchmai's powers of persuasion brought
Trystan, or Sir Tristram—after three years' absence owing to displeasure—back to the court
of Arthur, who had sent eight-and-twenty
warriors to seize him, but without avail. This
knight was a celebrated scientist, and one of the

three of whom it was said "there was nothing of which they did not know the elements, and the material essence."

Walwyn's Castle in Pembrokeshire, where it is better known as Castell Gwalchmai, is a memorial of this knight, who, according to William of Malmesbury, was buried near the shore in a province named Rhôs, in Pembroke county.

Arawn, or Aron, and Llywarch Hên were two of the "Three counselling knights" of the court of Arthur. Of them the Triads state:—"These three knights were the counsellors of Arthur, and whatever dangers threatened him in any of his wars, they counselled him, so that none were able to overcome Arthur; and thus he conquered all nations through three things which followed him; and these were good hope, and the consecrated arms which had been sent him, and the virtue of his warriors; and through these he came to wear twelve crowns upon his head, and he became Emperor of Rome . . . and he had nothing but success when he acted by the advice which he received from them, and reverses when he did not follow their counsel."

Llywarch Hên was the celebrated warrior-poet whose odes and elegies are among the grandest and most powerful in the Welsh language.

Peredur, the "Prince of Sunshine," is celebrated in the ancient romances as Perceval,

who with others went in quest of the celebrated
Sangreal, and recovered the Holy Lance, of
which it is written in the "Mabinogion":—
"Then Peredur and his uncle discoursed together, and he beheld two youths enter the hall
and proceed up to the chamber, bearing a spear
of mighty size, with three streams of blood flowing from the point to the ground. And when
all the company saw this, they began wailing
and lamenting. But for all that, the man did
not break off his discourse with Peredur. And as
he did not tell Peredur the meaning of it, he
forbore to ask him concerning it."

Cador of Cornwall was one of the blithe-
hearted knights who withdrew with Arthur to
the Tower of Heroes at Caerlleon to read the
letter from Lucius Tiberius demanding tribute.
And of him it is said:—"Cador of Cornwall
made merry remarks upon the prospect of war
as they climbed the stairs."

Owain, the son of Urien Rheged, is one of
the heroes of the "Mabinogion." His name is
mentioned in the Triads as one of the "Three
Knights of Battle," of whom it is recorded:—
"And this was their three characteristics, that
they would not retreat from battle, neither for
the Spear, nor for the Arrow, nor for the Sword,
and Arthur never had shame in battle, the day
he saw their faces there, and they were called
the Knights of Battle."

Lewis Glyn Cothi, in an ode to Gruffudd ap Nicholas, a Carmarthenshire chieftain, who was descended from Urien Rheged, sings thus—

> "Gruffudd will give three ravens of one hue,
> And a white lion to Owain."

Owain, the son of Urien Rheged, was the father of the celebrated St. Kentigern.

From the heraldic emblem of Owain, the White Lion became a popular tavern sign throughout Wales.

Cai, known also as Sir Kai, is represented in the Triads as "one of the Three Diadem'd Chiefs of Battle," and gifted with magic by means of which he was able to transform himself into any shape he desired. In the "Mabinogion" it is recorded :—"Kai had this peculiarity, that his breath lasted nine nights and nine days under water, and he could exist nine nights and nine days without sleep. A wound from Kai's sword no physician could heal. Very subtle was Kai. When it pleased him, he could render himself as tall as the highest tree in the forest. And he had another peculiarity,—so great was the heat of his nature, that, when it rained hardest, whatever he carried remained dry for a handbreadth above, and a handbreadth below his hand ; and when his companions were coldest, it was to them as fuel with which to light their fire."

That was the Kai of Romance, but the real
hero and valorous buffoon was celebrated for his
want of courtesy to Sir Gareth, the brother of
Gwalchmai, or Sir Gawaine. When Sir Gareth
presented himself before Arthur, and craved, as
a boon, permission to remain for a year as an in-
mate of the king's palace, Sir Kai the seneschal
was commanded to give him all meats and
beverages of the best, and to treat him "as
though he were a lordes sone." Whereupon,
according to the "Morte d'Arthur," "'that shal
lytel nede,' said Syr Kay, 'to doo suche cost
upon him. For I dare undertake he is a vylayne
borne, and neuer make man, for and he had
come of gentylmen, he wold have axed of you
hors and armour, but such as he is so he asketh.
And sythen he hath no name, I shall yeue hym
a name that shall be Beaumayns that is fayre
handes, and in to the ketchen I shalle brynge hym,
and there he shalle haue fatte broweys eury daye,
yt he shall be as fatte by the twelue monethes
ende as a porke hog.'" And in this manner Sir
Kai "scorned him and mocked hym." And
when a year had passed Beaumayns desired to
be knighted, whereupon Sir Kai derided him
and called him a "kechyn knave" and unworthy to be a knight. For which, later on,
Beaumayns unhorses Sir Kai the braggart, and
takes possession of his arms, in an adventure
undertaken on behalf of Luned, or Lunette, for

the sake of her sister, "dame Lyones of the Castel Peryllous." In the end Beaumayns, or Sir Gareth, married "Dame Lyones."

Cadawg, who with Illtyd and Peredur were guardians of the Grail, is better known to students of Celtic lore as Cattwg Ddoeth, Cattwg the Wise, and to others as St. Cadoc. He was renowned for his wisdom. A very large collection of his maxims and moral sayings, both in prose and verse, is preserved in the "Myvyrian Archæology." He was the first principal of the celebrated College of Llancarvan, which was founded in the fifth century. In the "Life of Saint Cadoc" he is described as "the most Blessed Cadoc, also called Sophia or Sophias, Bishop and Martyr, of the City of Beneventum." The celebrated Taliesin was a pupil of Cadoc, who gave the poet the following wholesome advice:—"The counsels which Cattwg gave to Taliesin, the Chief of Bards. Consider before thou speakest; secondly, why thou speakest; thirdly, to whom thou speakest; fifthly, what will come of what thou speakest; sixthly, what will be the benefit of what thou speakest; seventhly, who may be listening to what thou speakest. Place thy word on the end of thy finger before thou speakest it, and turn it these seven ways before thou speakest it, and no harm will ever result from what thou speakest. These were addressed by Cattwg

Ddoeth, the Chief of Bards, when he was giving him his blessing."

After Cadawg the knight, or Cadoc, quitted court life at Caerleon for a religious career at Llancarvan, many miracles were attributed to him. Thus it is written :—" When his sheep depastured on the aforesaid island Echni (The Flat Holmes), lo, two wolves from England, by swimming came to the place. Having torn many of the sheep, and slain some with their rapacious mouths, they attempted to swim towards the British sea; but when they had come to the middle, they were changed by divine judgment, because they had irritated and slain his sheep, into stones, and in the British language were called Cunbleid, that is Wolf Stones."

Two very dangerous rocks in the Bristol Channel are still known to mariners as "The Wolves."

Concerning the death of Cadawg, the following record appears in his " Life " :—" He heard an angel of the Lord mentioning to him in a vision of the night, ' Lo, an option is given to thee by the Lord ; now choose by what death thou wilt leave this mortal life, and migrate to the eternal kingdom.' He answered, ' Having my option, I choose martyrdom, as it is, before the Lord, the most excellent of deaths.' " The angel then fore-told that a " cruel king " would plunder the city

and kill him before the altar.   Accordingly, "as
he sang mass . . . one of the horsemen entered
the church . . . and with incited step and
raging fury, pierced Saint Sophias (or Cadoc)
with a lance, as he stood on the altar. . . .
Many . . . miracles were performed after his
death. . . . Sight was restored to the blind, and
walking to the lame, the leprous were cleansed,
and the demons were driven away from those
who were possessed by them. . . ."

Beneventum here mentioned is supposed to
have been Benevenna, now called Weedon, in
Northamptonshire, whereto St. Cadoc was translated, or "bodily carried . . . as Elias was in
a chariot of fire to Paradise . . . ."!

From the "Sayings of the Wise," which are
attributed to Cadawg, or St. Cadoc, the following
verses are selected :—

> " Hast thou heard the saying of Illtyd,
>   The studious golden-chained knight ?
>   Whoso does evil, evil betide him.
>
> Hast thou heard the saying of Caw ?
>   Though it is easy to un-freeze frost,
>   It is not easy to un-sort sort.
>
> Hast thou heard the saying of Cadwgi
>   The Little, who overcame giants ?
>   There is no sickness but sloth.
>
> Hast thou heard the saying of St. Ilid,
>   One come of the race of Israel ?
>   There is no madness like extreme anger.

" Hast thou heard the saying of ancient time
  Of worthy clearest utterance ?
  The fool will laugh when drowning.

  Hast thou heard the saying of Gyttyn,
  Who knew not which side of the loaf the butter was ?
  It is either a fox or a bush of fern.

  Hast thou heard the saying of Peredur,
  Sovereign of the Island of Britain ?
  Harder is the brave than a blade of steel."

Womanhood, even in those days, was not
exempt from scarcasm :—

" Hast thou heard the saying of Cadrawd
  Calchvynydd, of vast meditation ?
  The best woman is the one without a tongue."

Poverty also had its pithy proverbs :—

" Hast thou heard the saying of the poor old man
  When he could not get alms ?
  Whoso has meal shall have meal.

  Hast thou heard the saying of the poor hoary hermit
  Where there was no hand stretched out ?
  Every ditch is a shelter to a beggar.

  Hast thou heard the saying of Eleri
  Where there was not a bestowing hand ?
  It is not almsgiving that causes poverty."

In the other " Sayings," which are devoted to
nature, the following appear :—

" Hast thou heard the saying of the hawk
Conversing with the kite ?
The friend of the wolf is the slothful shepherd.

Hast thou heard the saying of the ant
In the winter, out of its mound ?
Summer sleep, winter famine.

Hast thou heard the saying of the blackbird
Hiding from the hawk ?
There is but a season for the proud.

Hast thou heard the linnet
Feeding on the bog-berries ?
Wait for evil, it will come."

In these proverbs the lame dog has his day :—

" Hast thou heard the saying of the dog
In the ditch, having become lame ?
Let judgment be understood, before hanging."

But women are denied a hearing :—

" Hast thou heard the saying of the jay,
Screaming about the divulging of secrets ?
Make not thy wife thy confidante."

These words of the wise conclude thus :—

" Hast thou heard my own saying
After all sayings have been rehearsed ?
There is no wisdom like choosing the best."

And this ends this portion of the " Sayings of the Wise ; and happy is the man who is as wise as the Pig," who said :—

> " Hast thou heard the saying of the pig,
> Recoiling from dirty actions ?
> There is none so hateful as the drunkard."

In the Iolo MSS. there are one hundred and sixty-four triplets of the above description and various other compositions by Cadoc, including :—

" THE CIRCLE OF THE MORAL WORLD.

> " Poverty causes exertion,
> Exertion causes prosperity,
> Prosperity causes wealth,
> Wealth causes pride,
> Pride causes contention,
> Contention causes war,
> War causes poverty,
> Poverty causes peace,
> The peace of poverty causes exertion,
> Exertion brings round the same circle as before."

Illtyd, the co-guardian of the Grail and renowned " officer, leaving his earthly warfare . . . for obtaining the highest crown" . . . was afterwards known as St. Iltutus, of whom the following account is given in the Iolo MSS. : —" Illtyd Varchog (knight), the son of Bicanus of Armorica. His mother was the daughter of the king of Morganwg (Glamorgan), and he was chief of all Arthur's knights. And there occurred a contention betwixt Illtyd and the Emperor Marcian, and the Emperor's chief officers desired to kill him. And they laid hold upon Illtyd

whilst he was at prayer, and they could not move
in the least; but Illtyd by his prayers restored
them. And when the Emperor knew this of his
officers, he degraded them, and gave property to
Illtyd to form a college on the site of the church
of Eurgen (Eurgain), the daughter of Caractacus,
king of Morganwg, who, after being carried captive to Rome, was, together with his daughter
Eurgen, converted to the Christian faith. . . .
And Eurgen formed a college of twelve saints,
. . . and . . . it became an exceeding eminent
monastery; and Illtyd made three large new
cells, . . . and it was the most celebrated of all
the monasteries for piety and learning, and there
were two thousand saints. And Arthur gave
lands and great rents to these cells. . . . Here
are the names of the cells of the college of Illtyd:
the college of Matthew—of Mark—of Luke—of
John—Arthur—Saint David—Morgan—Eurgain
—and Amwn. Of these eight colleges, Illtyd was
the principal; and the place was named Bangor
Illtyd. . . .", It is also stated that "Illtyd
founded seven churches, and appointed seven
companies for each church, and seven halls or
colleges in each company, and seven saints in
each college. . . . And prayer and praise were
kept up, without ceasing, day and night, by
twelve saints, men of learning of each company.
. . . Illtyd Varchog (knight) bore for his arms,
argent, three masts, three castle tops, or, and six

darts or. (The three masts for the three schools,
and the three castle tops for the three colleges of
saints, and the six gold darts for the six churches,
which he founded for teaching the Christian
religion;) such was the number of the churches,
and they were all in Caer Worgan in Morganwg,
the place now called Llaniltyd Vawr." This
locality is at present known as Llantwit Major,
Glamorganshire, where Illtyd, the knight and co-
guardian of the Sangraal or Holy Grail, lived and
toiled. There still is to be seen the shaft of an
inscribed cross, which has weathered the storms
of more than a thousand winters, and remains as
one of the most interesting memorials of the far
past and the heroes of King Arthur's court.

In the *Vita Sancti Iltuti* it is stated that this
knight "was named Illtyd, . . . one safe from
every crime; he was blameless in the five stages
of life, and was laudable and beloved by all persons. . . . He had so good a memory, that on
once hearing a saying of his master, he perfectly
retained it ever after. . . . No one was more
eloquent throughout Gaul than Illtyd the soldier
in reciting philosophical eloquence. . . . Outwardly he was a soldier who wore a military
dress, but inwardly he was one of the most intelligent of the natives of Britain. Therefore
he was appointed by King Paulinus (king of
Glamorgan) to be chief over the soldiers, on account of his exquisite eloquence and incompar-

able intelligence; no contemporary could be compared with him for mental ability, which was proved and confirmed by the testimony of learned men."

The later life of Illtyd was spent in "divine service; all his thoughts were in the holy Scriptures, which he fulfilled in his daily works; many scholars and learned persons in the seven arts flocked to him for instruction."

Geraint, the son of Erbin, was one of the most valiant heroes of Arthur's court. In the Triads he is described as one of the three naval commanders each of whom had sixscore ships, with sixscore men in each. This hero has been immortalised in ancient Welsh literature by that aged bard of sorrow and war, Llywarch Hên, who describes him as having "a face beaming with beauty; he was the glory of Britain." He adds, "When Geraint was born, the gates of heaven were open." The venerable poet then sings :—

"Before Geraint, the terror of the foe,
　I saw steeds fatigued with the toil of battle,
And after the shout was given, how dreadful was the onset.

　At Llongborth I saw the tumult,
　　And the slain drenched in gore,
And red-stained warriors from the assault of the foe.

　Before Geraint, the scourge of the enemy
　　I saw steeds white with foam,
And after the shout of battle, a fearful torrent.

At Llongborth I saw the raging of slaughter
And an excessive carnage,
And warriors blood-stained from the assault of Geraint."

Longborth is believed by some to have been
Portsmouth ; by others it is supposed to be Lang-
port, in Somersetshire.

The story of Geraint is so beautifully told
in Tennyson's " Idylls of the King," that any
further allusion to him would be a waste of
words.

Caradawc Vreichvras was another hero of
Arthur's camp and court. The Triads describe
him as one of the " Battle Knights of Britain."
He was the son of Llyr Merini, prince of Cornwall, and his valour is thus described by his
contemporary, Aneurin, the poet :—

" When Caradawc rushed into battle,
  It was like the tearing onset of the woodland boar,
  The bull of combat in the field of slaughter,
  He attracted the wild dogs by the action of the hand. . . .
  From Cattraeth and its carnage,
  From the hostile encounter . . .
  He saw no more the dwelling of his father."

Lluagor, Caradawc's steed, is described in the
Triads as one of the " Three Battle Horses of the
Island of Britain."

Ederyn, the son of Nudd, was another hero of
Arthur's court. With six thousand men under
his command, he led an expedition to assist
Gawaine and others, who had been treacherously

assailed while returning from their mission to the Roman camp, during Arthur's celebrated expedition against the Emperor of Rome. Of this hero, William of Malmesbury says that, in order to prove Ederyn's military skill, King Arthur "conducted him to the hill of Brentenol, for the purpose of fighting three most atrocious giants. And Ider (Ederyn), going before the rest of the company, attacked the giants valorously, and slew them. And when Arthur came up, he found him apparently dead, having fainted with the immense toil he had undergone, whereupon he reproached himself with having been the cause of his death through his tardiness in coming to his aid." For which neglect Arthur ordered the monks of Glastonbury to say Mass, and gave endowments of lands and money and ecclesiastical ornaments to the Abbey. Doubtless this act of the king helped later on to immortalise the hero, for in Rees's "Welsh Saints" it is recorded :—"Ederyn the son of Nudd . . . was a bard, who embraced a life of sanctity, and the chapel of Bodederyn under Holyhead is dedicated to him. .... Festival, Jan. 6."

Trystan, the son of Tallwch, who is more generally known as Tristran, of Chivalry, and Sir Tristram or Tristrem of Romance, was one of the celebrated chieftains of the sixth century. He is described in the Triads as one of the "Three Diademed Princes" of Arthur's court. Like

Sir Kai, he had the reputation of being able
to transform himself to any shape at his own
will and fancy.   His unfortunate attachment to
Essyllt, or Isolt, the wife of March ap Meirchion,
or Mark, is the subject of Swinburne's brilliant
and alliterative verse.

CHAPTER IX

SEMI-MYTHICAL HEROES

PASSING from the ranks of the real heroes of Arthur's court, the semi-mythical characters of it illustrate the humorous side of a life, in an age when attractions of barbaric splendour vied with martial excitement, while plunder and destruction were curiously united to fitful outbursts of religious contrition and fervour.

The bravest real heroes of this period thought little of attacking the churches and pilfering the goods of religious institutions and bodies, and afterwards making reparation in various ways. The following illustrations are particularly consistent with the spirit of the Arthurian era.

In the *Vita Sancti Paterni* it is recorded: "Maelgwn, king of the Northern Britons, . . . the great tempter of the saints . . . ordered two heralds to go before him, that they might

try Saint Padarn in some malicious manner, and
they . . . with a wicked intention . . . filled
their bags with moss and gravel, which they
feigned to be royal treasures ; and they brought
them to the saint, and requested him to keep
them until the king should return prosperously."
When the king returned from his warfare, " he
sent the wicked heralds that they might try the
saint." The manner in which these messengers
proceeded was mischievous and daring. Going
quickly to St. Padarn, they " took up the bags,
and, emptying them, laid down the moss and
gravel, and saucily exclaimed that the royal
treasures had been stolen, and gravel and moss
had been put in their place ; the saint on the
other hand declared that they were found in the
same state as they had been delivered. But
they threatened ruin to the whole building, if
the treasures were not restored." Whereupon
an ordeal of "very hot water" was arranged,
and "then in the warmth of the spirit, Padarn
orders the water to be made hot in a brazen
vessel until it boiled ; this was soon done, and
Padarn immediately put his hand into the water,
when it was in its greatest heat, which when
taken out appeared white and cold as snow.
Soon after, the heralds were required to place
their hands in the water, and their scalded
hands showed the malice of their minds ; and
being forthwith all burnt, they and their lives,

and their souls fled in the form of ravens over the channel. . . . Then the king Maelgwn himself became blind . . . and sick at heart, and staggered with weak knees, and . . . went immediately to Padarn, and on his knees asked for pardon, which was granted . . . and the king remunerated him with a quantity of land, that is from the mouth of the river Rheidiol, upwards, until at its head it touches the boundary of the river Clarach, and its boundary goes the whole length of the river to the sea. In that hour the king's eyes were cured, his heart was strengthened, and his knees rendered firm. . . . Saint Padarn and the king departed from each other in peace."

King Arthur appears as the offender in the next illustration, for it is said:—" Arthur traversed the countries on each side, and came on a certain day to the cell of Saint Padarn, the bishop, and while he spoke to Padarn, he looked at his coat, and being seized with the affection of avarice, asked if he should have it; and the saint answering, said, 'This coat is not suitable for the wearing of any malicious person, but for a clerical habit.' He went out of the monastery in a rage, and again returned in a state of anger that he might take away the coat against the wishes of the attendant saints. One of the disciples of Padarn, seeing him returning in a rage, ran to Saint Padarn, and said, 'The tyrant who was here before is returning in an insulting manner, and treading the ground, levels it with his feet.' Padarn answered, 'Yes, may the earth swallow him.' With the word, the earth opened its bosom to some depth, and swallowed Arthur as far as his chin, who immediately acknowledged himself guilty, and he began to praise both God and Padarn; until by asking pardon, the earth delivered him up. And in that place, with bended knees, he begged the favour of the saint, and obtained it; and he accepted Padarn for his perpetual patron, and so departed."

Near Llanbadarnfawr, in Cardiganshire, there is an ancient entrenchment known as Llys Arthur, or the Hall of Arthur.

The semi-mythical heroes of Arthur's court lead one back to regions of fairy-folk and giant lore, of weird enchantments and magic arts.

Sir Tristan and Sir Kai have already been described as heroes of battle and adventure, at the same time being endowed—according to Romance—with superhuman powers, but they are far surpassed by their grotesque and comical contemporaries who may be described as semi-mythical.

In the "Mabinogion," Morvran, the son of Tegid, is described as one of those who fortunately escaped being assailed in the battle of Camlan, "by reason of his ugliness; all thought he was

H

an auxiliary devil. Hair had he upon him like
the hair of a stag!" In striking contrast to
this character was Sandde Bryd Angel, of whom
it is said, "no one touched him with a spear in
the battle of Camlan, because of his beauty; all
thought he was a ministering angel!"

So fleet-footed was Henbedestyr that with
him "not any one . . . could keep pace, either
on horseback or on foot;" and with Henwas,
"no four-footed beast could run the distance of
an acre, much less beyond it."

Gwenhwyvar, the queen, had two attendant
messengers, named Yskyrdav and Yyscudydd,
whose "feet were as swift as their thoughts;"
and among the celebrated leapers who would
clear three hundred acres at one bound was
Gilla Coes Hydd, who not only gained much fame
in Wales, but became a champion in Ireland.

Sgilti, the messenger of the court, "when he
intended to go upon a message . . . never
sought to find a path, but knowing whither he
was to go, if his way lay through a wood, he
went along the tops of the trees." And so light
of foot was he that "a blade of reed grass bent not
beneath his feet, much less did one ever break."

Drem, the watchman, is thus described in the
"Myvyrian Archæology":—

> "Hast thou heard what Dremhidydd sang,
>   An ancient watchman on the castle walls?
>   A refusal is better than a promise unperformed."

Brave old Drem, the long and keen-sighted, looking from his hoary watch-tower in Gelli Wic, could see the gnat rising "in the morning with the sun," as it first peeped above the heights of "Pen Blathaon in North Britain."

Gelli Wic is supposed to have been in the neighbourhood of Callington, near which is the tor called Arthur's Hall and the rocky basins known as Arthur's Troughs, both in the parish of North-hill. Pen Blathaon is supposed to be Caithness, in Scotland. The distance between these points is about nine hundred miles, or the length of the "Island of Britain."

Sol boasted that without fatigue he could stand "all day upon one foot," while Gwadyn Ossol, standing on the "highest mountain in the world," found it merely as "a level plain under his feet." The feet of Gwadyn Odyeith "emitted sparks of fire" as they "cleared the way for Arthur," and to him the greatest obstacle was no hindrance. Sugyn is tersely described as "broad-chested," which he had need be, seeing that he could suck up the sea and strand hundreds of ships. Powerful Rhacymwri was able to thresh rafters, beams, and boards until they "were no better than small oats;" and one Uchtryd thought little of throwing his "red untrimmed beard over the eight-and-forty rafters which were in Arthur's Hall."

The child in the nursery is often rebuked for

"pulling a long lip," which expression owes its origin to Gwevyl, who, when sad at heart and fretful in spirit, "would let one of his lips drop below his waist, while he turned up the other like a cap upon his head!"

Curious, to say the least, were the three grandsons of Cleddyf. In the "Mabinogion" their shields are called "three gleaming glitterers;" their spears, "three pointed piercers;" and their swords, "three griding gashers." These men had three celebrated dogs, three wives, three daughters, three grandchildren, and three hand-maidens. Of Clust, the man of marvellous hearing, it is said that "though he were buried seven cubits beneath the earth, he would hear the ant fifty miles off, rise from her nest in the morning!"

Who, reading this record, and having a hearty laugh thereat, shall say there is no comedy, no burlesque, no subjects for pantomimic display, in the wonderland of Welsh romance?

To conclude this pause of a few minutes while contemplating the semi-mythical heroes of the Arthurian age, let us glance at the bards and minstrels who, in a long procession, passed before King Maelgwyn Gwynedd, and made obeisance to him. On this occasion, instead of behaving, as usual, in a dignified and proper manner, these men never uttered a single word, but made ugly mouths and wry faces at the king, and played "Blerwm, blerwm" on their pouted lips.

Whereupon the king, losing patience, and thinking the bards were "drunk with many liquors," became angry, as well he might at such vulgar behaviour, and naturally commanded them to "collect their wits." But although they were thrice ordered to "cease their funning," they remained refractory, and, worse than all, repeated the offence, and then the king ordered a squire to strike the chief bard on the head with a broom, until "he fell back upon his seat."

Then Heinin, the chief bard, confessed that their conduct was due to "the influence of a spirit that sits in the corner yonder in the form of a child." And that child was Taliesin, the bard, whose "blerwm" playing upon the lips was contagious. Taliesin subsequently, by means of his song, obtained the release of Elphin, who, in a family feud, had been taken prisoner by Maelgwn Gwynedd.

CHAPTER X

QUEEN GWENHWYVAR'S BOWER

IN that age, when loud and hoarse battle-cries mingled with songs of love and chivalry, when fair ladies made gay favours which were worn by courteous knights at the tourney, when gallantry was frequently followed by harshness and severity, and gentle deeds of kindness were often uncouthly received, society had its radiant lights and dark and gloomy shadows, among which lurked—

> "The little pitted speck in garnered fruit
> That rotting inward, slowly moulders all."

Knights were brave, but often faithless; and fair ladies were beautiful, but sometimes fickle and false; and in Arthur's court both were to be found, though the good and faithful preponderated.

First by right of precedence as Queen and beauty is Gwenhwyvar, who has been immor-

talised by Tennyson under her modernised name,
Guinevere. This lovely lady was also known
as Guenever, Genievere, and Geneura. Welsh
legends describe Arthur as having had three
wives, each bearing the same name. One was
the daughter of Gwryd Gwent, another of
Gwythyr ap Greidiol, and the third was daughter
to Gogyrvan Gawr. In the romances and some
of the ancient legends, Gwenhwyvar was the
daughter of Leodegrance. Gwenhwyvar the
golden-haired is described in old Welsh folk-
lore as the daughter of Gogyrvan the Giant, and
of her it is said—

> " Bad when little, worse when great."

Her beauty, dignity, and subsequent littleness
have been so well described by Tennyson and
others, that more than this short reference to her
name here is unnecessary.

Enid's beauty, constancy, and devotion form
one of the most charming " Idylls of the King."
In the Triads she is called one of the fairest and
most illustrious ladies of Arthur's court.

Elined, Luned, or Lunette was the " daymosel
saueage " of the " Castle Peryllous," and sister
to Dame Lyones, whom Beaumayns, or Sir Gareth,
married. The magic ring of Luned, by means
of which she released Owain, the son of Urien, is
mentioned among the precious articles of the
Island of Britain. Whoever wore this ring, and

carefully concealed the stone, would immediately become invisible.

Tegan Eurvron, whose name is not so well known as it deserves to be, was the wife of Caradawc Vreichvras. This lady, who was renowned for her virtue and her charms, is described in the Triads as "one of the three chaste" ladies of Arthur's court. Her mantle, her golden goblet, and her knife were among the precious possessions of the Island of Britain. The mantle of Tegan Eurvron would only cover those ladies whose conduct was above reproach, and no fair dame could drink from her golden goblet unless her fame was untarnished.

In the old legends and stories of the Arthurian era the following ladies appear, lending charms to the dark days of warfare or casting shadows upon the purity of romance.

There is the "Lady of the Fountain," described as—

> "The riche ladye Alundyne
> The dukes doghter of Llanduit."

An ardent Welshman of the present day believes the Llanduit here mentioned to be the Llanuit of Leland's "Itinerary," and now known as Llantwit.

This lady is pictured in the "Mabinogion" as having "yellow hair falling over her shoulders, and stained with blood; and about her a dress

of yellow satin, which was torn.   Upon her feet
were shoes of variegated leather."

Then there is the " chief of the maidens," who
lived in the many-towered castle surrounded by
bushes and weeds ; and Peredur of the Holy
Lance, describing her, said :—" She had an old
garment of satin upon her which had once been
handsome, but was then so tattered that her skin
could be seen through it.   And whiter was her
skin than the bloom of crystal, and her hair and
her two eyebrows were blacker than jet, and on
her cheeks were two red spots, redder than whatever is reddest."

Angharad of the Golden Hand was one of the
most liberal ladies of Arthur's court, and to her
Peredur said, "Thou art a beauteous and lovely
maiden ; and, were it pleasing to thee, I could
love thee above all women."   Whereupon the
fair lady somewhat brusquely responded, " I
pledge my faith that I do not love thee, nor will
I ever do so."   For that reason Peredur pledges
his faith never to " speak another word to any
Christian again, until the fair lady would come
to love him above all men."

Next we see the " golden-chained daughters of
the Island."   These include Indeg, whose beauty
is so often extolled by the bards ; Morvudd, the
daughter of Urien Rheged and sister to Owain ;
Essyllt, who became notorious as Yseult or Isolt
in the romance of Sir Tristan and Isolte.

Radiant and beautiful appears Olwen, the daughter of Yspaddaden Penkawr, of whom the poet wrote—

"Olwen of slender eyebrow and pure heart."

Like a star shining in dark cloud-rifts, Olwen looks with her golden hair, foam-white skin, and cheeks "redder than the reddest roses." For a long time and wearily Kilhwch sought the maiden who was destined to be his wife, and when at last he found her, most extraordinary obstacles were put in the way of the winning. In the "Mabinogion" Kilhwch is described saying, "Ah! maiden, thou art she whom I have loved; come away with me lest they speak evil of thee and of me. Many a day have I loved thee." Whereupon the maiden replies, ". . . I have pledged my faith to my father not to go without his counsel, for his life will last only until the time of my espousals. Whatever is, must be. . . . Go, ask of my father, and that which he shall require of thee grant it, and thou wilt obtain me; but if thou deny him anything, thou wilt not obtain me."

Yspaddaden Penkawr makes thirty-nine requests, all of which are proposed in order, if possible, to put off the "evil day" and hour of death for the giant. At length, with the aid of Arthur and his faithful knights, Hawthorn Head's commands are satisfied, after which the giant is bearded in his den, and slain. The end of the giant was accomplished thus :—All requests being fulfilled, Kilhwch asks, " Is thy daughter mine now ? " To which the giant replies, " She is thine, but therefore needest thou not thank me, but Arthur, who hath accomplished this for thee. Then Goren . . . . seized him by the hair of his head, and dragged him after him to the keep, and cut off his head, and placed it on a stake on the citadel. Then they took possession of his castle, and of his treasures. And that night Olwen became Kilhwch's bride, and she continued to be his wife so long as she lived. . . . And thus did Kilhwch obtain Olwen, the daughter of Yspaddaden Penkawr."

All these brave knights, fair dames and damosels, and more beside, made Arthur's court the scene of pleasure and centre of gaiety. Many a time, when the roar and din of battle echoed and re-echoed among the distant mountain ranges, the darksome glens, gloomy ravines, and dreary passes of Wales, high festivals were held at Caerlleon, where days of tilt and tournament were broken by recitations, music, and song, while lords and ladies played chess with golden pieces on boards of silver, or watched the magic and golden chessboard of Gwenddolen—another celebrated beauty of Arthur's court—whereon the silver chessmen played of themselves, as " they had been living men."

Even then the inward rotting that soon was to develop into slow mouldering had commenced.

When mirth was at its zenith and song was in its prime, when Arthur's face shone with a great light and Gwenhwyvar looked fairer than ever, treacherous eyes watched and sinister smiles curved the lips of two, as messages conveyed by glances passed from one knight to another in the king's presence-chamber.

One of these knights was Medrawd, the king's nephew, friend, and confidant, whose personal prowess and charms of speech—the qualities of which are described as being " calmness, mildness, and purity " — turned the heads of the damosels and the hearts of the dames. There he stood, the hero of many campaigns, the trusted knight and kinsman of Arthur, hatching in secret a treacherous confederacy, that craftily concealed future hostility. Near him lurked Iddog or Iddawc Cordd Prydain, the plotter and planner of mischief, ready to aid Medrawd against the counsels of the king, who, on that last Christmastide of his life, guessed not that his dearest friends and most faithful knights were his worst enemies. In the " Mabinogion " Iddawc is described as having " yellow curling hair " and a " beard newly trimmed." He " wore a coat of yellow satin sewn with green silk, and on his thigh was a gold-hilted sword, with a scabbard of new leather of Cordova, belted with the skin

of the deer, and clasped with gold. And over
this was a scarf of yellow satin wrought with
green silk, the borders whereof were likewise
green. And the green . . . was as green as
the leaves of the fir-tree, and the yellow was
as yellow as the blossom of the broom. So fierce
was the aspect of the knight, that fear seized
those who beheld him." Iddawc then explains
why he obtained the nickname of Cordd Prydain,
or Hammer of Britain, which could come down
heavily or lightly as he who wielded it pleased:
—" I was one of the messengers between Arthur
and Medrawd his nephew at the battle of Camlan;
and I was then a reckless youth, and through my
desire for battle, I kindled strife between them,
and stirred up wrath, when I was sent by Arthur
the Emperor to reason with Medrawd, and to
show him that he was his foster-father, and his
uncle, and to seek for peace, lest the sons of
the kings of the Island of Britain, and of the
nobles, should be slain. And whereas Arthur
charged me with the fairest sayings he could
think of, I uttered unto Medrawd the harshest I
could devise. And therefore am I called Iddawc
Cordd Prydain, for from this did the battle of
Camlan ensue. And three nights before the
battle of Camlan, I left them, and . . . I remained doing penance seven years, and after
that I gained pardon."

The last high festival of Christmas for Arthur

and his court at Caerlleon was spent in regal
splendour and fashion. When the drinking-horns,
filled with luscious metheglin, wine, or spiced
ale, went round, all present drank to the health
of the living and the memory of the dead, and
not one among the crowd of courtiers dared
prophesy how soon the traitor and his victim
should fall on unfair field, or the beloved king
and mighty warrior would be gathered to his
fathers.

So they "passed the night with songs, and
diversions, and discourse, and ample entertain-
ment, and when it was time for them all to go
to sleep, they went."

CHAPTER XI

THE EXIT OF ARTHUR

ITH day came the awakening. From the Romans in the south menaces and demands for tributes were sent; in the north the Saxons and Celts were engaged in obstinate struggles.

Hastily leaving his kingdom and Queen in charge of Medrawd, Arthur went forth to battle. During the king's absence Medrawd abused his privileges as Regent, and in that capacity exercised his power to overthrow the monarchy. According to some authorities, when Medrawd was engaged in treachery and sedition in South Wales and Cornwall, Arthur was fighting against foes in the north, whereto messengers conveyed the evil tidings. Then

> " Modred's narrow, foxy face,
> Heart-hiding smile, and gray persistent eye,"

came between the king, his subjects, his wife, and many of his knights.

Hearing that his wicked nephew had usurped the kingdom, Arthur quickly returned, to find the Saxons, Picts, and Scots allied with Medrawd, who obstinately resisted his uncle.

Though crushed in spirit by the treachery of his nephew, the faithlessness of Gwenhwyvar, and the loss of some of his bravest knights, lion-hearted Arthur pressed on and put the usurper to flight. Seizing the opportunity, Medrawd openly unmasked his plans, and with fire and sword laid waste his uncle's territory in Cornwall; and, in return, Arthur retaliated upon his nephew's possessions in the North.

Soon afterwards the eve of the last and fatal struggle approached.

Medrawd—whose infamous name still lives in strong contrast to Arthur's—and Iddawc met at Nanhwynian before the battle of Camlan, and this event is described in the Triads as one of the "three treacherous meetings of the Island of Britain."

Arthur once more, and for the last time, prepared to meet the foe. Tennyson, in some of his noblest and most patriotic verses, has described the king saying—

> " Now, I must hence ;
> Thro' the thick night I hear the trumpet blow :
> They summon me, their king, to lead mine hosts
> Far down to that great battle in the west,

Where I must strike against my sister's son,
Leagued with the lords of the White Horse, and knights
Once mine, and strike him dead and meet myself
Death, or I know not what mysterious doom."

King Arthur then collected his forces and
marched to Camlan, where the fate of war was
fiercely and desperately contested. The scene
of this battle was near Camelford, on the banks
of the river Camblan, now known as the Alan.

In that terrible conflict only three out of "a
hundred thousand" of the Cymry escaped, and,
according to the ancient records of Wales, they
were Morvran ap Tegid the ugly, Sandde Bryd
Angel the beautiful, and Glewlewyd Gavaelvawr
the gigantic, who "acted" as porter in Arthur's
court.

On that wild and wind-blown field of battle
Medrawd, the traitor, was slain, and Arthur, the
hero and king, though grievously wounded, was
borne to the island of Avallon to be healed.
There "mystic Uthyr's deeply-wounded son"
lingered a while and died.

Arthur's death in 542 dealt one of the most
savage blows to British independence, since it
robbed his country of her early heroic defenders.

The legendary and real Arthur are so deftly
interwoven as to render it impossible to unravel
the mysteries surrounding the last scene of the
great king's life.

I

The real Arthur, the renowned warrior, the invincible defender of his beloved land, the faithful friend of his people, the dignified lord of the Round Table, the hero whose lofty and patriotic soul yearned only for defence of right and redress of wrong, stands forth in history as the leader of that great and renowned Pendragonship which through all succeeding ages has made Britain a power alike on land and sea. His faults were those common to the semi-barbaric ages, when skill in warfare, valorous magnanimity, and unswerving persistence in the cause of freedom were among the highest attributes of kingly sway, and plunder, sanguinary revenge, sacrilege, abduction, and plurality of wives were the order of the day.

Though long and eventful centuries have passed since the battle of Camlan, the name of Arthur — as one of the " Three brave sovereigns " of Britain who could only be vanquished by treason, and one of the " blood-stained " and victorious warriors whose unswerving valour inspired wavering hosts and kept invaders at bay—shines with changeless and undiminished glow in Welsh history, where praise of him is not exaggerated and blame is not concealed.

The most perfect and beautiful record of this hero's legendary life exists, and will continue to live, linked with the renowned monarch's name

in Tennyson's "Idyls of the King" and the
"Morte d'Arthur."

Regarding the resting-place of Arthur, Giraldus
Cambrensis describes the discovery of a grave at
Glastonbury where a stone was then to be seen
bearing the inscription—

> "Hic Jacet Sepultus Inclytus Rex
> Arthurius in Insula Avalonia."

Many feet below the surface there was a
coffin of hollowed oak containing gigantic bones,
and a skull bearing the marks of ten wounds.
By command of Henry II., the bones were removed from the grave to the interior of the
church; and when Edward I., with his queen,
visited the place in 1276, the shrine was opened,
and "the king folded the bones of Arthur in a
rich shroud, and the queen those of his wife,
which also lay there, and deposited them reve-
rentially in the tomb."

In some of the ancient chronicles it is recorded that Gwenhwyvar's body was found
beside Arthur's, while Medrawd's was hard by,
although in the Welsh "Memorials of the Graves
of the Warriors" it is stated that—

> "The grave of March is this, and this the grave of Gwythyr.
> Here is the grave of Gwgawn Gleddyfrudd,
> But unknown is the grave of Arthur."

The Romancers, recognising Arthur as the
ideal of Christian chivalry and the honoured

favourite of the Fairies, described the king as
one whose

> "Grave should be a mystery
> From all men, like his birth."

And in all the varied forms of the beautiful
legend, Bedwyr, or Bedivere, appears as the
chosen knight to obey the king's last command
and throw Arthur's sword into "the middle
mere." But the celebrated Caliburn, or Excalibur, with its jewelled hilt, became a temptation
to Bedwyr, who thrice disobeyed the king. At
length the sword was thrown into the water,
where a mysterious hand seized it, and after
brandishing it aloft, disappeared. Then the
devoted Bedwyr, who was one of the "Three
Diademed Chiefs of Battle," carried the king to
the shore of the lake, and placed him in a boat
which ultimately conveyed the king to Fairy-
land, there to be healed of his wounds, and to
prepare for his return to the scenes of his former
exploits and victories.

In the "Morte d'Arthur" it is said that the
king, after receiving terrible wounds in the battle
of Camlan, was taken to the island of Avalon
"in a shyppe wherein were thre quenes, that
one was kyng Arthurs syster quene Morgan le
fay, the other was the quene of North galys,
the thyrd was the quene of the waste londes.
Also there was Nynyne, the chyef lady of the
lake . . ."

Here it may be mentioned that Bedwyr's name is recorded in the "Graves of the Warriors," and with it appears another knight of Arthur's court—

"The grave of the son of Ossvran is in Camlan,
   After many a conflict.
   The grave of Bedwyr is in the woody steep of Tryvan."

Some authorities are of opinion that the Tryvan mentioned in the above triplet is Tryfaen, or Trivaen, the three-pointed mountain, with its towering crags, at the head of the Valley of Nant-ffrancon, or the Valley of the Beaver, near Snowdon. Other chroniclers suggest Dindryvan, the site of the present castle of Dunraven, in Glamorganshire, as the grave of Bedwyr. The latter suggestion is the most probable, because of the proximity of Dunraven to Somerset, Devon, and Cornwall.

To return to the king. More in accordance with the old heroic spirit of the age in which Arthur lived, is the story of the huge cavern under the hazel-trees on Craig-y-Dinas, where the king and his knights of deathless fame lay held in charmed slumber until the black and the golden eagle should fight and rouse them to avenge and redress the wrongs of the Cymry, and deliver them from the yoke of oppression.

So powerful was the influence of King Arthur that belief in his return from the care of the queens in the mysterious island of Avalon was fondly cherished alike by patriotic enthusiasts and chivalric dreamers. The former regarded their hero as a mighty warrior waiting for an auspicious moment to march forth with his forces and assail the Saxons, or, with his spirit embodied in the mortal form of a later but all-powerful chieftain, he might yet completely deliver Wales from the English yoke. Chivalric dreamers pictured him as a solitary wanderer in lost Lionnesse, once a prosperous, and afterwards a submerged kingdom, the mountain-tops of which form the Scilly Islands of our days; or a lonely wraith restlessly pacing the Bréton forests; or a shadowy figure followed by spectre-knights whom the country folk beheld by moonlight in the wilds of Wendron; or a mourner on the heights of Gelli Wic; or a kingly ghost holding solemn and silent court at midnight among the ruins of "Old Caerlleon upon Usk."

Through the long-vanished centuries since this hero of reality and romance gave his life's blood for his country, other heroes, fighting for Britain in far fields of glory and renown, have yet wished for the time when the typical Arthur shall

"Come again, and thrice as fair;
  .   .   .   .   .   come
With all good things, and war shall be no more!"

CHAPTER XII

MERLIN THE SEER

AMONG the seers of olden story, not one has held a more important or prominent position than Merlin, known in the world of romance and song as the mighty enchanter, whose birth and death are alike involved in mystery. Many circumstances combine to elude any satisfactory investigation of this weird but enthralling character, whose interesting life, as the only great seer acknowledged by Wales, is full of striking events and curious anomalies.

In the ancient annals of the Principality three Myrddins appear. These are : — 1. Myrddin Emrys, sometimes described with the appellation Ambrosius. The surname Emrys may have been derived from Dinas Emrys, in Eryri, and that of Ambrosius from the King of Britain, known also as Emrys Wledig, who, with his brother Uthyr, fled into Brittany when Vortigern usurped the throne and leagued with the Saxons. 2. Myr-

ddin the Caledonian, whose patron was Gwenddolau, son of Ceidio, Prince of North Britain.
3. Myrddin *Wyllt*, or the Wild, the bard, and
son of Madog Morvryn, who, with other fugitives
of North Britain, sought refuge in Wales.

Mr. Thomas Stephens has identified Myrddin
Emrys with Myrddin *Wyllt;* while the Rev. Rice
Rees, in his " Essay on the Welsh Saints," under
heading, "From A.D. 464 to A.D. 500," writes
thus :—" The last saint to be mentioned of the
line of Coel," the North Briton, " was Madog
Morvryn, whose life must have extended into the
following century (*i.e.*, the sixth). He was a
member of the congregation or monastery of
Illtyd, where he is said to have distinguished
himself as a teacher ; but he is more generally
known as the father of the bard, Myrddin
Wyllt."

In the Iolo MSS. the following notice appears :—" The three primitive baptismal bards
of the Cambro-Britons : Madog, the son of
Morvryn, of Caerlleon upon Usk ; Taliesin, the
son of Saint Henwg, of Caerlleon upon Usk ;
and Merddin Emrys, of Maesaleg, in Glywysyg ;
after whom came Saint Talhaiarn the father of
Tangwyn, Merddin the son of Madog, Morvryn,
and Meugant Hên, of Caerlleon upon Usk, who
were succeeded by Balchnoe, the bard of Teilo
at Llandaff ; Saint Cattwg ; and Cynddylan,
the bard. These nine were called the Impul-

sive Stocks of the baptismal bards of Britain; Taliesin being their chair-president; for which reason he was designated Taliesin, chief bard of the West. . . . The institution was, also, called the Chair of the Round Table, under the superior privileges of which, Gildas the prophet and Cadocus the Wise, of Llancarvan, were bards; and also Llywarch Hên, the son of Elidr Lydanwyn, Ystudvach, the bard, and Ystyphan, the bard of Teilo."

Here are found Myrddin Emrys and Myrddin, the son of Madog Morvryn, described as two distinct persons.

In "Glimpses of Welsh Life and Character," my slight reference to Merlin was based entirely upon Mr. Stephens' identification of Myrddin *Emrys* in Myrddin *Wyllt*, the son of Madog Morvryn. I have since endeavoured carefully to trace the career of each character, and with the following result :—

Myrddin *Emrys* was the renowned Merlin of British and Bréton romance; Myrddin the Caledonian was the son of Madog Morvryn, and received the surname *Wyllt* after the fatal battle of Arderydd.

Merlin, the celebrated magician or enchanter, known at first as the boy of Carmarthen, became the prophet, astrologer, bard, and adviser in succession of Vortigern, Emrys, Uthyr, and Arthur. He first appears in the annals of

Wales in A.D. 453, immediately after the famous but treacherous "Battle of the Long Knives," when, according to the Iolo MSS., "the British chieftains were killed by the Saxons in the treachery of Ambrosbury Hill, called also the Hill of Caer-Caradog, in the district of Caersallawg, where they were assembled under the refuge of God's Peace and of national tranquillity."

This battle is described in the Saxon Chronicles thus:—"Hengist having been defeated by the Britons, sent ambassadors to Vortigern entreating for peace. The king invited the strangers to a friendly feast, where the treaty could be considered. Hengist gladly accepted the invitation, but secretly desired his chieftains to carry their short Saxon swords beneath their garments. All proceeded pleasantly, until Hengist exclaimed, 'Unsheath your daggers,' when every Briton present, with the exception of Vortigern, was slain."

In that fray Vortigern was taken prisoner, but ransomed himself by investing the Saxon leader with the sovereignty of the counties of Kent, Essex, Sussex, and Middlesex, thus allowing the invaders a permanent footing in the island.

Before his usurpation of the throne of Britain, Vortigern was a prince and chieftain of the northern parts of Radnor and Breconshire, while his dominions as leader of a clan extended all along the Wye valley. This famous but treacherous prince was also regulus of Erchenfield, in Herefordshire.

After the "Battle of the Long Knives," Vortigern, who in the Triads is described as the "arrant traitor," retired to the fastnesses of his native mountains, and there, in despair, consulted several magicians as to what he could do to protect himself against the Saxons, whose fair Rowena—called by the ancient chroniclers Alis Ronwen—had lured him to destruction.

The wise men of that period advised the wretched prince to build a very strong tower in a place of security, and Vortigern, having selected Dinas Emrys, in Eryri, as the site, ordered his builders to proceed with the work. To the vexation and dismay of the castle-builders, and the amazement of their royal master, as quickly as the foundations were laid they were swallowed up. Day after day all attempts to proceed with the work were unavailing, and it appeared as if the dethroned and deserted monarch was destined to have no refuge or resting-place wherein to end his unhappy days.

Again and again were the magicians summoned and consulted, and, after considerable pressure, one among them ventured to give counsel. The wise but fearful adviser told

Vortigern that he must find and slay a boy
who never had a father, and with the victim's
blood sprinkle the stones for the castle-building,
which could then be carried on without danger
of being engulphed.   Thereupon Vortigern sent
messengers all through Wales in search of a
boy answering to the description given by the
magicians, and at last, after weary wanderings,
they reached Caervyrddin, or Carmarthen.

Two boys playing ball in a street of that
ancient town wrangled, and one charged the
other with never having had a father.   This
being proved by Meugant, the clerk, to the
satisfaction of the magicians and Vortigern, the
boy was prepared for death.   Being told why
he was to be slain, he put so many perplexing
questions to the wise men with reference to the
site of the proposed stronghold, that they were
unable to answer him.   He then volunteered to
say why foundations could not be laid there.
Under the rushes in that swampy land the
marvellous boy said there was a pool of dank
and stagnant water, and at the bottom of it was
a stone chest containing two slumbering dragons,
who, whenever they awoke, fought desperately,
and the commotion of their conflict caused all
stones laid on the surrounding ground to be
immediately swallowed up.   The boy assured
the magicians that, without doubt, the spot
was celebrated as the place where Lludd, at

the suggestion of his brother Llefelys, buried
the dragons who caused the annual May-night
shriek. The rushes were speedily removed, and,
under the strange boy's direction, the pool was
drained. Then the magicians found the chest
and the dragons, between which a fierce conflict at once commenced. Eventually the red
dragon, though grievously wounded and almost
slain, chased the white dragon from the pool
until it disappeared. When the boy was asked
the meaning of this strange scene, he explained
that the red dragon was Britain, and the white
one represented the Saxons; but though the
Britons were oppressed, they would overcome
the invaders and drive them from the country.
He further said it was waste work to build
a castle or tower there, for Emrys and Uthyr
were coming from Brittany to regain their
father's kingdom.

Vortigern then spared the life of the boy,
who afterwards became the honoured companion of the king, to whom he foretold future
events in the solitary wilds of Wales.

Many stories are told of the lonely, dis-
appointed, and discontented monarch, who,
cheered by bardic song and enchanted games,
waited the doom that was fast approaching.

Soon the Britons went forth to meet the sons
of Constantine on their return from Brittany, and
having assembled in vast numbers, the people

unanimously elected Ambrosius, or Emrys Wledig,
as king. The latter immediately marched
against Vortigern, who fled to his castle of
Erging, or Erchenfield, in Herefordshire, there
to meet the fate foretold by Myrddin. According to Nennius, Vortigern's stronghold and all
within it were destroyed by fire, or otherwise
marvellously swallowed up.

Myrddin's fame, after the death of his patron,
rapidly spread through Britain, and he was
soon acknowledged as the only seer and one of
the greatest men of the age.

When Emrys Wledig had restored peace,
rebuilt the churches, revised the laws, and
replaced those who had been dispossessed of
their lands, he visited Caer-Caradawg, where
the bodies of those who had been slain by
Hengist were buried. Ancient annals record
the account of a great assembly of artisans
convened by Emrys Wledig to devise a fitting
monument to the memory of the British heroes.
After a fruitless conference, the Archbishop of
Caerlleon advised the king to send for Vortigern's
prophet, Myrddin, or "Merlin, who knew the
range of all their arts." When the great seer
appeared before the king and the nobles, he
astonished both by advising them to procure
the stones of the Giants' Dance from Killara,
Ireland.

The king and the people derided the suggestion, and were reproved by the prophet, who extolled the wonderful virtues of the celebrated stones recommended by him.

Thereupon the king and the people unanimously agreed that Uthyr, accompanied by Myrddin and fifteen thousand men, should at once proceed to Ireland, rout King Gillamori, and bring home the stones. But on reaching Killara, the men failed to move the great blocks, and then Myrddin, by his own art alone, conveyed them to the ships, and thus the Giants' Dance was removed to Britain.

When these stones, under the direction of Myrddin, were set up at Caer-Caradawg, Emrys Wledig was re-crowned, and he signalised the event by appointing Samson to the archbishopric of York, and Dubricius to that of Caerlleon.

About that time Myrddin first appeared with the surname Emrys, received either from the king, whose adviser, prophet, and astrologer he became, or from his former connection with Dinas Emrys, in Eryri.

In the Triads, the memorial erected at Caer-Caradawg is described as the building of *Gwaith Emrys*, which was one of the "mighty achievements" of Britain, and afterwards came to be known as Stonehenge, on Salisbury Plain. Henry of Huntingdon, writing early in the twelfth century, states that people could not then understand how such massive stones were erected and what purpose they served.   Later antiquarians, including Stukeley and others, have put forth various theories with reference to the religious and secular purposes of Stonehenge.

After the building of Caer-Caradawg, Myrddin Emrys was almost continually in the royal presence.   When the monarch was ill at Winchester, Myrddin accompanied Uthyr against the united forces of Pasgen, the son of Vortigern, who, with the Saxons and Gillamori, the angered king of Ireland, opposed Emrys; and then the great astrologer and magician predicted the death of the king and the succession of Uthyr, whose wonderful banner bearing the dragon's head inaugurated the great Pendragonship which was to exercise so great an influence in the sixth century.

From the day when the boy of Carmarthen went forth to be slain, and afterwards spared, at the command of the unhappy and remorseful Vortigern, to the last known hour of his existence, the mighty enchanter appeared with majestic aspect in the courts of Britain and Brittany.   He who masterfully held his own in the presence of Vortigern, the wavering regulus of Erchenfield; he who became the art counsellor of Emrys, the prophet and astrologer of Uthyr, and the revered friend of Arthur from his youth to his manhood, was in truth not only a lordly character, but a master-mind of the age.   This Myrddin of Carmarthen, and no other, whose magic influence was powerfully felt alike by the Britons and their kinsmen and allies in Brittany, was one

> " Who knew the range of all their arts,
> Had built the king his havens, ships, and halls,
> Was also Bard, and knew the starry heavens :
> The people called him wizard. . . ."

And although the wear and tear of about fifteen centuries have half effaced and almost obliterated the names of the great British philosophers, seers, and bards, the name of Merlin still survives, weaving its potent spell like a magical web around the imagination, and holding thought enthralled in day-dreams of the past.

Spenser, in his enchanting "Faerie Queen," thus describes Merlin :—

> "For he by wordes could call out of the sky,
> Both sunne and moone, and make them him obey ;
> The land to sea, and sea to maineland dry,
> And darksom night he eke could turne to day ;
> Huge hostes of men he could alone dismay,
> And hostes of men of meanest thinges could frame,
> Whenso him list his enimies to fray :
> That to this day, for terror of his fame,
> The feendes do quake when any him to them does
> name."

Numerous prophecies have been attributed to Merlin, but, as so many are spurious, it is almost impossible to separate the real from the fictitious.

K

The great enchanter's astrological predictions were probably orally delivered, and particularly well remembered by those to whom they were addressed, after which the sayings became household words. Like the astrologers of every age, he evidently foretold events that would probably come to pass in seven or ten years, and to his knowledge of the stars he added character-reading, known in later times as physiognomy. His exceptional gifts as an astronomer and astrologer were largely aided by keen foresight, sound judgment, and the capability of seeing in causes of the day the germinating results of the morrow, and, in common with all wise monarchs and far-sighted statesmen, he made strong and most enduring impressions upon the people.

Among the predictions attributed to Merlin are those contained in the celebrated "Prophetia Merlini," which forms the seventh book of the "golden legend" called by Geoffrey of Monmouth the "History of the Britons." The following extracts culled therefrom illustrate the nature of the great seer's prophecies :—" Six of his (Arthur's) posterity shall sway the sceptre, but after them shall arise a German worm. . . . Menevia shall put on the pall of the city of legions. . . . The German dragon shall hardly get to his hole, because the revenge of his treason shall overtake him. . . . The seed of the white dragon shall be swept out of our gardens, and the remainder of his generation shall be deci-mated. . . . They shall bear the yoke of slavery, and wound their mother with spades and ploughs. . . . The sixth shall overturn the walls of Ireland. . . ."

A few more sentences reveal the astrological tendencies of the so-called productions of Merlin : —" The tail of Scorpio shall produce lightning, and Cancer quarrel with the Sun. Virgo shall mount upon the back of Sagittarius and darken her virgin flowers. The chariot of the Moon shall disorder the Zodiac, and the Pleiades break forth into weeping. No officer of Janus shall hereafter return, but his gate being shut shall lie hid in the chinks of Ariadne. The seas shall rise up in the twinkling of an eye, and the dust of the ancients shall be restored. The winds shall fight together with a dreadful blast, and their sound shall reach to the stars." And again it appears—" At that time shall the stones speak, and the sea towards the Gallic coast shall be contracted into a narrow space. On each bank shall one man hear another, and the soil of the island shall be enlarged. The secrets of the deep shall be revealed, and Gaul shall tremble for fear."

According to the Triads, there were " three missing ones and losses from disappearance of the Island of Britain." One was Gavran ap

Aeddan, who, with his idle and dreaming followers, quitted the turbulent scenes,

"Where hosts in battle waver,"

and sailed far out to sea in search of the beauti-.
ful and enchanted "green islands of the floods,"
with their fairy folk and fairy castles, and
summer bowers where they could live at ease
for ever. Another disappearance was that of
"Madog ap Owain Gwynedd, who, with three.
hundred men, went to sea in ten ships, and it is
not known whither they went." The third disappearance was that of Myrddin Emrys, who in
"a ship of glass" sailed away and never returned.

Carmarthenshire tradition indicates Merlin's
Tree, Merlin's Hill, and Merlin's grave near Aber-
gwilli. In the latter it was said the great enchanter was held, not dead, but spell-bound by the
wicked and artful Nimue, or Vivien, who, learning
the magic secret, used it against the veteran sage.

Merlin, as the prophet of Emrys, Uthyr, and
Arthur, frequently visited Brittany, where his
name was as much revered as in Britain ; and the
final disappearance of the seer is the subject of
several traditions, one of which has been immortalised in magical verse by Tennyson in his
incomparable "Idyls of the King."

In the preface of the "Morte d'Arthur,"
Merlin is described as having been led by Vivien
into the Forest of Brécéliande, and there, under

a white thorn-bush heavily laden with flowers, the wily woman made the enchanter reveal his secret, after which, " with woven paces and with waving arms," she "nine times made the ring, and nine times made the enchantments," around him. When he awoke he found himself enclosed as in a strong tower, from which he never emerged.

The same authority describes Merlin addressing Sir Gawain, who was sent in search of the lost seer. The faithful knight of Arthur's court wandered through the Forest of Brécéliande, and being transformed into a dwarf, bemoaned his evil fate, when he heard some one "groaning on his right hand," while a cloud of smoke, like a silver mist or white fog, prevented his progress. Out of the mist Merlin spoke, and related the account of Vivien's mischief. The seer then said, "Ah, sir, you will never see me more, and that grieves me, but I cannot remedy it; and when you shall have departed from this place, I shall never more speak to you, nor to any other person, save only my mistress."

In the "Prophecies of Merlin," the scene of the incarceration is laid in the Forest of Arvantes, where the magician had constructed a tomb for himself. Vivien persuaded Merlin to lie down in the receptacle, and as soon as he entered it she closed the lid so securely that it never could be opened.

Ariosto, in his "Orlando Furioso," gives the same version, but sets the scene near the Garonne, in the south of France.

Tennyson adheres to the old British account of the "hollowed oak," while the folk-loreists of South Wales abide by the cave or grave of Merlin near Carmarthen. North Wales folk-lore describes the great enchanter ending his days in a "house of glass" on Bardsey Island, where, above the shrieking storm and the hissing wave, his voice is to be heard proclaiming prophecies to his successors in the bardic circle.

English historians are inclined to regard Merlin as a purely legendary character, around whose life many stories are entwined, all of which are more or less fabulous. In the annals of Wales, Myrddin Emrys, or Ambrosius, appears as a real and potent sage, whose counsel was sought and followed in succession by one princely usurper, and three rightful monarchs of Britain.

The position held by Merlin in Welsh history proves him to have been a skilled architect, surveyor, and original designer of various works of art. His knowledge of astral sciences was shared in common by men who still adhered to primitive Druidism, and Christianised bards whose creed was a strange combination of the worship of nature and the simple, almost child-like, faith of the early and first-born Church of

Britain, which was cradled in Morganwg by the pious Princess Eurgain.

Myrddin Emrys of Carmarthen, who was discovered by Vortigern, and patronised by Emrys, Uthyr, and Arthur, was the great and renowned enchanter, known as the Merlin of British and Bréton history and European romance, while the ill-fated bard of Strath-Clyde, subsequently known as Myrddin *Wyllt*, was the son of Madog Morvryn, the North Briton. This Myrddin was compelled by the successes of the Picts and Saxons to seek refuge in Wales, where he made the acquaintance and secured the friendship of Taliesin.

In Rees's "Essay on the Welsh Saints" it is recorded :—" To proceed with the line of Coel : Gwenddolau, Cof, and Nudd were the sons of Cedio ab Garthwys, a chieftain of North Britain. They were all instructed in the Christian faith in the college of Iltutus. . . . Gwenddolau was the patron of the bard, Myrddin the Caledonian, and was slain at the battle of Arderydd, A.D. 577."

According to the Triads, the great battle of Arderydd was one of the "frivolous" engagements, because "a lark's nest was the cause of it." Rhydderch Hael, the generous, lost this battle and eighty thousand Britons owing to the treachery of Aeddan, who is described as "the arrant traitor" because he made a raid upon

Rhydderch's court and destroyed all therein,
after which he went wholly over with his men
to the Saxons.

Myrddin, the bard of Gwenddolau, who fell
in the battle of Arderydd, appears as a warrior-
poet, who not only lost his patron but was deprived of his reason through an unhappy cause.
Fighting with his patron against the enemy,
Myrddin unfortunately slew the son of his twin
sister Gwenddydd. This fatality caused him
to lose his reason and wander aimlessly through
the great Caledonian forest, wherefrom his sister
vainly endeavoured to lure him by rich gifts
and costly trinkets.

In the "Kyvoesi Myrddin a Gwenddydd," a
poem on the conversation between Myrddin and
his twin sister, the following lines appear :—

GWENDDYDD.

"Thy head is the colour of hoary winter :
    May God relieve thy necessities !
    Who will reign after Urien ?"

MYRDDIN.

"Heaven has pressed heavily upon me,
    And I am ill at last ;—
    Maelgwn Hir will rule over Gwynedd."

The lines addressed by Gwenddydd to her
twin brother Myrddin, surnamed *Wyllt*, give the
impression that, owing to his insanity, the bard

had become prematurely aged, and in great necessity, but yet regarded as one who had not lost
the gift and power of foretelling future events.
This Myrddin, of Strath-Clyde, appears to have
ended his days in the haunts of his youth and
childhood, where, in imagination, he communed
with the " sevenscore chieftains," who

> "Were turned into spirits;
> In the wood of Celyddon
> Were they transformed."

During his sojourn in Wales, Myrddin, the
son of Madog Morvryn, became a Christianised
bard, and was baptized at Caerlleon. This was
probably the result of his acquaintance with
Taliesin.

The two Myrddins, who are incorrectly known
by the one appellation of Merlin, appear in
chronological order thus :—

Myrddin, or Merlin, the enchanter and sage,
was discovered by Vortigern's messengers in
A.D. 453. Supposing him to have been about
fourteen years of age at that time, he would be
about one hundred and three when Arthur died
in A.D. 542. There are no records to prove that
Merlin survived Arthur, but many British and
Bréton traditions describe him to have been
missing or virtually dead before the fatal battle
of Camlan.

Myrddin *Wyllt*, of Strath-Clyde, is known to

have outlived Taliesin, who died about A.D. 570, and to have survived his patron Gwenddolau, who was slain at the battle of Arderydd in A.D. 577. He appears to have returned from his exile in Wales to support his patron in the conflict against the Picts and Saxons in the northern parts of Britain, after which he lived for some years as a partially insane wanderer in the Caledonian forest.

Myrddin *Wyllt*, like the greater Myrddin, was skilled in bardism and occult studies, but did not possess the master-mind which makes the seer of Arthur's court stand like a giant among the distinguished men of his time. As in the case of his name-sharer, the later days and death of Myrddin the North Briton were surrounded with mystery. He is described as a restless and insane wanderer, whose eyes were troubled and "boiling like the water of a pot upon the earth," and whose beard was "like the grey moss on the trunk of an old oak." In short and lucid periods he was persuaded to go home, but escaped again and again to the wild forest, where he could hear the spirit-voices of his lost and loved friends who fell in battle. At last his devoted sister Gwenddydd had a palace or house of glass—probably an observatory—built for him, and there, star-gazing, he passed the twilight of his life, and waited for Death to lead him to his friends of the long ago.

CHAPTER XIII

CHILDREN OF SONG

THROUGH the wild and desolated low-lands of Wales, where fierce battles were fought, and the red glow of sunset mingled with the deeper crimson of precious life-blood; or among grim mountain ranges and passes, where human bodies remained unburied, and the pale moonlight fell kindly upon pallid faces wet with death-dew; or away where brave princes and warriors paused awhile from warfare for the tournament, or Arthur's knights with sparrow-hawks won the ladies' favours, the children of song were to be seen.

Sons of song perhaps it should be said.

But children of Nature were they, who had ever held their mother's tokens close to their hearts, and whose influence still kept them child-like in simplicity, even though heroic in character.

Three of these singers were known to each

other, shared the same century, and their names,
linked as in a golden triad, have survived the
"scorns of time," and are still as fresh as ever—
Aneurin, Llywarch Hên, and Taliesin.

All three are seen in the court of Arthur, that
old-time sanctuary for those who fled from battle
or captivity.

Aneurin came thereto from imprisonment after
the terrible carnage of Cattraeth, the battle-
strand of Northumberland, and in Arthur's halls
sought peace after the great conflict where the
flower of Britain had fallen, and ease after the
fetters of bondage that were removed by a friend
and fellow-warrior.

Of his sufferings and the rescue Aneurin thus
sang :—

> "Pierced were the soles of my feet,
>   Lacerated was my knee,
>   In the house of earth,
>   With a chain of iron around my knees."

> "From the power of the sword (noble was the succour),
> From the cruel prison-house of earth he released me,
> From the place of death, from the cheerless region,
> He, Cenau, son of Llywarch, magnanimous and brave."

Aneurin believed his life was spared because
of his muse, for he says, " And I too was saved
from the shedding of my blood as the recom-
pense of my fair song."

By-and-by he grew tired of court life, and

left Caerlleon for Llancarvan, in the Vale of
Glamorgan, that classical spot where he spent
the remainder of his life and wrote his celebrated
"Gododin," and frequently received his friend
Taliesin.

And there, in the monastery or college of
Catwg at Llancarvan, we find him still singing:—

> " Of the mead and of the horn,
>   And of the assembly at Cattraeth,
>   I, Aneurin, will frame what Taliesin knows,
>   A song of participation,
>   Which shall be offered by Gododin
>   Before the dawn of the day of toil."

In response comes the song of Taliesin :—

> " I know the fame of Aneurin,
>   That celebrated genius,
>   Even I, Taliesin,
>   From the banks of the Lake Ceirionydd."

The "Gododin," by Aneurin, holds the first
rank among the poems of Wales, and for bold
grandeur, vivid style, and historic details, it is
celebrated as the finest heroic and lyric pro-
duction in the Welsh language. It is said that
the original composition was very extensive, but
only about nine hundred lines remain. The
number of the stanzas are supposed to have
been equal to the number of chieftains who
were present at the battle of Cattraeth. The
following and opening lines of the "Gododin,"

translated and rhymed, appear in the " Cambrian
Wreath " :—

> " Of years though brief, the youthful chief
> Was nerved and armed for manly deed ;
> And for the field, his broad light shield
> Hung on his slender, thick maned steed.
> Oh ! he was graceful to behold,
> With bright blue sword and spurs of gold.
> A princely, gay, and ermined garb,
> An ashen spear with point and barb,
> 'Tis not for me to envy thee,
> A kinder, nobler part be mine—
> To sing thy praise, for brief thy days,
> Soon closed that bright career of thine.
> Ah ! sooner comes thy bloody bier
> Than nuptial day, or festal cheer.
> On thee, on thee shall ravens feed,
> Ere thou achieve the hero's deed.
> Brave Owen's dear and gallant friend,
> The fierce prey-birds thy steed shall rend,
> His bones alone remain to tell
> What spot the son of Marco fell."

The poet then continues :—

> " The warriors went to Gododin, a laughing phalanx ;
> Soon the embattled host rose against them
> In hateful contest.
> They slew with blades shining
> Without din. . . .
> They went to Cattraeth ; a talkative host.
> Pale mead had been their feast,
> And proved their poison. . . . .
> They went in a mass ;
> Their overthrow was complete."

He describes the

> " Powerless throne, a land all desolate.
> Godebog's progeny, a faithful band,
> On biers are borne to glut the yawning grave."

His tribute to one of the chieftains runs thus—

> " None made the social hall so free from care
> As gentle Cynon, Clinion's sovereign lord ;
> For highest rank he never proudly strove,
> And whom he once had known he ne'er would slight.
> Yet was his spear well-pointed, and well knew
> To pierce, with truest aim, the embattled line.
> Swift flew his steed to meet the hostile storm,
> And death sat on his lance, as with the dawn
> He rush'd to war in glory's brilliant day."

Mourning over the friends who fell while he escaped, he sings—

> " Miserable am I
> After the toil of conflict,
> Suffering in the pangs of others
> The anguish of death.
> Doubly bowed down am I
> In sorrow to have seen
> Our men falling on all sides,
> And to have felt anxiety and grief
> For the valiant men
> Of the social land ;
> For Rhuvawn, Gwgawn, Gwiawn, and Gwylyget."

Aneurin lived for many years in the seclusion of delightful Llancarvan, where many a knight of deathless fame paused to gain a word or more of inspiration and encouragement from the poet-hero of Cattraeth and author of the celebrated "Gododin." This renowned son of song, who had suffered so much himself and so keenly sympathised with the sorrows of others, experienced a cruel fate, for he was murdered by a blow from an axe dealt by Eidyn, the son of Einygan, the crime being mentioned in the Triads as "one of the accursed deeds of the Island of Britain." Turner, the historian, in his "Vindication of the Ancient Welsh Bards," describes the "Gododin" as so many "poetic memoranda of a disastrous conflict, penned by a friend who had witnessed its events, in all the confusion in which they had occurred, than a well-conceived and artfully-arranged series of individual conflicts like the poems of Homer, which, though genuine as to the author, yet contain incidents which the poet's invention has arranged as it pleased him."

Llywarch Hên, described as "one of the disinterested princes of Britain," was a Cumbrian refugee at the court of Cynddylan, Prince of Powys. He too fought at Cattraeth under Urien Rheged, and fled to the south, where he remained for some time. But calamity again pursued and overtook him. The Loegrians attacked Cynddylan, in whose defence Llywarch and his sons took up arms; but the battle went against them, and the poet survived to lament the death of his children and his noble patron. Some of the lines of his lamentation run thus—

> " The hall of Cynddylan is silent to-night
> After having lost its lord :—
> Great God of Mercy, what shall I do ?
>
> The hall of Cynddylan, how gloomy seems its roof !
> Since the Loegrians have destroyed
> Cynddylan and Elvan of Powys. . . .
> The churches of Bassa are near to-night
> To the heir of Cyndrwyn :
> The grave-house of fair Cynddylan ! "

Urien Rheged, who commanded at Cattraeth and fled to Wales, fell in this battle, and of him, in an elegy, Llywarch sighs—

> " This hearth, will it not be overgrown with nettles ?
> Whilst its protector was yet alive
> More familiar with it was the foot
> Of the needy petitioner."

In the evening of his days he wrote his " Ode " to his " Crutch," which is considered one of the finest poems in the Welsh language. Bowed down by many sorrows and heavy losses, succeeded by a lingering age and infirmity, the poet lived to grieve that—

> " Before I went on crutches I was bold,
> I was admitted into the congress-house
> Of Powys, the Paradise of the Cymry."

His brave sons were military chieftains, and, as their father sang—

"Wearing the golden wreath, leaders of armies,"

went forth to war, and were slain.

One of his sons had his horse killed under him in battle, and soon afterwards was himself slain. The skull of the horse remained instead of a stepping-stone near the brook where it fell, and one day a man reminded Llywarch that it belonged to the charger of his own son Gwên. Whereupon the poet promptly remarked—

"I have seen that horse's day,
    (That horse with the looks of a stag, the thrower up of
        sods,)
    When none would have trodden on his jaw,
    As he carried Gwên the son of Llywarch."

This poet spent the close of his life at Llanvor, in Montgomeryshire, where he died at the age of one hundred and fifty years.

This is corroborated by the fact that Llywarch was about forty years of age when Arthur died in A.D. 542, and outlived Cadwallon, whose death took place in A.D. 646, when the poet wrote an elegy on that chieftain.

Twelve poems composed by Llywarch Hên are preserved in the "Archæology of Wales," and the metre used is of the most ancient description. His "Elegy on Geraint" is very beautiful. He sings—

"When Geraint was born, the portals of heaven were open,
Christ vouchsafed what was supplicated,
A countenance beaming with beauty, the glory of Britain."

Geraint fell fighting against the Saxons at Llongborth, the poet immortalising his name thus :—

"At Longborth I saw the conflicting edges of blades,
Men quaking with terror, and blood on the brow,
Before Geraint, the worthy son of his father.
At Longborth I saw severe toiling
Amidst the stones, and blood on the brow,
And on the chieftain's brow a crimson gash."

In a secluded spot near Llanvor, known as Pabell Llywarch Hên—Old Llywarch's Cot—the aged poet ended his earthly pilgrimage, but his name survives as that of one whose life and poetry are deeply pathetic and melancholy.

Taliesin has priority in order of bardic precedence and talent, but was the youngest of these three children of song.

Romance and mystery surrounded his birth, and the highest praises are attached to his name.

The story of Taliesin's early years is thus told in the Iolo MSS. :—" He with Elphin, the son of Urien, being once fishing at sea in a skin coracle, an Irish pirate ship seized him and his coracle, and bore him away towards Ireland ; but while the pirates were at the height of their drunken mirth, Taliesin pushed his coracle to the sea, and got into it himself, with a shield in his hand which he found in the ship, and with which he rowed the coracle until it verged the land; but the waves breaking then in wild foam, he lost his hold on the shield, so that he had no alternative but to be driven at the mercy of the sea, in which state he continued for a short time, when the coracle stuck to the point of a pole in the weir of Gwyddno, Lord of Ceredigion, in Aberdyvi; and in that position he was found, at the ebb, by Gwyddno's fishermen, by whom he was interrogated; and when it was ascertained that he was a bard, and the tutor of Elffin, the son of Urien Rheged . . . 'I, too, have a son named Elffin,' said Gwyddno; 'be thou a bard and teacher to him, also, and I will give thee lands in free tenure.' The terms were accepted; and, for several successive years, he spent his time between the courts of Urien Rheged and Gwyddno, called Gwyddno Garanhir, Lord of the Lowland Cantred; but, after the territory of Gwyddno had become overwhelmed by the sea, Taliesin was invited by the Emperor Arthur to his court at Caerlleon upon Usk, where he became highly celebrated for poetic genius and useful meritorious services. After Arthur's death he retired to the estate given to him by Gwyddno, taking Elffin, the son of that prince, under his protection. It was from this account that Thomas, the son of Einion Offeiriad, descended from Gruffudd Gwyr, formed his

romance of Taliesin, the son of Cariadwen,—
Elffin, the son of Goddnou,—Rhun, the son of
Maelgwn Gwynedd,—and the operations of the
Cauldron of Ceridwen." Iolo states that this
version of Taliesin's origin was taken from
Anthony Powel of Llwydarth's MS.

The very beautiful and romantic story of
Taliesin appears in the "Mabinogion" of the
late Lady Charlotte Guest. Therein it is stated
that Elphin, the son of Gwyddno Garanhir, was
a luckless youth, and "born in an evil hour,"
wherefore his father "granted him the drawing
of the weir"—between Dyvi and Aberystwith—
for one year to see if fortune "would ever befall
him, and to give him something wherewith to
begin the world." It is then stated that when
poor Elphin went to the weir he saw nothing
but a "leathern bag upon the pole of the weir."
When Elphin examined the bag he found therein
an infant boy, who, having a fine forehead, was
thereupon named Taliesin, or "Radiant brow."

The story of Elphin's release through the
influence of Taliesin's song has already been
told, and it only remains to be stated that this
distinguished poet received his education at the
College of Illtutus at Llantwit Major, and also
spent some years in the Monastery of Llancarvan, under its first abbot, Catwg the Wise.
Taliesin's whole soul and heart were in the faith
of his fathers, and none of the poets went so

deeply into the ancient Bardic mysteries as he did. One of his great poems turns on the transmigration of souls; another dealt with the "Excellence of the Bards;" in addition to which he wrote the "Reproof" and the "Spite of the Bards."

From his curious poem, entitled "One of the Four Pillars of Song," the following extracts are taken. The translations appear in the late Thomas Stephens' "Literature of the Kymry" :—

> "The Almighty made,
> Down in the Hebron vale,
> With His plastic hands,
>   Adam's fair form :
>
> And five hundred years,
> Void of any help,
> There he remained and lay
>   Without a soul.
>
> He again did form
> In calm paradise,
> From a left-side rib,
>   Bliss-throbbing Eve. . . .
>
> Twice five, ten and eight,
> She was self-bearing
> The mixed burden
>   Of man-woman. . . ."

With reference to Eve, the poet continues—

> "An angelic hand
> From the high Father,
> Brought seed for growing
>   That Eve might sow ;

But she then did hide
Of the gift a tenth,
And all did not sow
    Of what was dug.

Black rye then was found,
And not pure wheat grain,
To show the mischief
    Thus of thieving.

For this thievish act,
It is requisite
That all men should pay
    Tithe unto God. . . ."

Taliesin then describes how he obtained his learning, and goes on to prophesy that the Brython would be swayed by strangers "from Saxony;" after which—

    "Their Lord they will praise,
    Their speech they will keep,
    Their land they will lose
        Except Wild Walia.

    Till some change shall come,
    After long penance,
    When equally rife
        The two crimes shall come.

    Britons then shall have
    Their land and their crown,
    And the stranger swarm
        Shall disappear.

    All the angel's words
    As to peace and war
    Will be fulfilled
        To Britain's race."

This great and illustrious poet is supposed to have died in the same year as Aneurin, A.D. 570. His life appears to have been tranquil and free from sorrow, and his name is still held in veneration as the monarch of the ancient British bards.

CHAPTER XIV

MASTERS OF MYSTERY

LOOKING back into the far past, when, like the Chaldeans of old, Celtic astrologers intently watched the heavens, and the masters of alchemy tried to turn base metals into gold, and solemn men went in quest of the philosopher's stone, and sages sought the *elixir vitæ,* is like gazing into a magic crystal, wherein strange scenes and curious characters appear.

Long before the Christian era, the giant Idris studied the stars from the top of the lofty mountain that still bears his name, and in later days "Gwydion the son of Don, and Gwyn ap Nudd . . . by the extent of their knowledge concerning the stars, their natures and their qualities, they could prognosticate whatever was wished to be known unto the day of doom."

In the Iolo MSS. it is stated that "Don had a son called Gwydion, King of Mona and Arvon, who first taught literature from books to the Irish of Mona and Ireland; whereupon both those countries became pre-eminently famed for knowledge and saints."

According to the Triads, the three masters of mysteries and secret science of the Island of Britain were " Mâth, the son of Mathonwy, and he disclosed his secret to Gwydion the son of Don, Mengw the son of Teirgwaedd, who taught his secret to Uthyr Pendragon; and of Rhuddhom Gawr, and he learned his mystery Eiddic Gôr and Coll the son of Coll Frewi."

Gwydion, the son of Don, was one of the three celebrated " Herdsmen of the Island of Britain," and kept the cattle of the tribe of Gwynedd above the Conway. These primitive herdsmen were persons of distinction and importance, whose duty it was to look after vast herds of cattle and milch cows belonging to their own particular tribes. Some of these herds consisted of thousands of kine, and the chief herdsman had a large staff of servants under his control. This celebrated herdsman and enchanter was a renowned astronomer. He gave his name to the constellation of Cassiopeia, which in Welsh is called Llys Don, or the Court or Hall of Don, and bestowed upon the Corona Borealis the appellation Caer Arianrod, after the " silver-circled " daughter of Don, who was one of the " three beauteous ladies of the Island of Britain." He learnt his magical arts from Mâth, the son of Mathonwy, and is described as

> "Gwydion the son of Don, of toil severe
> Formed a woman out of flowers. . . .
> The bold traveller, out of plaited twigs
> Formed a cavalcade,
> And perfect saddles."

In the "Mabinogion" of "Mâth the son of Mathonwy," Gwydion is described as "the best teller of tales in the world, and he diverted all the court that night with pleasant discourse, and with tales, so that he charmed every one in the court, and it pleased Pryderi to talk with him." But ultimately Gwydion, "by force of strength and fierceness, and by magic and charms," slew Pryderi. Gwydion was buried in Morva Diullen. Mâth the son of Mathonwy's name has been immortalised in the "Mabinogion" of the late Lady Charlotte Guest. There it is stated that Mâth, "by charms and illusion," formed a woman "out of flowers," and in the following way :—" So they took the blossoms of the oak, and the blossoms of the broom, and the blossoms of the meadow-sweet, and produced from them a maiden, the fairest and most graceful that man ever saw. And they baptized her, and gave her the name of Blodenwedd."

Blodenwedd, or "Flower-Aspect," was transformed by Gwydion into an owl as a punishment for her infidelity to her husband, Llew Llaw

Gyffes. Dafydd ap Gwilym describes this fair lady saying—

> "Gwydion son of Don, in scorn,
> With his wand of magic sway
> Changed my beauty's proud array
> For the aspect you behold!
> In revenge, because of old
> Gronwy, Pevyr, Garanhir,
> Of tall form, and noble cheer,
> Penllyn's lord to me was dear!"

Coll, the son of Collfrewi, was a man of "Illusion and Phantasy," of whom Lady Charlotte Guest, in her notes to the "Mabinogion" of "Geraint the son of Erbin," says :—"May it not be fairly said that it is to the Coll mab Collfrewi above mentioned, whose fame had descended to his times, that Chaucer alludes in the following lines ?—

> 'There I saw Coll Tragetour
> Upon a table of sicamour,
> Play an uncouth thing to tell,
> I saw him carry a wind-mell
> Under a walnote shale.'
>> '*House of Fame*, B. iii.'"

This master of magic was one of the "Three swineherds of the Island of Britain," and he was chiefly located in Cornwall.

Gwyn ap Nudd is described in the Triads as one of the "Three happy astronomers of the

Island of Britain." In the fairy lore of Wales he receives the dignity of King of the Fairies and supreme controller of the Tylwyth Teg and the Bendith i Mammau, who were fond of showering their blessings upon mankind. He had for his minions the fantastic Ellyllon, or Elves, and the mischievous "goblins and their tribes" who frequented the turf bogs called by Dafydd ap Gwilym the fish-ponds of Gwyn ap Nudd. The king of Welsh fairies dwelt mostly on the mountain-tops of Wales, wherefrom he could watch his tiny subjects, and at the same time contemplate the grandeur of the heavens.

Gwyddno Garanhir appears as the owner of a marvellous basket, which is described as one of the precious possessions of the Island of Britain. If food for one person were put in it, when opened it would be found to contain sufficient provender for a hundred people. Among the other marvellous treasures of the Cymry was the sword of Rhydderch Hael, which was so charged with electricity, exhibiting itself in dangerously flashing flames, that people feared it. Then there were the chariot of Morgan Mwynvawr, which instantly conveyed people wherever they wished to go; the halter of Clydno Eiddyn, hanging at the foot of his bed, where he could find a horse whenever he desired one; the mantle of Arthur, a garment through which he who wore it could see everybody and yet remain invisible; and the robe of Padarn Beisrudd, which suited a man of gentle birth, but misfitted the churl.

Gwyddno Garanhir was the Prince of the Cantref y Gwaelod, which in an evil hour, and owing to the recklessness of Seithennyn, the drunken son of Seithyn, King of Dyved, was inundated by the sea. The dominions of this unfortunate prince were protected from the sea by a high embankment, the care of which was left to Seithennyn, who neglected his charge, and allowed the tide to break through the bank and submerge the whole country. This great inundation, which took place about A.D. 500, totally destroyed sixteen of the largest fortified towns in Wales, and reduced their monarch to poverty.

In the "Myvyrian Archæology" a poem on the subject of this terrible inundation is preserved.

It is attributed by some authorities to Gwyddno Garanhir, and by others to Llywarch Hên.

Among the most striking passages are the following :—

" Stand forth, Seithenin,
  And behold the dwelling of heroes,—
  The plain of Gwyddno the ocean covers !
  Accursed be the sea guard,
  Who after carousel,
  Let loose the destroying fountain of the raging deep ! . . .
  A cry from the sea arises above the ramparts ;
  Even to heaven does it ascend,—

After fierce excess comes the long cessation ! . . .
A cry from the sea arises above the winds !
A cry from the sea
Impells me from my place of rest this night !
After excess comes the far extending death ! "

The last line of this sublime lamentation is a poem in itself, and a fitting conclusion to the narrative of the terrible disaster that caused the deepest tribulation to Gwyddno Garanhir.

CHAPTER XV

"TYRANTS," AND OTHERS

FROM the death of Arthur to the close of the sixth century, although the struggles between the Welsh and the Saxons were frequent and prolonged, there was a dearth of heroes in the noblest sense of the word, but warriors and fierce fighters for the cause of their country were numerous.

Three of these appear in the Saxon Chronicles as "tyrants." They were "Constantinus the tyrant," son of Cador of Cornwall and Devon; "Vortiporius" or Vortimer the Second, the "tyrant" of South-West Wales; and "Maglocunus" or Maelgwyn Gwynedd, the "tyrant" of North Wales. The latter, who was contemporary with Arthur, survived the great king, and lived to a very advanced age.

In the records of the Ancient British Kings the following list is given:— "*Maelgwyn Gwynedd* (the 22nd in succession) . . . with longe hande . . . was kinge of this lande of

Brittaine. He buylded three towns or citties,
viz. Caer-ddigoll, Argaer-golloyn, Argaer-gyffin,
in the British tongue ; in English, Soronsbury,
Harloch, and Aberconwe ; and he had a sone and
a daughter. Ryn was the name of the sone, and
Engainge was the name of the daughter. . . ."

Gildas, in his celebrated letter, charges " Maglocunus," or Maelgwyn Gwynedd, with disregard-
ing and neglecting " the praises of God, uttered
by the sweetly modulated voices of Christ's disciples, and the breath of church-melody," for
self-praise "roared out, bacchanal-wise by the
mouths of scoundrel-brawlers, foaming with lies
and wickedness."

This monarch was successful in war, and
courageous, but terribly wicked. He was the first
after Arthur to make six countries tributary to
him. The *Brut* states that the possessions he
added to Britain were, Norway, Denmark, Goth-
land, Orkney, Ireland, and Iceland. Of this king
and his court Teliesin, singing for the release of
his friend and benefactor, Elphin, predicted—

> " If you be primary bards formed by Heaven,
> Tell your king what his fate will be. . . .
> I shall liberate Elphin . . .
> And will tell your king what will befall him.
> A most strange creature will come
> From the sea-marsh of Rhianedd
> As a punishment of iniquity on Maelgwyn Gwynedd ;
> His hair, his teeth,
> And his eyes being as gold ;
> And this will bring destruction on Maelgwyn Gwynedd."

This prediction was verified by the pestilence of the Vad Velin, or Yellow Plague, of which Maelgwyn died.

In the *Vita Sancti Cadoci* it is recorded that "Maelgon . . . sent some of his young men to the region of Gwynllwg, that they might there receive tribute; who coming to the house of the steward of Cadoc, seized his very beautiful daughter, and took her away with them." For which liberty the men of Gwynllwg retaliated, and the result was that Maelgon "became greatly excited with anger," and went forth to add injury to insult by plundering the country, whereupon the people of Gwynllwg appealed to Cadoc, who forthwith proceeded by night to the tents of the enemy. There the holy man prayed, and when in the morning he "arose from prayer, . . . lo, a pillar of cloud preceded him, which also covering all the tents," obscured the troops, until "day was as a dark night to them." In the dense and alarming darkness, Cadoc suddenly "appeared before the tent of the king, and, after saluting him he asked, 'Why hast thou come to my country with an armed force for the purpose of plundering and destroying . . . ?'" The king then, in great fear of the darkness, confessed that he had sinned, and prayed for pardon. He asked that, by the intervention of Cadoc, "the darkness may depart, whereby we may return uninjured to our habitations." Cadoc then answered, "Thy very great crimes are forgiven thee." Immediately "the light of summer spread all around, and . . . when the king saw this miracle, he arose from his chair, and fell upon his face." The conscience-smitten monarch then promised to "ratify the refuge which Arthur the bravest of heroes bestowed" upon the saint, and also said, " To-day I choose thee before all others, to be my confessor among South Wales men."

In the traditions of Wales he is described as shutting himself up in Llan Rhos Church, in the parish of Eglwys Rhos, to avoid the plague ; but, in the parabolical language of Taliesin, who personified the disease in the form of a hag so hideous that to look upon her would be fatal, the king, incautiously peeping through the window or keyhole, caught a glimpse of the creature, and died soon afterwards. Maelgwyn takes a prominent position in the semi-mythical period of Welsh history. In it he is described as being a resolute and relentless tyrant and autocratic sinner. Roughly remorseful for his evil deeds, this monarch, when sickness assailed him, vowed that he would enter upon a religious life, and the Triads record his name as chief elder at Caerlleon. Geoffrey of Monmouth states that Maelgwyn honourably buried St. David, who died in the monastery of his own foundation at Menevia.

Maelgwyn's son, Rhun, the wearer of the golden torque, was a hero who, with his hosts, went forth to fight the men of the North for burning Arvon. It appears that Elidyr the Courteous, of the North, was slain at Arvon, whereto Clydno Rhydderech the Benevolent, and Nudd the Generous, with other heroes, marched to avenge their friend's death. On the banks of the Gweryd disputes arose as to who should take the van, and it was accorded to the men of Arvon. Of this battle Taliesin sings—

" Behold ! from the ardency of their blades,
    With Rhun the reddener of armies,
    The men of Arvon with their ruddy lances."

Rhun, in common with the chieftains of those days, went on many plundering expeditions, and in the Romance of Taliesin he appears very unfavourably. Thus he is seen coming to " rob the southern Britons of their possessions and riches, and utterly ravish the country." Thereupon Maelgwyn ordered Rhun not to injure St. Cadoc or his territory, because he depended on their friendship, and this reckless son " promised with an oath " to obey his father. But, alas ! the temptation was too great, and Rhun, with his men, went onward, plundering to their hearts' content, until they were thirsty, and, going to the farm of Cadoc's cowherd, demanded " a sufficiency of milk to drink." This was refused, on the ground that Cadoc had " one hundred clergymen, and as many soldiers, and the same number

of workmen, besides women and children," for
whom the daily supply was only sufficient. Rhun
was angered, and his men tried to set the barn
on fire, but "it would not burn, but only
smoked." At this time "Rhun was in his tent
playing at dice with his eunuchs, and the smoke
like a wooden post" went direct from the barn
of Saint Cadoc to the king's tent, with the result
that all in the place were blinded. Rhun then
set the blame upon his esquires, and begged for-
giveness for the "great crime" his men had
committed, which was the least they could do,
having completely lost their eyesight. Cadoc's
prayers were efficacious, and Rhun confirmed the
refuge accorded by his father. And the king, in
gratitude, gave to Cadoc his "own messenger,
with complete horse accoutrements and three
principal articles of armour, namely, a shield, a
sword, and a spear."

Cadvan was a successful warrior and hero,
whose name is preserved in Llangadwaladr
Church, where his epitaph runs thus :—

> " Catamanus Rex,
>   Sapientissimus, Opinatissimus,
>   Omnium Regum."

Under the command of Cadvan, who became
the Pendragon of Britain, the Northumbrians
were driven beyond the Humber. In a treaty
of peace it was agreed that Ethelfrid was to hold

all the territory north of the Humber, and Cadvan was to keep Britain south of that river.

After Cadvan comes the name of his son, Cadwallawn, the "twenty-third" monarch, who is
described as a "mightie kinge, hee fought with
his enemyes the Saxons often tymes, and drove
them astraye, and had alwayes the victorie over
them, hee reigned xlviii yeares, and when hee was
dead his bodie was anoynted with holie oynt-
mente or oyle, and caused his bodie to be sett
in an image of brass upon one of the gates in
London, as Merlyn said in his profesie unto
Kinge Vortiger, that a Saxon woulde never enter
into Brittaine while his bodie remained there,
and that was proved to be true untile hee was
taken away."

This "image of brass" was placed on a brazen
horse over the western gate of London, where a
church was built and dedicated to St. Martin.

Cadwallawn fought many desperate battles
against the Saxons. In one of them he was
defeated by Edwin, King of Northumbria, and,
driven from his dominions, went over to Ireland,
where he remained as an exile for seven years.
On his return he once more fought against Edwin,
who was slain, and whose army was routed and
partially destroyed. This Pendragon was very
victorious, and according, to Bede, many of the
Anglian princes were captured and put to death
by him, while he ravaged the country, slaughtered

the inhabitants, and, though a Christian, was more barbaric and savage than any pagan. So successful was this king that the Britons believed he would be able to expel the Saxons and regain possession of the whole island. But at last Cadwallawn was suddenly and unexpectedly defeated and slain by the Saxons under the command of Oswald the Bernician.

According to some of the Welsh traditons, when Edwin, on October 12, A.D. 633, was defeated and slain at Heathfield, the leek was adopted as the national emblem, and the fray is described as the " famous battle at Meigan." Cynddelw, a bard of the twelfth century, wrote thus—

"Men of Powys! a people renowned;
By a skillful contest of joyful result,
Fourteen immunities strenuously upheld and respected
They gained at Moigan !"

CHAPTER XVI

CADWALADER THE "BLESSED"

THIS monarch, according to the Iolo MSS., was celebrated as being the "last king of Britain descended from the primitive royal lineage of the Island, until it was restored in the person of Henry VII." He was the last of his race to assume the royal title, and although not a hero in a warlike sense of the word, he shared with Arthur the reputation of being one who was to reappear in a dateless age, expel the Saxons from the Island of Britain, and restore the Welsh to their primitive and ancient possessions. The Chronicles describe him as the twenty-fourth and last monarch of the royal line of Wales. Of him it is said he was "kinge of Brittaine 51 years, and hee was the last kinge of the first 100 kinges of the Brittones. He buylded the Towne of Abergeveney, where an oulde buyldinge was before made by a giant called Eigas Orgo, hee de-

fended this Realme of Brittaine, and warred
allwayes against his enemeys the Saxons, and in
the meane space hee fell into a great sickness,
and theire in Brittaine there was a great discorde
between the lords of the land, that each one
warred upon the othere, and in that tyme there
fell so great dearthe and scarcety of corne and
other victualls in the lande that a man myghte
goe 3 or 4 dayes from towne to towne, that he
shoulde not fynd to buye for goulde, nor silver,
breade, wyne, nor enye othere victualls wherewith a man myght live, but onlie the people
lived upon roots of herbes, for othere living had
they none, soe that yet to this misadventure
there fell soe great mortalitie and pestilence
among the people bye the corruptione of the
ayre, that the living people sufficed not to burie
the deade bodies, for they died so sodeynlie,
both greate and small. Master and servant
in eating, going and speaking, they fell down
and died. When Cadwalader sawe those great
hunger, mortalitie, and pestilence, and the
lande all poore and faylinge corne and othere
vitayles, and his foldes perish, and saw also the
most part of his lande all wasted, and void of
people, hee appeared hyme and his folks that
were lefte alyve, and passed over to Little
Brittaine, unto Kinge Alayne, that hee muche
loved that was Cozene, and, as they Sailed on
the Sea, he made muche lamentation, and soe

did all those that were with hyme, and said
*dediste dire taman ones escaru et in gentibus
despersisti nos.* Among this great companyes
that came from Germanye unto this lande, came
the noble queen Saxburga, with the 400 thousand men and womene, and childrene, for here
there was none that Might theme lett, for all
the lande was desolate and void of people, but
the fewe poore Brittones that were left on
mountaines and in woods until that tyme, and
from thence forth lost the Brittons this realme
for all their dayes, and the English people began
to araigne and departed the lande betwixt
theme, as they would themselves accordinge to
theire owne will and pleasure, and when Kinge
Cadwalader had knowledge that the Mortalitie
and Pestilence were overpassed, and that the
lande was replenished with a livinge people, hee
thought good to come againe into this land, and
praid his cozene Kinge Alayne, a succoure and
helpe, that he myght be restored to his owne
proper realme, and first dignity, and King
Alayne granted hym his askinge. Then did
Cadwalader apparaile himself to take his waye
and voiage into this land, and prayed God
Almightie devoutedly that he would make to
him demonstration, whether his prayer to return
to this lande was pleasant or not, for againste
the will of God Almightie he woulde nothinge
doe; when he had thus devoutedlye made his

prayers, a voice from heavene said to hyme,
and bade hym to leave that journey into Eng-
lande and that hee should goe to the Pope of
Rome, for hitt was not the will of the Almightye
God that the Brittons should raigne anye more
in Brittaine, nor never recover the land until
the tyme that the prophecies that Merlin,
Scibill and Festoine said be fulfilled, and that
shoulde never be untile the tyme be come that
the relickes of his bodie should be brought from
Rome, and translated into Brittaine. And when
the relickes of other saints that have been hid,
for the persecution of the Panyme folke should,
be founde and openlie shewed, thene shall they
recovere theire lande againe which they had
soe longe tyme lost through theire deservinge.
Whenc Cadwalader had herd this answere, hcc
marveailled greatly, and told it to the Kinge
Alayne, thene Kinge Alayne sent for the clergie
of his lande, and made them to bringe the
stories and prophecyes that Merlin and Scibill
had said in theire prophecyes accorded to the
divyne answere that Cadwalader had herd, he
Counsailed hyme to leave his people and his
navye, and to submit hyme to the disposition
of God, and doe all that the Angel had commanded hyme. Then Cadwalader called Ivor
his sone, and Ivorye his sister sone, and some
saye he had two other sones, Alaen and Idwal,
the Roe in the British tongue, Idwal, Iwrch,

and said to them, take, said he, my folke and
my navye, that is here already, and passe into
Walles, and be lorde of Brittons that noe dishonour come to them bye interruptions of the
Paynyms folke, for defaulte of lordes, and then
hee hymeself leaft his realme of Brittaine and
his folke forevermore, and tooke his waye to
the Pope of Rome Sergius the which worshipped
hyme muche and hee was confessed, and tooke
penanc for his sines.   Hee had not longe
dwelled there butt that hee died, the XIIth
of Maye, in the yeare of grace v.c. LXXIX.
(679).   Thus endeth the reigne of the Kinges
of Brittaine, in this Cadwalader, and from
thence, beginneth the reigne of the Princes of
Walles, which endured in the Brittons for the
space of 700 years or thereabouts."

A similar account of Cadwalader, taken from
the MS. of Hafod Uchryd, appeared in the old
Welsh "Greal," dated London 1805.   In Rees's
"Essay on the Welsh Saints," the death of this
monarch is fixed at A.D. 664.

There are several versions of the death of
Cadwalader, and historians find it difficult to
unravel fact from fiction, but this much is known
for a certainty.   For many centuries after the
death of Arthur and Cadwalader, the leaders
of Welsh warfare excited the patriotism and
national spirit of their followers by predictions
that both ancient heroes would one day return

and lead them onward and upward to years of
brilliant victories, after which the Saxons would
be completely defeated, and ultimately wholly
annihilated.

Geoffrey of Monmouth represents Myrddin
the bard prophesying :—"Cadwalader shall call
upon Cynan, and take Albania into alliance.
Then shall there be a slaughter of foreigners;
then shall the rivers run with blood. Then
shall break forth the fountains of Armorica, and
they shall be crowned with the diadem of Brutus.
Cambria shall be filled with joy, and the oaks of
Cornwall shall flourish. The island shall be
called by the name of Brutus, and the name
given it by foreigners shall be abolished. From
Cynan shall proceed a warlike boar, that shall
exercise the sharpness of his tusks within the
Gallic woods. For he shall cut down all the
larger oaks, and shall be a defence to the
smaller."

The same prophet and bard is described as
singing in the " Avallenau " attributed to
him—

"Yet shall my prophetic song announce the coming again
  Of Medrawd, and of Arthur, leader of hosts;
  Again shall they rush to the battle of Camlan,
  And only seven escape from the two days' conflict.
  Let Gwenhwyvar remember her crimes
  When Cadwaladr takes possession of his throne again,
  And the religious hero leads his armies ! . . . .

Sweet apple-tree! of richest fruit; that grow'st
In solitary woods of Celyddon,
All seek thee for thy fruit, but seek in vain,
Till Cadwaladr to Rhyd Rheon come
For conference, and Cynan shall advance
Against the Saxons; then shall victory
The Britons crown, led by their graceful chief,
Who shall restore to every one his own;
And by the horn of gladness is proclaim'd
The song of peace, and days of happiness."

The "Arymes Prydain Vawr," or "Oracle concerning Great Britain," contains the next verse—

" Cadwaladr and Cynan, men of might
In battle; be they bless'd! till day of doom
Famous; steadfast kings, profound in council;
Two, who the Saxons will through God defeat;
Fearless and ready men; men of one faith,
One end; of Britain's comely armies, shields; . . .
Theirs shall be all the land from Brittany.
To Man, from South Wales unto Thanet Isle,
From heaven unto earth, their word shall rule. . . .
A strong support of Kymru shall arise.
Unto the faithful kingdom of our God,
Fleets from all countries shall invited be;
Trouble shall end; in peace shall all men live."

In later centuries Cadwalader received the
surname of " Bendigaid," or " Blessed," and in
the Triads he is called one of the " Three
Canonised Kings of the Island of Britain," and
one of those who gave sanctuary in all parts
of his dominions to those who fled before the
oppression of the Saxons.

After the death of Cadwalader the ancient Welsh princes never regained the monarchy, and the centuries passed in many wars both among themselves and against the Saxons.

From the death of this last king of Britain, in A.D. 664 to the end of the ninth century, there were many heroes fighting for independence and freedom that were slowly but surely departing before the encroachments and power of the Saxons.

One of the most eminent of the British chieftains at this period was Rhodri Maelwynawg, who bravely resisted and defeated the Saxons in several battles, particularly in that of Mount Carno, Monmouthshire. Later on, Rhodri, after many deeds of heroism in border warfare, was driven to North Wales, and, at his death in A.D. 756, he was succeeded by his son Cynan, whose name is only slightly mentioned in the Welsh records. The next heroes that appear are those whose fiery blood was roused by the making of Offa's Dyke, and in A.D. 796, Caradawg, King of Gwynedd, with many other distinguished and princely warriors, were slain by the Saxons at Rhuddlan, in the Vale of Clwyd. In some of the ancient Welsh records it is stated that the touching lament, called "Morva Rhuddlan," was composed by the bards on the occasion of this battle.

For twenty years after the desperate and fatal

battle of Rhuddlan Marsh continual expeditions
were made, and border foray, warfare, and fierce
conflict were ceaselessly carried on in the Welsh
marches between the Saxons and the Celts.

In A.D. 816 or 822, Dyganwy, the home of
the kings of North Wales, was burnt. This
fortress was called by the Romans "Gannoe,"
but its Welsh name means "The white waves
breaking along the shore." This celebrated
stronghold has a conspicuous place in the annals
of Wales from the time of the Romans until the
tragic death of Llewelyn in A.D. 1282.

In A.D. 844 the crown of Gwynedd passed
from Mervyn Vrych—who, with Essyllt, made a
stout resistance against the Saxons in the rugged
mountain passes of Snowdon and the wilds of
Montgomery—to Rhodri Mawr, or Rhodri the
Great. According to some of the Welsh national
records, Rhodri inherited Gwynedd from his
mother, Powys and the Isle of Man from his
father, and with his wife Angharad he received
South Wales. For that reason he was recognised
as the first prince of the whole of Wales.

Early in the reign of Rhodri the Great the
Danes first visited Wales, and in A.D. 853
"Mona was ravaged by the black Pagans," who,
from the wide estuaries of the Dee and the
Severn, penetrated into the centre of the land,
and made many incursions along the shores of
Anglesea and Glamorgan. In the reign of

Rhodri the seiges of York, Ash-down, Alcluyd,
took place, and in all the great battles this
prince proved himself to be among the most
distinguished chieftains and warriors of his age.

At his death the dominion was divided into
three parts between his sons, who subsequently
came to be known as the Three Sons of Rhodri,
described in the Triads as the " Three diademed
princes." The eldest son, Anarawd, received
Gwynedd, or North Wales; Cadell, the second
son, had for his dominion Dinevwr, or Dehu-
barth, in South Wales; and Mervyn became
king of Powys, which consisted of all the
country extending between the Wye and the
Severn.

This division, though equitably arranged
according to the then existing law of gavel-
kind, proved injudicious, and became the cause
of quarrels and battles between the brothers.
Cadell conquered Mervyn, and became king of
Powys, and left his realm and possessions to his
son Hywel, afterwards known as Hywel Dda,
or Howel the Good, who in after-time was
regarded as the " chief and glory of the
Britains."

CHAPTER XVII

HYWEL THE GOOD

AT the death of his cousin, Idwal Voel, the Welsh unanimously elected Hywel to rule the whole Principality, thus re-uniting the kingdom which had been divided by his grandfather, Rhodri the Great.

The illustrious Hywel Dda appears in striking contrast to the warlike kings, princes, and chieftains whose brilliant successes or unhappy failures fill the long pages of Welsh history. Glory, power, triumphs of warcraft, acquisition of territory, and fierce battles and forays to keep the Saxon from crossing the mountain-barriers of wild Wales, formed the sole desire of the spirited Celt; but Hywel Dda was a patriot prince, quite ready to take up arms against the enemy, though more willing to apply the arts of legislation to the security of peace.

Fierce domestic feuds, broils between chieftains, and skirmishes of petty princes were unavoidable in his time; but while Hywel reigned, the general condition of the country was peaceful, and undisturbed by foreign invasion. His heroic spirit kept the volcanic turbulence of the Celt in temporary subjection, and, under his sway, insignificant intrigue, baneful dissension, and civil turmoil smouldered among the mountains of Wales, only to be rekindled at his death, and continued for centuries without intermission.

In solitary grandeur, as a hero of peace among the distinguished war-kings, princes, and chieftains of Wales, Hywel Dda—holding the olive branch, and the tablets of the law instead of sword and shield—stands pre-eminent in the annals of Wales, as Alfred the Saxon appears in the history of England.

Hywel was one of those remarkable men who clearly understood what should, and what could, be done, and it is one of the strongest points in his character that, instead of spending his strength against foreign foes, he did his utmost to fortify his own dominions. Calling his wise men together, he drew up a revised code of laws, and next proceeded to see that the law-courts did their duty. With the highest interests of his country at heart, Hywel, seeing many abuses and much anomaly, directed his mind to alter and improve them. At the same time, he was not a hasty and impetuous reformer, who, like an impatient disputant, goes about his work in reckless fashion; nor did he resemble many of the erratic law-alterers of to-day, who, caring little for traditions of the past or emergencies of the future, go forth much like the Mael-gwyns and Rhuns of old, now rushing wildly along with the sword, and then falling on their knees in humble submission.

This monarch entered upon this patrimony in A.D. 907, and his first public work was in A.D. 926.

During those years he had closely watched the affairs and requirements of his people, and then went out to see how other lands were governed. Having decided upon a visit to Rome, Hywel, attended by several bishops, and other clerical and lay dignitaries, set forth on a pilgrimage for the purpose of consultation, as Caradoc of Llancarvan says, "with wise men respecting the means of improving the laws of the realm of Cambria, to obtain a knowledge of the laws of other countries and cities, and to know the laws which the emperors of Rome put in force in the Isle of Britain during their sovereignty."

On his return home Hywel convened a great assembly of all the learned men, the clergy and nobility, of Wales, to meet him at Ty Gwyn ar Dâf, the White-House on the Tâf, or Tav, beside

Whitland Abbey, near Tenby. And, by the way, this royal hunting-seat in Carmarthenshire was so called because it was built of white wood —possibly a wattle and daub erection.

This convocation consisted of a hundred and forty ecclesiastics, six men of learning from every *cymwd* or commote in his kingdom. Each commote comprised twelve manors and two hamlets. Blegwryd, Chancellor of Llandaff, who was the first scholar and lawyer of his day, was appointed head commissioner over twelve other commissioners, to examine the Welsh laws and draw up an improved code. After much deliberation, the laws of Dyvnwal Moelmud were chosen as the basis of the new and reformed system, which was submitted by the commissioners to the judgment of the convention, and, being thereby approved and ratified, passed on to Hywel Dda, and received the royal assent.

The king ordered three copies of the laws to be written out in full. One was kept for his own use, another was deposited at Dinevwr, and the third went to the palace of Aberfraw.

The laws of Hywel Dda reveal the state of society in Wales in the tenth century, and prove this monarch to have been one of the most conscientious and enlightened rulers of Wales and the Welsh. In the "Ancient Welsh Laws" the code is divided into three books:—The first contains the laws of the royal court, the second the laws of the country, and the third appertained to wild and tame animals.

It is interesting to examine the laws of that far past, and look into the condition of Wales before the Normans set foot in the land.

First for consideration comes the royal court, the arrangement of which appears in the following order:—Twenty-four servants were appointed. Of these there were sixteen for the king, and eight for the queen.

The king's suite consisted of the chief of the household, the steward, the priest or chaplain, the bard, the judge of the court, the page of the chamber, the silentiary, the candle-bearer, the door-ward or porter, the chief falconer, chief groom, chief huntsman, the mediciner, butler, mead-brewer, and cook.

The queen's suite comprised the steward, the priest, the page of the chamber, the handmaid, candle-bearer, door-ward or porter, chief groom, and cook.

The Chief or Master of the Household was the king's representative during his absence, and, in addition to his general duties, he had to settle domestic accounts and family quarrels; and it is recorded, "If the king receive any man of the family in anger, the master of the household must invite him into his presence, and reconcile him to the king." In those days of marauding expeditions it was necessary to make provision for them; therefore the master of the king's household was commanded what to do " when it is necessary for the family to go to pillage!"

The priest or chaplain was also Secretary of State and Chancellor, but although he " said grace" at the king's table, he is described as having "his lodging with the sexton, and the scholars with him; his allowance is one dish of meat and a hornful of liquor." The steward, as chief of the servants, had not only the care of food and beverage, with other serving duties, but " he must swear for the king." The silentiary, or crier, " must proclaim silence by striking the pillar above the head of the priest;" and the page, who was king's messenger, treasure-keeper, and wardrobe-man, had " to be punished for what he may lose." The master of the hawks, or chief falconer, " has his lodging in the king's barn, lest his birds should be injured by the smoke. He must bring his vessel to the palace, to get drink in it; for he ought only to quench his thirst, lest his birds be injured by neglect. He is entitled to a stag in October, and the skin of a hind in May, to make gloves to train his hawks, and also to make their jesses. He must be honoured with three presents the day the hawk kills one of these birds—a bittern, a crane, or a heron. He claims the mantle in which the king rides on the three great festivals," and he received a " handbreadth of wax-candle from the steward for feeding his birds and making his bed." The door-ward, with his rod of office, cleared the way for the king; and the cook not only prepared but tasted every dish, and served the same at the royal table.

Three times a year, at Christmas, Easter, and Whitsuntide, the twenty-four officers received their woollen garments from the king, and their linen garments from the queen.

The judge of the palace " receives his pillow and bed-linen from the queen, while the cushion upon which the king sat during the day shall be under him at night. . . . He is entitled to receive a chess-board, made of the bones of a sea-fish, from the queen, and another from the domestic bard; and these toy ornaments he must neither sell nor give whilst he lives. . . . The porter must open the large gate for him when coming to the palace . . . for he must never go through the small gate whether in going or coming."

The heir-apparent was allowed "meat and drink without measure," and all his expenditure was defrayed by the king; but he could not give away even a dog or a ring, or the smallest ornament, without the monarch's permission. The master of the horse " claims fourpence for every horse which the king gives, except to three men ; these

are the bishop, the master of the hawks, and the
buffoon. He receives nothing for a horse given
to the bishop, because he is the king's confessor,
rises up before him, sits behind him, and holds
his sleeves while the king washes himself. He
receives nothing from the master of the hawks,
for the king serves him on three occasions. . . .
Neither does he get anything from the buffoon,
because he must tie the halter round the horse's
tail, and ride the contrary way when he goes
from the palace."

A very peculiar court officer was the foot-
holder, who "must hold the king's foot in his lap,
from the time he begins to sit at banquet until
he goes to sleep; and he must rub the king;
and during that space of time, he must guard
him, lest he should suffer any misfortune. He
has the privilege of eating upon the same dish
with the king, with his back towards the fire."
At the same time, though he should have a dish
of meat and liquor for himself, " he is not to join
in the feast," but " his land shall be free, and
he shall receive a horse from the king, and shall
have a share of the visitors' gift money." In
some instances the office of foot-holder was
bestowed upon a damsel, as recorded in the
" Mabinogion " of Mâth, the son of Mathonwy,
who " could not exist unless his feet were in
the lap of a maiden, except only when he was
prevented by the tumult of war." This maiden

bore the curious name of Goewin, and "she was the fairest maiden of her time."

The apparitor was obliged to stand "between the two pillars, with his rod in his hand, lest the house should take fire whilst the king is eating and drinking with his officers; but he must not sit in the hall. If the apparitor be caught sitting, and be insulted for it (this was in legal cases), when causes are tried, he can only claim a sieve of oats and an egg-shell for the insult."

The chief huntsman, "from the eighth night of February, must take his dog, his horns, and his greyhounds, to go and hunt the young stags. His horn must be buffalo, and its value is one pound. From that time to the middle of summer, being the Feast of St. John, he must hunt the young deer, and during that time he is not bound to do justice to any one who may have a claim upon him, unless it be one of his fellow-officers. Some say that he ought only to swear by his horn and his leashes. He is entitled to the skin of an ox in winter to make leashes, and to a buck's skin in summer to make boots. On the morrow after the Feast of St. John, being the middle of summer, he must go to hunt deer; and unless he can be taken before he has risen from his bed and put on his boots, he is not obliged to do justice to any one who has a claim on him."

Among the various perquisites of the porter were "a billet of wood from every burden of fuel which is brought through the gate which he may be able to pull off without stopping the horse, having his hand on the gate." Moreover, he was entitled to "every pig that comes through the gate without a tail!" He was obliged to do his errands gratis, but could claim the leavings of the cheese which he toasts."

According to these laws, a son came of age at fourteen, and a daughter at twelve, and in North Wales the latter could not succeed to property on the paternal side. The king was heir to the private property of the bishops, and his Majesty was next-of-kin and heir-at-law to many people, especially placeholders of every description.

In those days to *see* a fire was sufficient to make a person an accessary to the burning, and wilful homicide was legally expiable by a pecuniary fine, which proves the prevailing extent of revenge by murder for various offences.

The *saraad*, or fine, had special provision. Of these fines the following are the most curious :— "The fine due to the king for violating his protection was a hundred cows for every cantred or hundred, and a white bull with red ears" with each hundred of cows. The fine to the lord of Dinevwr was "as many white cows with

red ears as would extend in close succession
from Argoel to the palace of Dinevwr ; " while
that due to the king of Aberfraw consisted of
" a rod of gold as tall as himself, and as thick
as his little finger." The fine for other kings
was a " silver rod that would reach from the
floor to their lips as they sat, and as thick
as their middle finger, with three nobs at each
end."

Curiously, the king of Aberfraw was entitled
to a fine of " a plate of gold, as broad as his
face, and as thick as the nail of a ploughman
who had been at his work for seven years ; "
while for other kings the fine consisted of " a
gold cup that would hold the king's full draught,
and a golden cover, as broad as his Majesty's
face," of the thickness already mentioned, or of
" the shell of a goose's egg."

According to the code of Dyved, " twenty-
four pence was the worth of the blood of every
kind of persons ; for thirty pence was the worth
of the blood of Christ ; and it was unworthy to
see the blood of the Son of God and the blood
of men appraised of equal worth ; and therefore
the blood of a man was of less worth." It was
also decreed that " whoever shall pull a person's
hair, let him first compensate for the insult, and
pay a penny for every finger that touches the
head, and two pence for the thumb ; and a legal
penny for every hair pulled by the root from

the head; and twenty-four pence for the front hair!"

In a case of extreme and ferocious hair-pulling, it must have been difficult to number the hairs in order to impose the fine.

A still more curious branch of Hywel Dda's legislation includes the following :—

"THE LAW OF A CAT.

" 1. Whoever shall kill a cat that guards a house and a barn of the king, or shall steal it, it is to be held with its head to the ground, and its tail up, the ground being swept, and then clean wheat is to be poured about it, until the tip of its tail is hidden : and that is its worth. If corn cannot be had, a milch sheep, with her lamb and its wool, is its value.

" 2. Another cat is four legal pence in value."

The qualities of " a cat are, that it be perfect of ear, perfect of eye, perfect of tooth, perfect of tail, perfect of claw, and without marks of fire; and that it kill mice well; and that it shall not devour its kittens; and that it shall not be caterwauling every moon."

The finder of a swarm of bees was entitled to a penny, or the wax, and the owner of the land received the swarm. The worth of martens, ermines, and beavers, wherever killed, became the king's property, because the fur was made into royal garments. Wolves, foxes, and all mischievous animals were free for any one to kill.

Those laws compelled every landed proprietor or squire to maintain an armed man, and every householder had to be furnished with a bow and twelve arrows, while the chief of the king's household could choose those who were to "go on a foray." The king might lead his hosts "out of his own dominions for no longer a time than six weeks," and as the spoils of warfare or forays were shared, the domestic bard was to sing the song of "the monarchy of Britain." That must have been the original National Anthem, about which it would be interesting to know more.

There is a valuable and ancient copy of the Laws of Hywel Dda preserved among the Cotton MSS. in the British Museum, and another in the Welsh School in Gray's Inn Lane, while "The Ancient Laws and Institutes of Wales," edited by Mr. Aneurin Owen, is the most valuable modern record extant.

In A.D. 948 the long and peaceful reign of Hywel Dda, or, in English, Howel the Good, one of the most enlightened monarchs of Wales, came to a close, and his death was almost immediately succeeded by renewals of civil wars, in which it is said his four sons ultimately perished.

Leland, who made his celebrated itinerary through Wales about 1530, states in his Latin "Collectina" that Hywel Dda was buried in the Church of St. Iltutus, or, as the old historian renders it, "Llaniltud Vawr Church."

CHAPTER XVIII

EARLY BORDER WARFARE

ACCORDING to the Welsh records, in the bitter contests that followed the death of "the chief and glory of the Britains," Dyvnwal and Rhodri, two of Hywel's sons, died fighting against Idwal at the battle of Carno; and, later on, another son of the great king fell in the prevailing and continual strife.

In A.D. 958, Owain, the son of Hywel Dda, entered and ravaged Gower and Glamorgan, where Morgan Hên, or Aged, reigned. With reference to this Morgan, it is stated in the Iolo MSS. that he "was a mighty, brave-hearted king; and great, beyond measure, in generosity, justice, and mercy; for which he was designated a second Arthur. He married Olwen, the daughter of Rhodri the Great. . . . Morgan had a palace at Cardiff, where formerly stood the court of the Roman general, Aulus Didius, but that palace was reduced to heaps of ruins by the Saxons in the time of Cadwalader the Blessed. He had also a royal residence at Margam, and another at Brigan, where he usually held his national and juridical courts. He lived to the age of one hundred and twenty-five years."

The remains of the ancient castle of Breigan are still to be seen in the parish of Llansannor, in the Vale of Glamorgan. The Iolo MSS. thus continue :—"Owen, the son of Morgan the Aged, was involved in war by Owen, the son of Howel the Good ; but Edgar marched an army against the latter, and compelled him to abide by his wise men's decision in favour of Morgan the Great. Owen, the son of Howel, was now excommunicated ; but, having made restitution to Owen, the son of Morgan, he was absolved. This Owen, the son of Morgan, built a church and castle at Ystrad-Owen, where he and his wife were buried." In the notes attached to this record it is stated that at "Ystrad-Owen ;— a village near Cowbridge. There is a large tumulus within the churchyard of this place, which, probably, was raised in commemoration over the grave of Owen and his wife." The tumulus is still to be seen outside the walls of the present church and in the grounds of Ash Hall, the venerable owner of which is Daniel Owen, Esq., J.P., part proprietor of the *Western Mail*, Cardiff. It is singularly interesting to find the ancient home of Owen, the son of

Morgan the Aged, occupied in the nineteenth century by a later Owen, who is himself a bard and patriotic Welshman.

To return to Owain, the son of Hywel Dda. When he ravaged Gower and Glamorgan his spite knew no bounds, and because some noble Saxons were being educated at the Colleges of Illtutus at Llantwit, and Cadoc of Llancarvan, this fiery Welshman greatly damaged both, and carried many of their treasures away. While these civil broils were being carried on in various parts of Wales, the Saxons gradually made progress and gained power, and in A.D. 973 Chester was the scene of the partial submission of the Welsh to Saxon sway. In the English annals, Edgar, surnamed the "Peaceable," and called "The Honour and Delight of the English Nation," is described as having, on one occasion, received eight kings at Chester to do homage to him as their superior lord. These vassal kings rowed Edgar along the river Dee to the Church of St. John the Baptist, and, on his return, the Saxon king is said to have exclaimed, "My successors may think themselves kings when they can command the services of a like number of regal vassals." These "regal vassals" were Kenneth, King of the Scots, and Malcolm, his son, King of Strathclyde; Maccus, "Lord of the Isles;" Iago, King of the Galloway Britons; Idwal, King of Westmere; Siferth and Hywel, Kings of Wales; and Dyvnwal, King of Dyved. In the Iolo MSS. the following reference to this submission on the part of the Welsh is given:—" Gwaethvoed, Lord of Cibwyr and Ceredigion, lived in the time of King Edgar, who summoned the Welsh princes to Chester, to row his barge on the river Dee. Gwaethvoed returned an answer to Edgar, saying that he could not row a barge; and if he could, that he would not do so, except to save a person's life, whether king or vassal. Edgar sent a second and very imperious command, but no answer whatever was given to the messenger, who, consequently, begged, with submission, to know what kind of reply he should return to the king. 'Say to him,' said Gwaethvoed, ' " Fear him who fears not death : " ' whereupon Edgar went to him, and giving him his hand in great kindness, entreated that he would become his friend and relation; and so it was; and thenceforth the motto of all descended from Gwaethvoed has been, ' Fear him who fears not death.' The arms of Gwaethvoed were vert, a chevron or, between three wolves' heads, dropping blood, until the time of Henry VIII., when the armorial bearings of the princes of Powis were given to the lineage of Gwaethvoed; but some of his descendants continued to bear the original coat-of-arms, with the motto already mentioned."

The next name of importance appearing in the
annals of Wales is Meredydd ap Owain, who, as
his enemies said, subjugated all North Wales
"by extreme craft and cunning." In A.D. 991
Meredydd's nephew, with a host of Saxons,
marched across Wales, and in their course plundered towns, villages, cathedrals, including St.
David's, and took hostages everywhere, in order
to win his uncle's dominions.   Meredydd, finding himself sorely pressed, is said to have been
obliged to hire Danish soldiers, with whom he
ravaged Glamorgan, then ruled by Ithel Ddû,
who is described in the Iolo MSS. as a "very
valiant and potent king, and lived mostly at his
new summer house, called Ton Ithel Ddu (Ithel
the Dark), from his very black hair and beard."

By-and-by the "black host" gained a firm
footing in the North, and in A.D. 995 Meredydd,
whose dominions were famine-stricken, was defeated in the south of Denbighshire.   Three
years later the Danes entered the Severn, and
ravaged Wales and the West of England, and
almost depopulated St. David's, and Idwal ap
Meirig obtained the sovereignty of North Wales,
leaving heroic Meredydd, who had made stout
resistance against much oppression and cruel
wrongs, to die dethroned in his own country.

Subsequently the Welsh are seen aiding
Edmund Ironside against Canute, and Llewelyn
ap Seisyllt obtained supremacy of all Wales.

Several attempts were made to dethrone him and in A.D. 1022 a native of Scotland, named Reyn, appeared as pretender to the crown of Wales. This Reyn proclaimed himself as son to Meredydd, and lawful king of all Wales, and as such was accepted by the people of the South. By this time the country, under the sway of Llewelyn ap Seisyllt, was in a prosperous condition, and, having for some years ceased warfare, was both rich and powerful. The men of Gwynedd, exasperated with their brothers of Dyved for taking the part of the pretender, marched forth under Llewelyn, fought against and routed the offenders ; whereupon the South Welsh joined the North, and both used their united efforts against the pretender, whom they pursued, and went onward, as the *Brut* says, "slaying his men, and devastating the country, pillaging every place, and destroying it as far as Mercia." Soon after this Llewelyn ap Seisyllt died.

Wales afterwards continued to be the scene of fierce turmoil and divided parties until A.D. 1039, when Gruffydd ap Llewelyn took possession of the kingdom. He proved himself ready to use the sword so unsparingly as to be the source of perpetual annoyance to the Saxons. Under his rule border warfare became fiercer, more bitter, and continual

In A.D. 1056, Leofgar, Bishop of Hereford, yearning for the excitement of warfare, threw

aside his crosier for the sword, and went forth
to take the field against Gruffydd. Of this encounter, which took place in the summer, the
chronicler says, " It is difficult to tell the distress
and the camping, and the travail and destruction of men, and also of horses, which all the
English army endured." Early in June, Leofgar
and his priests, with many of the followers, were
slain, and others fled away, and for a time
at least Gruffydd promised to be to "King
Edward a faithful and unbetraying under-king."
Gruffydd, ever restless and fond of warfare, soon
forgot his promise, and wishing to free himself
from the thrall of England, made another raid
against his enemies. Thereupon Harold, with
his forces, crossed the borders, and in his attempt
to subjugate North Wales, was encountered by
Gruffydd ap Llewelyn on the plain near Cefn
Ogof, and after a sanguinary battle was defeated
and driven back to Rhuddlan.

Harold then was determined to conquer the
brave but restless King of Gwynedd, and with a
large fleet circumnavigated Wales, while the land
forces marched on towards Snowdon. Right
valiantly Gruffydd fought, but his bravery of
heart and fearlessness were soon to come to an
end. Harold, with his superior forces, marched
among the heights and ravines of Snowdon, and
everywhere defeated the Welsh. He hemmed
in his brave-hearted but desperate enemy, but

even then Gruffydd would not yield. Dauntless
and resolute, he faced the enemy, and fought
until the allegiance of his people gave way, and
he had not a friend left. Of the manner of his
death there are several versions. The Saxon
Chronicle says :—" This same year (1064), during
the harvest in the beginning of August, was
King Gruffydd slain, by his own men, by reason
of the war that he warred with Harold the earl.
He was king over all the Welsh race; and his
head was taken to Harold, who presented it to
the king along with the prow of his ship, adorned
with ivory."

The Welsh record states :—" Thus Gruffydd
ap Llewelyn, the head, and shield, and defender
of the Britons, fell through the treachery of his
own men. The man who had hitherto been invincible was now left in the glens of desolation,
after taking immense spoils, and after innumerable victories, and countless treasures of gold, and
silver, and jewels, and purple vestures."

Of this prince the following story, illustrative
of the plundering tendencies and superstitious
sentiments of the age, is recorded in the "Lives
of the Cambro-British Saints" :—It appears that
Gruffydd ab Llewelyn, fearing his enemies, retired to the "Orcades Islands," and there induced
the islanders to assist him in revenging himself
against the English. Therefore twenty-four
ships well filled with men sailed under the com-

mand of Gruffydd along the Irish Sea, "and
after a long and dangerous voyage, came to the
Severn sea, which washes the banks of Glamorgan ;
then sailing along the sea, they very greedily
went for plunder to the mouth of the river Usk,
and cast anchor. The fleet being secured, they
take their hatchets, and armed with lances,
hostilely invade the fields and woods. From
these invasions they collect much prey ; the inhabitants, who were cautious, escaped through
watching, but the incautious were taken to the
fleet with their impious hands. The very wicked
pirates observing that the church of St. Gwnllyw
(supposed to be St. Woolos Church, Newport,
Monmouthshire) was locked, and thinking that
valuable articles were therein for safety and protection, broke the lock, and after breaking it
entered. And whatsoever was found valuable
and useful they took away, and after the sacrilegious robbery left the plundered church.
Then they returned burdened to the ships,
heavier with crimes than with great burdens.
. . . Having loosed the anchors, and hoisted up
the sails, they rejoicing, went to the Island of
Barry. . . . When they began to raise the sails
and return to the Orcades Islands and Ireland,
they saw a terrible man riding by day and night,
and pursuing them in every part ; that terrible
horseman was the holy Gwynllyw, who was sent
from heaven to oppose the sacrilegious persons."

A great storm arose; many of the ships were wrecked, and before Ireland was reached the whole fleet, with the exception of two vessels, "was overwhelmed." It appears that the two fortunate ships were owned by Gruffydd, who "would not destroy nor yet be a partaker of the robbery; neither did he enter the church, but with his companions waited on the shore the coming of the pirates. After some time he made peace with William, King of England, and related the miracles which he had manifestly seen performed for the sanctity of the most holy Gwynllyw."

When Gruffydd ap Llewelyn died many parts of Wales were converted into English provinces, which henceforth remained nominally governed by its native princes.

Bleddyn ap Cynan, King of North Wales and Powys, a monarch who was dearly beloved by his people, bought peace at the sacrifice of a very precarious freedom, and, acknowledging himself a tributary, did homage to keep his crown. After his death by assassination in 1073, Welsh independence soon became a name only, to be crushed out by the Normans, but occasionally hopelessly revived in succeeding centuries.

CHAPTER XIX

THE ADVENT OF THE NORMANS

IN 1077 Rhys ap Tewdwr, the last actual prince of South Wales, began to reign, and at that time Gruffydd ap Cynan was last Lord of Mona.

These names bring the record down to the days of William the Conqueror, who, in 1079, under pretence of making a devout pilgrimage to the "holy shrine" of St. David, marched through Wales, to the far metropolis of the West; and the Welsh princes, awed by the terror of the great and powerful Norman, reluctantly paid homage and took the oath of fealty.

In the Iolo MSS. the following record appears: —". . . Rhys, the son of Tewdwr, began to govern South Wales, as the rightful heir, in paternal descent, from Rhodri the Great; and at the same time, Griffith, the son of Cynan, became the just heir to the principality of North Wales; so that, now, all Wales had reverted to its lawful princes; and it would have been well for the country had this state of things been allowed to continue: but Iestyn, the son of Gwrgan, now governed Glamorgan after his father. . . ." It is then stated that Iestyn, or Jestyn, claimed the "kingdom of South Wales for his family, in the persons of his great grand-children. To effect this object, he collected a numerous host against Rhys, the son of Tewdwr; and Madog, Cadwgan, and Rhyryd, the sons of Bleddyn, the son of Cynfyn, aided his enterprise; consequently Rhys fled to Ireland, where he experienced much kindness, receiving aid both in men and ammunition; whereupon he returned with a heavy fleet to South Wales, and became victorious over his opponents. . . ." According to the same authority, Rhys ap Tewdwr, during these conflicts, seized the possessions of Einion, the son of Collwyn, "for whose apprehension he had proclaimed a high reward; offering to give three hundred heads of cattle and a thousand acres of land, in free lordship, to any one who would either take him prisoner or bring him, dead or alive, to his presence. Thus circum-stanced, and surmising treachery, Einion fled to Glamorgan, to Iestyn, the son of Gwrgan, who was his uncle; and having made his complaint, and related the whole affair, Iestyn advised him to go to London, where he was well known to the great men of King William Rufus, and in high esteem with the sovereign himself; for he had filled a distinguished office under him, in his wars."

Rhys ap Tewdwr appears in Welsh history as a brave and heroic prince, who returned from long years of exile in Brittany, and put forth his claim of heirship to the vacant throne of South Wales, which had been usurped by Rhys ap Owain. His legitimate claims, and his reputation as a wise and dignified prince—fourth lineal descendant of Hywel the Good, from whom he inherited many excellent qualities of head and heart—received the immediate recognition of his countrymen, who promptly invested him with the power accorded to his forefathers. Thereupon Trahaiarn ap Caradog, the usurper of North Wales, became full of ire to Rhys, whose success had roused Gruffydd ap Cynan to regain his hereditary dominions, and the result was a challenge from the rightful successors of the two thrones to the illegal holder of northern sovereignty.

The rival armies met in A.D. 1079 at Carno, among the mountains that divide North from South Wales, and there one of the most terrible and sanguinary battles recorded in the annals of Wales took place, with the result that Trahaiarn the usurper, his two kinsmen, and the greater part of his army were slain, while Gruffydd and Rhys were victorious.

Gruffydd ap Cynan celebrated his accession to the throne of North Wales by making a raid into Powys, then occupied by the Normans, who were represented by Cadwgan ap Bleddyn. The Earls of Shrewsbury and Chester, who were then lords of the border in the North, invited Gruffydd to meet them near the Berwyn Mountains, and treacherously explained it was for the purpose of a conference with the new ruler of Gwynedd on the subject of border rights. With only a few followers, Gruffydd proceeded to meet the Normans, who promptly loaded him with chains and despatched him to Chester Castle. It is said that Gruffydd's attendants, on the fatal journey to the Berwyns, had the thumbs of their right hands cut off, after which they were sent back to their native hills and valleys. For twelve years the unfortunate prince, who had so long been deprived of his rights by the usurper, was kept prisoner, while Hugh Lupus, who received from the Welsh the sobriquet of Hugh Vrâs or the Fat, went to and fro at his own wild will, without let or hindrance, through Gwynedd. Meanwhile Gruffydd's friends were planning his rescue.

Brave Cynwrig Hir went marketing into the grand old city of Chester. In those days the neighbourhoods of baronial halls and stately castles were the only places in which good things could be obtained. Cynwrig Hir knew that well, and with his purpose in close view, he entered Chester, laughed and talked with the pretty maidens and buxom matrons of the border-land, and cracked coarse and fair jokes with the castle guards. So successfully did he elude the gossipers' scrutiny and the guards in their jollity, that, after watching the golden opportunity, he made his way into Gruffydd's prison. There was no time for speech, for the removal of fetters, or the snapping of chains. Cynwrig Hir quickly and bodily seized his friend and prince, who suddenly found himself shouldered, fetters, chains, and all, by the devoted Welshman, who carried him away to a place of safety, wherefrom, with the aid of others, Gruffydd was borne home to Gwynedd. Heroic Cynwrig was rewarded in seeing his master free, but the freedom was precarious. Gruffydd, often in danger of being recaptured by the grim earl, had to hide in the dense forests and among the impassable mountain barriers of his beloved land, until at length, emerging from his hiding-places, he fought repeatedly with the Norman foe.

When Gruffydd ap Cynan, of North Wales, was held in bondage at Chester, the fierce struggles in South Wales were becoming more formidable.

Jestyn ap Gwrgant, whose family held the sovereignty of the South during the exile of

Rhys ap Tewdwr, revolted against the rightful claimant to the throne, and at once commenced the series of sanguinary conflicts that culminated in his last treacherous scheme. The son of Gwrgant had long been celebrated for his ambition and daring, but his obstinacy and treachery obtained for him lasting dishonour. Although, at the death of his father in 1030, he was unanimously excluded from the lordship of Glamorgan, he succeeded his uncle Hywel, and appears as the secret prompter of the sons of Bleddyn against Rhys. In his own affairs he stands boldly forth as principal actor, and, because of his close connection with the complete downfall of independence in South Wales, his name survives as an unjust and cruel prince, whose few good qualities are totally eclipsed by the severest censure of his countrymen, who regard him as the immediate and precipitate cause of the Norman conquest of Glamorgan.

Jestyn having thrown down a defiant challenge against Rhys ap Tewdwr, the latter struck the first blow, and forthwith marched into Glamorgan, laying waste the whole territory. Jestyn's castles of Dinas Powys, Boverton, and Dunraven were destroyed, and the feud increased, until, at length, the hour of vengeance approached. Rhys, who once more was compelled to quit his native land, fled to Ireland, but subsequently returned, with a largely augmented force, and met his opponents at Lechryd, on the borders of Pembrokeshire.

About 1088, Cadivor, Lord of Dimetia, died, and his sons, Llewelyn and Einion, induced Gruffydd ap Meredydd to fight against Rhys. Being defeated, Gruffydd received his meed as a traitor, and was ignominiously put to death, while the others fled. Rhys seized their lands, and offered a hundred head of cattle for Einion, alive or dead. Einion fled to his uncle, Jestyn ap Gwrgant, and induced him to seek the temporary aid of the Normans against Rhys. According to some authorities, Einion had been a visitor at the English court, and while there had formed the acquaintance of several of the Norman knights. Einion the wily promised to secure the assistance of the Normans, provided Jestyn agreed to bestow upon him his daughter Nest, with considerable territory as a marriage dower. After a formal treaty signed by both parties, Einion set forth upon his fateful journey, and soon returned with Robert Fitz-hamon and a powerful body of Norman knights and men, who landed at Porthkerry. This was about 1090—1.

Both armies met at Hirwaen Wrgant, among the Black Mountains, near Brecon, where, after a desperate and determined battle, Rhys ap Tewdwr was defeated at Bryn-y-beddau and obliged to take flight. Ruthlessly pursued by

his own countrymen, aided by the Normans, the
grand old patriot was overtaken on the brow of
a hill in Glyn Rhondda and relentlessly slain.
With the death-blow of this prince the first
wail of impending doom ran through the south
of Wales, and before the life-blood of Rhys
had dried upon the sward, the thin edge of the
Norman wedge had begun to lever Welsh independence in Glamorgan.

Jestyn paid the Normans in gold for their
assistance against Rhys ap Tewdwr, and the
spot where the transaction took place is known
as the Mill-tir-aur, or the Golden Mile, near
Bridgend.

The Normans, well satisfied with their bargain,
departed, and Einion asked for his bride and
guerdon, but was refused by Jestyn, who declared
he would not give his daughter to a traitor
against his country. This so greatly enraged
Einion that he hastened to the sea-shore, and
just as the Normans set sail, the Welsh chieftain
recalled them. Einion's love for his country was
totally quenched by the sudden and remorseless
hatred of Jestyn, who had insultingly refused to
fulfil his compact. Robert Fitz-hamon was persuaded to return to shore, where the Welsh
chieftain and traitor explained how easily, under
his directions, Morganwg might be conquered.
Attempts at a compromise did not accord with
Jestyn's turbulent and fiery disposition, and the

P

result was a battle at Mynydd Bychan, or Great
Heath, near Cardiff, where the Lord of Glamorgan and his forces were defeated. Jestyn escaped
and took flight, leaving the Norman conquerors to
part and parcel out his territory as they pleased.

The foregoing story of the Norman conquest
of South Wales was the undisputed national
version for long centuries. Leland heard it
nearly four hundred years ago, when Henry
VIII. sent him on his celebrated itinerary
through Wales; and Powell, in his "History
of Cambria," published in 1584, records the
same account. But during recent years some
attempts have been made to prove that the
conquest of Glamorgan was a planned campaign.
Mr. Floyd, in the *Archæological Journal*, vol.
xxviii., believes the conquest was made under
the direct and personal command of William
Rufus. Mr. Geo. T. Clark, in his excellent work
entitled "The Land of Morgan," writes :—"The
proceedings of Fitz-hamon during and upon his
conquest have been woven into a legendary tale,
very neat and round, very circumstantial, but as
deficient in evidence as though it had proceeded
from the pen of Geoffrey himself. . . . By whom,
or when, this story was concocted is not known.
It was certainly accepted without challenge in
the reign of Elizabeth, and could scarcely have
been circulated before the extinction of the Le
Despencers, early in the fifteenth century. Pro-

bably its author was some follower of the Stradlings of St. Donats, a family somewhat given to literature, whose fictitious pedigree it sets forth as true. What is certain is, that whatever may have been the cause alleged, the invasion was not really due to any local quarrel, but was part of a settled policy for completing the English conquest; a policy which, if not undertaken by Fitz-hamon, would have been carried out by Rufus in person, or by some of the adventurers who about the same time were taking possession of Monmouth and Brecknock, and the whole of South-West Wales. Indeed, Rufus awaited the result of Fitz-hamon's expedition at Alveston, between Bristol and Gloucester, and is supposed to have been only prevented by illness from bearing a share in it."

Thierry, in his "History of the Norman Conquest," expresses the belief that after Robert Fitz-hamon had been paid by Jestyn ap Gwrgant on the Golden Mile, he returned to his own manor at Gloucester, and there reflected greatly upon the terrible effect of his steel-clad knights fighting against the lightly armed and clad forces of Rhys ap Tewdwr. And, having considered the aspect in all its bearings, Fitz-hamon, without the invitation of Einion, invaded Morganwg. · ·

In all the national annals of Wales the names of Rhys ab Tewdwr and Jestyn ap Gwrgant appear in strong contrast.

Rhys is justly described as a patriot and hero, who, under the most trying and harassing circumstances, stood resolutely unmoved, as the victim of relentless revenge and cruel treason. Of him it is written in the ancient records :— " Prince Rhys was mightily grieved to find his country so unmercifully harassed, and though at this time being very antient, being above 98 years of age, he could not restrain but meet his enemies; and, having with all possible speed raised a convenient army, he met them near Brecknock, where, after a terrible Fight, and a great slaughter on both sides, he was unhappily slain. With him fell the Glory and Grandeur of the Principality of *South Wales,* being afterwards rent in pieces, and divided into several parts, and piece-meal, among these *Norman* Captains."

In the Iolo MSS. Jestyn appears as " a very wicked, cruel, and merciless king, incurring the hatred of his countrymen and subjects. Great animosity arose between him and Rhys, the son of Tewdwr, King of Dehenbarth ; and he entered into an unjust war against him ; for which object he engaged the mercenary aid of Sir Robert Fitz-hamon ; with whom came twelve knights, twenty-four esquires, and three thousand men. . . . After the departure of the Normans, contention sprang up between Iestyn, Einion, and Cedrych ; whereupon the two latter went after the mercenaries, and having related the injustice

of Iestyn's conduct, invited them back to
Glamorgan. . . . Sir Robert . . . expostulated
with Iestyn on his conduct ; but he behaved with
great arrogance and scornful pride towards them ;
so the contention ended in war. . . ." It is also
recorded that "after Iestyn had thus been dispossessed by the French he fled to seclusion, and
died at Keynsham."

The death of Rhys ap Tewdwr and the entry
of Robert Fitz-hamon into South Wales marked
the first stage in the complete downfall of ancient
British power in the Principality. From that
time the Normans rapidly gained territory and
became masters of the whole land, in the north
of which the "Lords Marchers" were already
in the ascendency.

Ordericus Vitalis, referring in his ecclesiastical
history to the border aggression of the Normans,
mentions the name of Robertus D'Avranches,
one of the vassals of the renowned and detested
nephew of William the Conqueror, Hugh Lupus,
who built Rhuddlan Castle. This vassal knight
assumed the name of Robertus de Rhuddlan,
and, according to Ordericus, the Saxon monk
and historian, for fifteen years intolerably oppressed the Britons ; ruthlessly pursued them
through dense woods and swampy marshes ;
chased them into their mountain fastnesses,
slaying some "out of hand like cattle," holding some in bondage and slavery, and im-

prisoning others for the sake of obtaining heavy ransoms.

In 1079 Hugh Lupus, Earl of Chester, gained possession of nearly all North Wales; Fitz-hamon and his twelve knights obtained Cardiff and Glamorgan in 1090; Dyfed and Ceredigion succumbed in 1091; Bernard Newmarch seized Brycheiniog in 1091; Brecknock was wrested from the Welsh in 1092; and in 1100 Gilbert Fitz-Richard was given permission to take Cardigan. The province of Ewyas fell to Hugh de Lacey, the founder of Llanthony Abbey; Hamelin became Lord of Over Went, and built Abergavenny Priory and Castle; Beaumont, Earl of Warwick, built Swansea Castle; Martin de Tours received the territory of Kemeys; Montgomery fell to the lot of the Earl of Shrewsbury; Pembroke was the prize of Arnulph Montgomery; to Martin went Fishguard; Gilbert Strongbow, the builder of Aberystwith, gained Cardigan; and Henry de Newbury received Gower.

CHAPTER XX

UNDER THE NORMANS

ITZ-HAMON in South Wales had parted
and parcelled out the lands among his
Norman knights, when Gruffydd ap
Cynan, after many years of imprisonment, re-
appeared as the hero of North Wales. Now
chasing the Saxons, then fleeing to Ireland in
order to return strengthened in his endeavours
to regain his kingdom, the ever-restless Prince
of Gwynedd is seen flitting among the mountains
in his ceaseless quest for lost independence.

In the old Welsh records it appears that while
the Normans were "carving for themselves in
Glamorgan," and Brecknock, Cadwgan and Rhy-
rid, the sons of Bleddyn ap Cynvyn, ravaged and
destroyed Dyved, and later on, when William
Rufus was warring against his brother Robert
in Normandy, "*Gruffydh ap Cynan*, Prince of
North Wales, and *Cadogan ap Blethyn*, who
now ruled in *South Wales*, with joynt Forces

entered into *Cardigan*, and slew a great number
of *Normans*, whose Pride and excessive Cruelties
towards the *Welch* were altogether intolerable."

Soon after, the ancient chronicler quaintly
asserts, "the *Welch* so abhorr'd their (the
Normans) Pride and tyrannical Dominion over
them when they were masters that they were
resolved not be subject to any such Tyrants
again; and therefore they boldly met them . . .
and set upon them so manfully, the very apprehension of Servitude whetting their Spirits, that
they put them to flight with great slaughter,
and drove them out of the Country. The *Normans*, however, were not so absolutely routed
with this Overthrow, but like a Fly in the night
which destroys itself in the Candle, they must
needs covet their own Destruction; their greedi-
ness egging them on to venture with few what
was not practicable to be effected by many.
Therefore, on they came as far as *Brecnock*,
with this absolute Vow and Resolution, not to
leave one living thing remaining in that Country.
But they fell short of their Policy, the People of
the Country being removed to a narrow Streight,
to expect their passing through; whither the
Normans being advanced, they fell upon them,
and killed a great number of them."

By-and-by William Rufus returned from Normandy and "gathered all his Power together,
and with great Pomp and Ostentation entered

the Marches, resolving utterly to eradicate the rebellious and implacable humour of the *Welch* Nation. But after all this Boast and seeming Resolution, he durst venture no farther than the Marches, where having built some few Castles, he returned with no greater Honour than he came."

From the time of Rhys ap Tewdwr's death and Jestyn ap Gwrgant's flight, the Welsh princes and the Normans were involved in continual struggles, and to enhance the difficulties, civil dissensions spreading among the chieftains, led to a long succession of warfare, pillage, and terrible disorder.

Gruffydd ap Cynan's daughter Gwenlliant married Gruffydd ap Rhys, son of the celebrated Rhys ap Tewdwr. Of him, in A.D. 1112, it is stated in the Welsh annals :—"This year the rumour of *Gruffydh,* Son to *Rhys ap Theodore,* was spread throughout South Wales, who, as the report went, for fear of the King had been from a Child brought up in Ireland, and having come over about two Years afore, past his time privately among his Relations, particularly with *Gerald* Steward of *Pembroke* his Brother-in-Law. And now the noise of a new Prince being spread abroad, it came at last to the Ears of the King of *England,* that a certain Person appeared in *Wales,* who pretended to be the Son of *Rhys ap Theodore,* late Prince of *South Wales,* and laid

Claim to that Principality, which was now in the King's Hands. King Henry being somewhat concerned with such a Report, and fearing lest his new Starter should create him some greater trouble, he thought to nip him in the bud, and sent down Orders to apprehend him. But *Gruffydh ap Rhys*, being aware of the Traps laid against him, sent to *Gruffydh ap Conan*, Prince of *North Wales*, desiring his Assistance, and that he might have Liberty to remain safe in his Country, which *Gruffydh* for his father's account readily granted, and treated him honourably." During this period Gruffydd ap Rhys married Gwenlliant, the daughter of Gruffydd ap Cynan.

On one occasion, in 1136, while her husband was absent in Gwynedd, where he went to seek his father-in-law's aid in his struggle to wrest his country from the "Franks," Gwenlliant appeared at the head of a large army against the enemy. This Welsh princess is described as having "espied" a good opportunity for trying to regain the family's lost possessions. Gathering all the forces she possibly could, Gwenlliant, accompanied by her sons Morgan and Maelgwn, marched to Kidwelly, and was there met by Maurice de Londres with his Normans. A great battle was fought, and although for some time Gwenlliant appeared successfully at the head of her forces, the Welsh were disastrously defeated.

Her son Morgan was slain, and Maelgwn with many of his followers were taken prisoners. Later on, Gwenlliant was captured, and as a warning to other "rebels," Maurice de Londres put the brave Welsh princess to death, with several of her men. Her son Maelgwn was, for some reason, liberated.

Early in 1137 Gruffydd ap Rhys died, and towards the end of the same year Gruffydd ap Cynan, Prince of North Wales, was gathered to his fathers. Of Gruffydd ap Cynan it is recorded that at his death, "he had reigned 57 years;" and died "to the Great Grief and Discontent of all his Subjects, as being a Prince of incomparable Qualities, and one, who after divers Victories obtained over the *English*, had thoroughly purged *North Wales* from all Strangers and foreigners. . . . There were several good and wholesome Laws and Statutes enacted in his time; and, among the rest, he reformed the great Disorders of the *Welch* Minstrels which were then grown to great Abuse."

Of Gruffydd's regulations of the bards, and his statute, the following account is given:—

"There were several good and wholsom Laws and Statutes enacted in his time; and among the rest, he reformed the great Disorders of the *Welch* Minstrels, which were then grown to great Abuse. Of these there were three sorts in *Wales;* the first were called *Beirdh*, who

composed several Songs and Odes of various
Measures, wherein the Poet's skill was not only
required, but also a natural Endowment, or a
Vein which the Latins term *furor Poeticus.*
These likewise kept the Records of all Gentle-
mens Arms and Pedegrees, and were principally
esteemed among all the Degrees of the *Welch*
Poets. The next were such as plaid upon
Musical Instruments, chiefly the Harp and the
Crowd; which Musick *Gruffydh ap Conan* first
brought over into *Wales;* who being born in
Ireland, and decended by his Mother's side of
Irish Parents, brought with him from thence
several skilful Musicians, who invented almost
all the Instruments as were afterwards plaid
upon in *Wales.* The last sort were called
Atcaneaid, whose Business it was to sing to
the Instrument plaid upon by another. Each
of these, by the same Statute, had their several
Reward and Encouragement allotted to them;
their Life and Behaviour was to be spotless
and unblameable, otherwise their Punishment
was very severe and rigid, every one having
Authority to punish and correct them, even to
the deprivation of all they had. They were also
interdicted and forbidden to enter any Man's
House, or to compose any Song of any one,
without the special leave and warrant of the
Party concerned; with many other Ordinances
relating to the like purpose."

CHAPTER XXI

"IN PRAISE OF OWAIN GWYNEDD"

OWAIN GWYNEDD, the son of Gruffydd ap Cynan, was, in the words of the old British proverb, "fed at the point of the sword." From his earliest childhood he had been accustomed to the sound of strife, the din and clamour of warfare, and the miseries of incessant disorder. He was probably born when the dying throes of the eleventh century were stifled by Norman force, and all the pent-up heroism of a race, that for long years had bravely struggled under Saxon oppression and Danish torture, burst forth with renewed energy against the power of the new conquerors and masters of Britain.

Gruffydd ap Cynan, who had experienced more than an ordinary share of conflict, was getting old, and his noble ally, Rhys ap Tewdwr, had met the fate of the brave, to whom death is preferable to dishonour.

Anarchy and civil dissension tortured the princes of the royal and legitimate lines of North and South Wales, and Henry the First's arbitrary introduction of the Flemings to Wales enhanced disorder. These foreigners, to the pain and annoyance of the Welsh, were given lands in Pembrokeshire, and, assisted by the English and the Normans, appropriated and held territory without regard to right or justice.

Owain Gwynedd first appeared on the field in A.D. 1121, when, under the direction of his father, he went with his brother Cadwallon to regain from the Prince of Powys the lands he had unjustly taken from his nephews. Gruffydd ap Cynan's sons were successful in redressing the wrongs of the oppressed kinsmen of Meredydd ap Bleddyn, and continued to vindicate the rightful claims of those who had been cruelly dispossessed of their personal property and landed possessions.

In 1135 the spirited young warrior, accompanied by his brother, marched from North Wales into South Wales, with the express design of assisting the inhabitants of the last-named territory in expelling the strangers. After seizing several Norman castles, these brave men of the North retreated for a time, but again invaded South Wales with a larger and well-disciplined army, augmented by many native princes and chieftains, and succeeded in subduing the country so far as the town of Cardigan, which was then the headquarters of a Norman governor. The latter, at the head of a large body of forces consisting of English, Normans, and Flemings from Wales and the marches, went forth to meet the Welsh at Cardigan. The result was a glorious victory for Owain Gwynedd, the expulsion of the foreigners, and the reinstatement of the lawful possessors of the land.

In 1137 Gruffydd ap Cynan died, and his eldest son Owain ascended the throne of Gwynedd; and of him it is recorded:—"No sooner had he entered upon the government, but together with the rest of his Brethren, he made an expedition into *South Wales;* and having demolished and overthrown the Castles of *Stradmeyric, Stephan,* and *Humffreys,* and laid in Ashes the Town of *Caermardhyn,* he returned home with no less Honor than Booty and Plunder."

From the hour of his accession to the last moment of his existence, Owain Gwynedd's life was one long scene of conflict and successful opposition to the English, who, by this hero's indomitable courage and skilful warcraft, were completely driven out from North Wales.

In 1142 Owain Gwynedd was actively engaged in one of those domestic feuds which were of frequent occurrence in the Principality.

Owain's brother Cadwaladr quarrelled with his son-in-law Anarawd, and caused the death of the latter, who was regarded as "the hope and stay of Dinevwr." Greatly incensed at the result of this broil, Owain, who spared not even his dearest friends in the cause of right, ravaged Cadwaladr's lands and burnt his castle at Aberystwyth.

Cadwaladr, being unable to defend himself against his brother, sought the aid of Irish and Scotch mercenaries, with whom he landed at Abermenai, in Carnarvonshire, and commenced hostile excursions in Owain's territory, but without much avail. When the rival armies met, the brothers became reconciled, and the Irish adventurers, in vexation and disappointment, seized Cadwaladr, and would not liberate him until they received two thousand head of cattle, and were allowed to retain the booty they had taken in Owain's territory.

For this act they received just retaliation. Immediately Cadwaladr regained his freedom, Owain Gwynedd suddenly and unexpectedly attacked the Irish, slew a great number of them, captured the cattle and booty they claimed as ransom, and compelled the last miserable remnant of marauders to retreat to Ireland.

Two years later Owain Gwynedd lost his son Rhun, on whom he had centred his most sanguine hopes and devoted affection. The shock of the young prince's death was so great a blow to his father, that for a long period the latter became utterly prostrated and almost totally inconsolable. Owain Gwynedd gave way to deep despondency and gloom, that developed into painful melancholy, from which it was difficult to rouse him.

Of this circumstance the following record appears:—"*Run*, the Son of Prince *Owen* of *North-Wales*, a Youth of excellent hopes, and incomparable qualifications dyed, whose Death his Father took so much to heart, that for some time he seemed to be past all Comfort, being faln into such a melancholy Disposition, that he was diverted by nothing but Retirement."

With reference to Owain Gwynedd's son, Caradoc of Llancarvan curiously writes thus:—"At the close of this year (1144) died Rhun ap Owain, a youth the most praiseworthy of the whole race of the Britons, and who had been educated with a liberality suitable to his princely birth. In his form and appearance he was comely, in his discourse mild. He was affable to every one, and circumspect in his bounty. Amongst his family condescending, dignified amongst strangers, terribly violent towards his enemies, and facetious amongst his friends. He was of a tall person, his complexion fair, his hair curly and flaxen, and his visage long. His eyes were of a pale blue, wide and full; his neck long and thick, his chest broad, and his body slender. His thighs were stout, his legs long and tapering, with long and narrow feet, and fingers perfectly straight."

In this quaint and ancient portrait the English reader will observe quite a different type from the dark curly-haired, short and stout, race, with which the name Welshman is generally associated.

Prince Rhun, in common with his countrymen of later centuries, inherited the old Celtic enthusiasm and irascibility, of which the cold-blooded and calculating English took ample advantage, to the subsequent detriment of Welsh independence.

Owain Gwynedd was aroused from his melancholy and sorrow by the Seneschal of Chester, who, holding the castle of Mold, in Flintshire, defied the Welsh and ravaged their territories. From the days of Eustace St. Omer, who did homage to William Rufus at the close of the eleventh century, the castle was the stronghold of the Normans, who continually molested and annoyed the Welsh.

Exasperated by the latest ravages of the English, and animated by an intense desire to conquer the enemy and obtain the castle, Owain Gwynedd, with a large army, laid siege to the fortress. For a time he was repulsed, but defeat only served to rekindle Owain's energy and increase his exertions. Urging his men and strengthening his arms, Owain made another attempt, and this time with success. Laying siege to Mold, he not only took the castle, but levelled the fortress with the ground.

After this celebrated victory Owain Gwynedd's triumphs continued almost without interruption.

In 1149 the English commenced a series of vigorous hostilities against this heroic and patriotic Welsh prince. Randulph, Earl of Chester, assisted by Madog ap Meredydd, Prince of Powys, who was jealous of Owain's power, marched into Flintshire, where he was promptly met and defeated by the dauntless Prince of Gwynedd. So vigorously were they attacked by Owain Gwynedd that the English had to seek security in ignominious flight, and the pursuit of the fugitives was so keen that those who reached Chester owed their escape entirely to their fleet-footed merlyns.

After the siege of Mold the English for many years ceased their attempts to keep North Wales in subjection, and henceforth Owain Gwynedd became a participator in the renewal of those internal dissensions which in Wales always succeeded the suspension of external conflicts.

The sons of Owain frequently and persistently fought against their uncles, and were generally successful. In one of those unhappy frays which arose entirely from family jealousy and rival ter-

ritorial claims, Owain unfortunately had recourse
to acts of inhumanity, which could only be
equalled by the worst physical forms of Oriental
barbarity, and this circumstance forms the only,
but very terrible, blot upon his irreproachable
fame.

When, in 1154, Stephen died, and Henry II.
ascended the throne, the English once more re-
sumed their attacks upon Wales. Marching into
Flintshire, and camping at Saltney, King Henry
in person opposed the Welsh, who, under the
command of Owain Gwynedd, met the English
at Basingwerk, after which, to frustrate the
enemy, the prince retired to Cil Owain, known
afterwards as "Owain's Retreat."

On this occasion the English expedition nearly
came to a disastrous end at the commencement
of the campaign, owing to the terror of the forces
upon finding themselves hedged in among the
forest thickets and marshes of Coed Enlo. When
marching through the narrow and difficult pass
of Coleshill, the English soldiers, finding themselves assailed by terrible cries and shouts where
the enemy was unexpected, fled. Robert de
Courcy and Eustace St. John were slain, and
this so alarmed the Earl of Essex, the king's
standard-bearer, that, suddenly dropping his
banner, he cried aloud, "King Henry is slain!"
Thereupon, in order to rally his forces and lead
them back to the fight, Henry uncovered his

face, and succeeded in reassuring his hosts that
there was no danger; but ultimately the king
retired to Rhuddlan, and garrisoned that fortress
and Basingwerk.

After this, the patriotic desire to defend their
country against the English caused the Welsh
for a time to forget their civil jealousies and
animosities, and to unite in the common cause
under the command of Owain in opposition to
King Henry. Many battles were fought and
much skirmishing took place, in which Owain
was generally successful.

In 1164 the English monarch, for the third
time, marched into North Wales, and pitched
his camp at Oswestry; while Owain, with his
forces, augmented by those of Rhys ap Gruffydd
and Owain Cyveiliog, Princes respectively of
South Wales and Powys, encamped to the south
of the village of Cynwyd, near Corwen. Henry
used every art and endeavour to induce the
Welsh princes to an engagement, but failed.
The Welsh contented themselves with harassing
the enemy in various ways, so that the English,
whose supplies were intercepted, found themselves in terrible difficulties, which, combined
with the bad weather, compelled Henry to
abandon his projects. When the English king
returned home he signalised his revenge by
barbarously depriving his Welsh hostages—two
of whom were Owain's sons—of their eyes.

Soon after this Henry again started forth against the Welsh, but after sending his troops by sea to Chester to effect a descent on Anglesea, where they were defeated, he suddenly disbanded his army.

Once more Owain Gwynedd took part in an intestine struggle, and this time he marched forth with Rhys ap Gruffydd against Owain Cyveiliog, Prince of Powys, who had dispossessed Iorwerth Goch of his lands. Owain and Rhys proceeded to divide part of the regained territory among themselves, whereupon the Prince of Powys, with the aid of foreign adventurers, succeeded in obtaining his own rightful possessions.

In 1169 Owain Gwynedd, who for thirty-two successful years had defended his country against foreign invasion, died. During his reign he had but few reverses, and his fame as a politic and valorous warrior, distinguished general, and ardent patriot, shines forth in history as a beacon-light to all generations. As the resolute opponent of Henry the Second's ambitious designs upon Wales, his character has been described as combining the " heroism of Hector with the wisdom of Solomon." At the same time, it is impossible to overlook, or endeavour to conceal, the fact that his name was involved in so many purely domestic feuds and miserable jealousies, while his cruel treatment of his nephew Cunedda deserves no excuse. But, taking into consideration the restless and disturbed spirit of the age, Owain Gwynedd, the heroic prince of North Wales, has no rival as a fortunate and successful opponent of the aggressive designs of the English, and a truly patriotic, intrepid, and faithful guardian of Welsh independence.

This grand old hero of Wales found a resting-place in Bangor, and Giraldus Cambrensis, who saw the grave about twenty years after Owain Gwynedd's death, thus describes his visit to the spot:—"On our return to Bangor from Mona, we were shewn the tombs of Prince Owain and his younger brother Cadwaladr, who were buried in a double vault, before the high altar, although Owain . . . died excommunicated by the blessed martyr St. Thomas, and the Bishop of that See has been directed to seize a proper opportunity of removing his body from the church."

In the Hengwrt MSS. it is recorded that soon afterwards the body was removed into the adjoining churchyard; but in order to escape the indignation of the people, the sacrilegious deed was effected by means of a subterraneous passage excavated expressly for the purpose.

Gwalchmai ap Meilyr, the celebrated warrior-poet of North Wales, addressed a very spirited ode to Owain Gwynedd on the occasion of the defeat of the English troops sent by King Henry by sea to Chester. Some of the lines, which have been translated by J. H. Parry, Esq., run as follows :—

> " The generous chief I sing of Rhodri's line,
>   With princely gifts endow'd, whose hand
>   Hath often curb'd the border land,
>   Owain, great heir of Britain's throne,
>   Whom fair ambition marks her own,
>   Who ne'er to yield to man was known ;
> Nor heaps he stores at Avarice's shrine. . . .
>
>   Now thickens still the frantic war,
>   The flashing death-strokes gleam afar,
>   Spear rings on spear, flight urges flight,
>   And drowning victims plunge to-night ;
>   Check'd by the torrent-tide of blood,
>   Backward Menai rolls his flood ;
>   The mailed warriors on the shore,
>   With carnage strew'd, and dyed with gore,
> In awful anguish drag their mangled limbs along,
>   And high the slaughter'd throng
>   Is heap'd the king's red chiefs before."

The poet then goes on to describe that England's flight on the occasion would—

> " Raise great Owain's sword to fame ;
> Whilst sevenscore tongues of his exploits shall tell,
> And all their high renown through future ages swell."

Another ode by Gwalchmai, in praise of Owain Gwynedd, the translation of which is taken from the *Cambro-Briton*, runs thus—

"THE PRAISE OF OWAIN.

"Gruffydd's noble son I sing,
Cynan's heir, high-gifted king:
Owain his glorious name,
Of bold and manful fame;
Who in him aught might blame,
Save his warm, impetuous ire,
Warlike rage, and soul of fire?

There upon the battle-plain,
Lion-like, with gory hand,
Where insulting terrors reign,
Foremost signal see him stand; . . .

Prostrate arms together blending,
Like the whelming waves, that ride
O'er some found'ring vessel's side:
There, Lloegria, fought thy warriors;—there, to thee
Came ruin and disgrace;—to Owain victory!"

It may here be mentioned that Owain's son, the brilliant but early blighted Hywel, was a celebrated warrior-poet, and the only one of the early Welsh singers who dedicated his songs to the fair sex.

Owain Cyveiliog, at one time the friend, companion, and faithful ally of Owain Gwynedd, but afterwards his adversary, was not only a warrior and hero, but one of the most celebrated poets of the twelfth century. His "Hirlas Horn" and "The Circuit through Powys" are ranked among the most important poems of that age. The first‑mentioned poem consists of stanzas, each of which contains a command to

the cup-bearer to present the filled horn to the
living hero of the battle then described, or to
the memory of those fallen in the fray.   From
Mr. Fenton's translation of Owain Cyveiliog's
"Circuit through Powys" the following lines
are taken :—

> "Quick proceed, the mountain crost,
>   That not a moment may be lost ;
>   Fast by the margins of the deep,
>   Where storms eternal uproar keep—
>   The road to shorten, mend thy pace,
>   By thy speed contracting space ;
>   And faithful to thy message, say,
>   We take Ardudwy in our way. . . .
>
> Messenger, set off again,
> Forerunner of our gallant train,
> Hurry at our chief's command,
> Prince of liberal heart and hand ;
> And as through Arvon winds thy way
> Armed knight, we charge thee say,
>   That having journey'd many a mile,
>   We mean to visit Mona's isle.
>
> We are Oaiwn's princely host,
> Spoils of foes the wealth we boast ;
> Tyrant Lloegyr overthrown
> Gives us title to renown ;
> Then our toilsome marches o'er,
> Who can want an opening door ?
>   Shall we not find on Rhos a bed
>   Whereon to lay the weary head ? "

While Owain Cyveiliog's poems breathe chiefly
of the joys of battle and the raptures of success,

Gwalchmaï's gifts were more varied, ranging from odes to warriors and songs of warfare to simple melodies expressive of the beauties of nature. From " Gwalchmai's Delights " the following lines have been culled :—

> " Fearless in battle, with my golden torque,
> A lion in the first rank of the host
> Am I, and all the livelong night have watch'd
> The boundary river . . .
> No foot hath press'd the grass . . .
> The limpid waters murmur'd as they pass'd ;
> The skilful songster, Philomel, ne'er ceased
> His warbled story ; whilst the sea-mews play'd
> In amorous sport . . .
> The nightingale in May I love to hear,
> Singing at break of day, at evening's close."

CHAPTER XXII

PRINCE MADOG'S VOYAGE

IT has already been mentioned that, according to the Triads, one of the "Three Lost or Missing Ones of the Island of Britain" was Madog, the son of Owain Gwynedd, who "went to sea along with three hundred men in ten ships, and it is not known whither they went."

In an ancient record the following account appears under date 1170:—"*Madawc*, another of *Owen Gwynedh's* sons, finding how his Brothers contended for the Principality, and that his native country was like to be turmoil'd in a Civil War, did think it his better Prudence to try his Fortune abroad; and therefore leaving *North-Wales* in a very unsettled condition, sailed with a small Fleet of Ships, which he had rigg'd and man'd for that purpose, to the Westward; and leaving *Ireland* upon the *North*, he came at length to an unknown Country, where

most things appeared to him new and un-
customary, and the manner of the Natives far
different from what he had seen in *Europe*."

This circumstance, which developed into the
alleged discovery of America by Madog ap
Owain Gwynedd, has been the source of end-
less controversy and ceaseless contradiction, and
forms one of those difficult problems of which
various solutions have been rendered, but to
little or no purpose.

Yet the subject is one upon which the poet
Southey wrote, and historians persistently agree
to differ, and it is curious to examine what the
quaint old Chroniclers have recorded about it."

In 1583 a pamphlet appeared entitled, "A
True Reporte of the late discoveries and pos-
session taken in the right of the Crown of Eng-
lande of the Newfound Landes by that valiaunt
and worthye Gentleman, Sir Humfrey Gilbert,
Knight. At London. Printed by J. C. (John
Charlewood) for John Hinde, dwelling in Paule's
Church-yarde at the signe of the Golden Hinde.
Anno 1583."

The author was Sir George Peckham, one
of the enthusiastic patrons of those *voyageurs*
whose discoveries and adventures form brilliant
episodes in the reign of good Queen Bess. The
third chapter of this pamphlet "doothe shewe
the lawfull tytle which the Queene's most excellent Majestie hath unto those countries, which

through the ayde of Almightie God are mente to be inhabited." The writer then continues :—

"And it is very evident that the planting there shall in time right amplie enlarge your Majestie's Territories and Dominions (or I might rather say), restore to your Highnesse Auncient right and interest all those countries into the which a noble and woorthy personage, lyneally descended from the blood royall, born in Wales, named Madocke ap Owen Gwyneth, departing from the coast of England about the year of our Lord God 1170, arrived and there planted himselfe and his Colonies, and afterward returned himselfe into England, leaving certaine of his people there, as appeareth in an auncient Welch Chronicle, where he then gave to certaine Ilandes, Beastes and Fowles sundrie Welch names, as the Iland of Pengwyn, which yet to this daye beareth the same.

This Iland was discovered by Sir Humfrey and his company in this his last journey.

There is likewise a Fowle in the sayde Countries called by the same name at this daye, and is as much to saye in Englishe as whiteheadde, in trueth the sayde Fowles have white heads. There is also in those countries a fruite called Gwynethes,[1] which is likewise a Welch word. Moreover there are divers other Welch wordes at this daie in use, as David Ingram aforesaide reporteth in his relations. All which most

[1] From *gwenith*, wheat.

strongly argueth the saide Prince with his
people to have inhabited there. And the same
in effect is confirmed by Mutuzuma,
that mightie Emperor of Mexico, Who hath
who in an oration unto his subjects also seene berded men there,
which can not
for the better pacifying of them, bee naturall
made in the presence of Hernando cuntrimen, for
that the Ameri-
Curtese, used these subjects follow- cans are voide
of berdes.
ing :—My kinsemen, freends and
servaunts, you do well know that eigteene
yeeres I have been your king, as my Fathers
and Grandfathers were, and alwaies I have
beene unto you a loving Prince, and you unto
me good and obedient subjects, and so I hope
you will remaine unto me all the daies of my
life. You ought to have in remembrance that
eyther you have heard of your Fathers, or else
our divines have instructed you that we are
not naturallie of this Countrio, nor yet our
Kingdome is durable, because our Forefathers
came from a farre countrie, and their King
and Captaine who brought them hither returned againe to his natural countrie, saying,
that he would send such as should rule and
governe us, if by chance he himselfe returned
not, &c., which Oration was made about the
yeere 1520. These be the very words of Mutuzuma set downe in the Spanish Chronicles, the
which being thoroughlie considered because they
have relation to some strange noble person who

long before had possessed those countries doo
all sufficientlie argue an undoubted title of her
Majestie : For as much as no other Nation can
trulie by any Chronicles they can finde make
prescription of time for themselves before the
time of this Prince Madocke."

In 1584 David Powel's "Historie of Cambria"
was published, and therefrom the following
slightly altered account has been taken :—

"Madoc, another of Owen Gwyneth his
sonnes, left the land in contention betwixt his
brethren, and prepared certaine ships with men
and munition, and sought adventures by seas,
sailing west, and leaving the coast of Ireland
so far north that he came to a land unknown,
where he saw manie strange things. This land
must needs be some part of that countrie of
which the Spaniardes affirme themselves to
be the first finders sith Hanno's time; for by
reason and order of cosmographie, this land to
the which Madoc came, must needs be some
part of North Hispania or Florida. Whereupon
it is manifest that that countrie was long before
by Brytaines discovered afore either Columbus
or Americus Vesputius lead anie Spaniardes
thither. Of the viage and returne of this
Madoc there be manie fables fained, as the
common people doo use in distance of place
and length of time rather to augment than to
diminish : but sure it is, that there he was.

And after he had returned home and declared
the pleasant and fruitfull countries that he had
seene without inhabitants; and upon the con-
trarie part, for what barren and wild ground
his brethren and nephewes did murther one
another : he prepared a number of ships, and
got with him such men and women as were
desirous to live in quietnes, and táking leave
of his freends tooke his journie thitherward
againe. Therefore it is to be presupposed that
he and his people inhabited part of those
countries ; for it appeareth by Francis Loues
that in Acusanas and other places the people
honoured the crosse : whereby it may be
gathered that Christians had beene there before
the comming of the Spaniards. But because
this people were not manie, they folowed the
maners of the land they came unto, and used
the language they found there."

In Hakluyt's "Voyages," first edition, dated
1589, it is recorded :—"The most ancient Discovery of the West Indies, by Madoc, the sonne
of Owen Gwyneth, Prince of North Wales, in
the yeere 1170 : taken out of the history of
Wales lately published by M. David Powel,
Doctor of Divinity.

"After the death of Owen Gwyneth, his
sonnes fell at debate who should inherit after
him : for the eldest sonne borne in matrimony,
Edward or Iorwerth Drwydion, was counted

R

unmeet to governe, because of the maime upon his face : and Howell, that tooke upon him all the rule, was a base sonne, begotten upon an Irish woman. Therefore David gathered all the power he could, and came against Howel, and fighting with him, slew him ; and afterwards enjoyed quietly the whole land of North Wales, until his brother Iorwerth's sonne came to age."

With the exception of this short introduction, the account in Hakluyt's "Voyages" is copied *verbatim* from Powel's "Historie of Cambria."

The earliest reference to Madog appears in Llywarch ap Llewelyn's poem, wherein the poet describes his own experiences, when put to the ordeal of the Hot Iron, in order to get him to make a confession regarding the mysterious disappearance of the Welsh prince. He sings—

" Good iron ! free me from the charge
Of slaying Madog. Show that he
Who smote the prince with murderous hand
Heaven's kingdoms nine shall never see,
Whilst I the dwelling-place of God
Shall share safe from all enmity."

Addressing Rhodri, Madog's brother, the poet continues—

" Two princes were there, who in wrath dealt woe,
Yet by the people of the earth were loved ;
One who in Arvon quench'd ambition's flame,
Leading on land his bravely toiling men ;
And one of temper mild, in trouble great,
Far o'er the bosom of the mighty sea,

> Sought a possession he could safely keep,
> From all estranged for a country's sake."

Cynddelw, the poet and contemporary of Llywarch ap Llewelyn, in his Elegy on the family of Owain ap Gwynedd, writes thus—

> "And is not Madog by the whelming wave
> Slain? How I sorrow for the helpful friend!—
> Even in battle he was free from hate,
> Yet not in vain grasped he the warrior's spear."

About three hundred years later, Meredydd ap Rhys, in 1440, refers to the missing prince in the following way :—

> "Madoc the brave, of aspect fair,
> Owain of Gwynedd's offspring true,
> Would have no land—man of my soul—
> Nor any wealth, except the seas."

Another version of Madoc's voyage appears in a volume of "Travels" by Sir Thomas Herbert, a member of the Pembroke family. In the first edition, dated 1634, p. 355, Sir Thomas writes—

"A Discourse and proofe that Madoc ap Owen Gwynedd first found out that Continent now call'd America. For albeit I have formerly in two lines vindicated the honour of our Countrie, lost in the greater part by protract of envious time, or want of wel-willers to defend it, I shall here somewhat more largely shew the ground of my conjecture, which with the most censorious may happily beget admittance, if analogie of Language and authority of

good Authours may finde it, touching the first
Discoverer of the Western World, commonly
(tho' improperly) called America, and to redeeme
an errour formerly by a printed mistake of
David for Madoc, of whom we treat of. We
may entertaine some lights out of authentique
story, and peradventure whereby at first Madoc,
and his brother David, adventured upon those
Discoveries, and since them Colon, Vesputius,
Magellan, and others. . . . Madoc ap Owen
Gwynedd (to say truth) was the first and sure
discoverer of those Countries, his Plantations
and other Reasons prooving it, which I trust
will not offend any, because hurtfull to none,
that wish well to us or our Countrie, being
withall a great Honor buried in modern silence,
and rapt from us, by all the Christian world,
who unanimously accumulate the glory of it to
the aforenamed Columbus, Americus, and many
others.

"And least any may thinke the person to
whom we attribute a Trophee of so great honour
subject to invention or not worth a memory, I
will first give you a word of his Discent, with
the occasion of his honourable voyage, and so
goe on.

"His name was Madoc, brother of Prince
David, and sonne of that famous Owen Gwyneth,
Prince of Wales, who for above thirty yeares
governed there with great wisdome, courage

and good fortune : his Father was that Gruffith
ap Conan that did homage to William the Con-
querour, at Saint David's, for his Principalities
in Wales, and other places, and lineally descended
from King Rodrimawr, or Rodericke the Great,
who in many conflicts beat the Saxons, especially is renowned by those overthrowes he gave
Burchred, King of Mercia, Athelwolfe, King of
the West Saxes, and Merick, a valiant Prince
amongst them, in foure severall Battailes at
Gwerthen, Bangelu, Monegid and Anglesea,
Anno Dom. 846.

"Enough to satisfie the modest, touching the
worth and value of this Madoc, this added, that
so soone as his Father Prince Owen was dead,
a great and implacable enmitie arose betweene
Iorwerth (sirnamed Drwyndwn, by reason of
his broken nose), Howell and David, sonnes of
Owen. . . . During which turmoiles and un-
naturall strifes, the said Madoc, loath to be an
Agent of Discord to either party, and seeing
propositions of peace ineffectuall, studies by all
good meanes to avoid the knowledge of it, and
aymes at some forren place of ease and profit,
neither discouraged by improbabilities nor likely
disasters.

"These (no doubt) were causes moving Prince
Madoc to this Heroicke Employment, added by
those foretelling southsayers before named, and
which without question were known unto Madoc,

who, according to his dignitie, was instructed in several sorts of arts and learning. [Then follows a copy of "That Prophetique Song, made by that honorable bardh or poet Ambrose Teleyssen," in which is the well-known verse *Ei ner a volant,* &c.] Madoc, ingeniously perusing the older illuminations, and seeing in some things the prophecie of this authentique bardh accomplished (for till they [*i.e.,* the Cymry] forgat God no strangers infested them), employing his Patrimonial estate upon men, ships, and provision, scarce bidding farewell to brother or kindred, left his honourable designes, by preposterous ceremony and complement (actions when affected, sure remonstrances of shallow braines and vanity), might find lets or discouragement to himselfe or servants, Anno 1170 hee left his Country, and after long saile and no lesse patience, blest with some happy windes, at last they discried land in the Gulph of Mexico, not farre from Florida, a land affoording health, aire, gold, good water and plenty of Nature's blessings, by which Prince Madoc was over-joyed, and had reason to account his happy estate superiour to that his brothers strove for, so eagerly emulating with ambitious hate and bloud each other, even for a little Territory, incomparable to that, good destiny allotted him, being a vast and wealthy Kingdome, obtained in some part without opposition, and able to satiate the most covetous.

There he planted, fortified some advantageous places, left a hundred and twenty men to finish what hee had begun, and returned home after some bad windes, guided by supreame providence (his large compasse) and the benefit the Pole-starre gave him on the night.

"When he was landed and had accounted his happy and miraculous Voyage, told the hopes of succeeding Conquests, and other motives of perswasion and admiration, these and the worth of Madoc himselfe drew so many willing minds and purses to a returne, that he attempted it with ten good Barques, loaded with all necessary provisions, a matter of that consequence required. At his arrivall hee found many of his Brittaines dead, caused by the Natives Villany or alteration of the Clime, which notwithstanding he digested patiently, and with Edwall and Eneon his Brothers, bettered the first intentions, living with content, and dying in no lesse distance from Heaven, than when at home, unhappiest in this, that their owne Nation forgot them quite, either judging them lost, because never after hearing from them, or because their owne Beings were turned topsie turvy, by the fatall end of that last unhappy Prince .Lluellyn ap Gruffith (who married Elianor, Daughter of Simon Mountfort, Earle of Leicester), slaine at Buelht by Francton an Englishman, in base and cowardly fashion, Anno Dom. 1282.

"And though the Cambrian issue in the new found world may seeme extinct, the Language to this day used amongst those Canibals, together with their adoring the crosse, using Beades, Reliques of holy men and some other, noted in them of Acusano, and other places, testified by Franciscus Louez, by Columbus, and other Spaniards at their first discovery, points at our Madoc's former being there, being impossible these ceremonies should come amongst them without instruction.

"For Ferdinando Curtez, Ambassadour and Generall for Ferdinando King of Spaine, confesses that Matezuma (second sonne of Antzol and Father of Quabutymoc, last King of Mexico) told him, upon demand how such venerable things came first amongst them, that they had it by tradition that many yeares before, a strange nation lived amongst them, but whence derived or how named hee could not satisfie, though by any indifferent man it may be granted it could be no other save Madoc, confirmed by the Records yet extant, writ by Cynwric ap Grono and Gutyn Owen, and no lesse orthodoxall, by that language left by the Cambrians to Birds, Rivers, Rocks, Beasts, and the like.

"Some of which words are these : *Gwrando,* signifying in the Cambrian speech to give eare unto or hearken. *Pen-gwyn,* with us a white head, refered by the Mexicans to a Bird so called,-

and Rockes complying with that Idiom. Some promontories had like denominations, called so by the people to this day, tho' estranged and concealed by the Spaniard. Such are the Isles *Corroeso*. The Cape of *Brutaine* or *Brittaine*. The floud *Gwyndowr* or white water, *Bara* bread, *Mam* mother, *Tate* father, *Dowr* water, *Bryd* time, *Bu* or *Buch* a Cow, *Clugar* a Heathcocke, *Llwynog* a Fox, *Wy* an Egge, *Calaf* a Quill, *Trwyn* a Nose, *Nef* Heaven; and the like then used : by which in my conceit, none save detracting Opinionatists can justly oppose such worthy testimonies and proofes of what I wish were generally allowed of. And if recitall of Authours may beget more credence, wee referre the Reader to those Records writ two hundred yeares agoe and more by Cynwric ap Grono, Gutyn Owen who lived in King Edward the Fourth's time, Humphrey Lloydd, David Powell, Sir John Price, Richard Hackluyt, Purchas, Davis and others. Enough to the wel-willers of Truth and Justice, too much for carping Zoylists, and such as take pleasure in sophistry and opposition."

It is stated in the *Cambro-Briton* that Sir Thomas Herbert had access to the celebrated and valuable library at Raglan Castle, before its destruction during the Civil Wars. In the *Encyclopædia Britannica* it is recorded : "Herbert's own share in the work has an air of truthfulness, and contains much valuable information not readily accessible elsewhere."

The foregoing records are only a few of the numberless testimonies in favour of Madog's discovery and colonisation of America, while there are numerous Chroniclers who contend that there is no proof whatever in support of the allegation.

CHAPTER XXIII

A REMARKABLE LAW.

ONE of the most curious laws affecting the succession to the throne of Wales was that which prevented any one becoming king who had a physical or mental defect.

A blind, deaf, dumb, or maimed man or woman, even though the first-born and legal heir of the family, could not inherit land or any kind of possession, and one of the most remarkable laws on the subject of inheritance was the equal division of territory amongst sons to the third generation, and the assignment of only half-shares to daughters.

In the ancient chronicles it is thus recorded: —" Prince *Owen Gwynedh* being dead, the Succession was of right to descend to his eldest legitimate Son *Iorwerth Drwyndwn*, otherwise called *Edward* with the broken Nose ; but by reason of that blemish upon his Face, he was

laid aside as unfit to take upon him the Government of *North Wales*. Therefore his younger
Brothers began every one to aspire, in hopes of
succeeding their Father."

Whereupon Hywel, the natural son of Owain,
assumed the government, but was speedily
opposed by David, whose escutcheon was not
blemished by the *bend sinister*, and who, therefore, in the quaint words of the old historian,
"made all the Preparations possible to pull
him down. *Howel*, on the other hand, was as
resolute to maintain his ground, and was not
willing so quickly to deliver up what he had
not very long got possession of; and so both
Brothers meeting together in the Field, were
resolved to try their Title by the point of the
Sword. The Battel had not lasted long, but
Howel was slain; and then *David* was unanimously proclaimed and saluted Prince of *North-
Wales*, which Principality he enjoyed without
any Molestation."

When Davydd ap Owain Gwynedd ascended
the throne, the princes and people of Gwynedd
and Dinevwr were bitter enemies, and in illustration of the feeling existing between them
the following story is told :—

When some fugitives from South Wales
sought refuge in the territory of Davydd, the
people of Gwynedd declared it was unseemly
condescension to receive the subjects of a rival

prince, who would not allow a similar privilege
to the inhabitants of North Wales.

Davydd declared he would send a messenger
to Rhys ap Gruffydd, merely to prove whether
or not that irascible prince would receive him
honourably. For some time there was great
difficulty in finding any one willing to undertake the task, but at length Gwgan of Caer
Einion consented to go. After a long and
weary journey through dense forests, almost
impassable paths, and over lonely mountains,
the messenger reached the palace of the Prince
of Dinevwr.

There a strange scene awaited him.

In the great courtyard of the palace the
warrior-prince strode to and fro, shouting and
raving, and almost uncontrollable in the fierce
heat of a furious passion. He cudgelled his
servants from right to left, flung his sword
after the frightened pages, hurled his boots of
untanned leather at the shivering maids, and
completed the scene by hanging all the dogs
that were unfortunate enough to hinder his
progress.

Gwgan, looking on, wisely postponed seeking
audience of the prince until the next morning.

Then, with caution, aided by mild, persuasive,
and somewhat flattering speech, he told the
prince that it was a great honour to appear
before the lordly " descendant of the line of

Rhys ap Tewdwr Mawr," and that he came there from "Davydd, son of Owain, of the kingly race of Cynan." He added that he was sent with "friendly greeting," and if he received "welcome and honour, so, in Davydd's name," was he "to thank the Lord of Dinevwr."

Rhys then asked what would be the most honourable kind of reception for the messenger of Davydd ap Owain Gwynedd.

Gwgan, surprised and delighted with the aspect of affairs, boldly answered, "Thou shalt give me a better horse than my own on which to ride back to Gwynedd, five pounds of money, and a brave new suit of clothes. I also ask for my servant who holds my bridle, a suit of new garments and one pound of money. Thus, O Prince, shalt thou honour the messenger who hath come from the descendant of the royal Cynan."

The man of Caer Einion, in Powys, was not only a bold but a successful beggar. His manner, possibly because it was daring, pleased the prince and renowned warrior of South Wales, who promptly said, "Come in; come in. For the sake of thy royal master, and thine own venturesome air, thou shalt have the best steed in my stables. I will also give thee twice as much money and twice as many clothes as thou hast asked. And never again will Rhys ap Gruffydd fail to do honour to the King of Aberfraw."

Gwgan's successful mission was the source of great pleasure to Davydd ap Owain, who rejoiced at being able to prove to the satisfaction of his people that he had not misinterpreted the real feelings of Rhys ap Gruffydd towards him.

Early in the reign of Davydd a terrible incident occurred. It is mentioned in the annals of Wales as the great massacre of Abergavenny, which in many points bears a striking resemblance to the Treachery of the Long Knives.

William de Breos—into whose keeping Henry II. gave the castle of Abergavenny—possessing the spirit of the early Normans, resolved to subdue the whole of Gwent. With this aim in view, he invited the Welsh chieftains and others of distinction to a grand banquet in Abergavenny Castle. When mirth was at its zenith and the feasters quaffed the rich wine, the sparkling metheglin, and the foaming bragget, De Breos proposed that all the Welsh present should bind themselves by an oath, in accordance with the king's orders, henceforth to travel unarmed through the country. They were not to carry bows and arrows, javelins, spears, or swords. On hearing this the Welsh were greatly surprised, and indignantly refused to obey the command. Two of the most obstinate Welshmen present were Seisyllt ap Dyvnwal and Ienan ap Rhiryd, who declared they would not go unarmed. Then, at a signal from De Breos, the banqueting-hall was instantly crowded with English soldiers, who assailed the unarmed chieftains and massacred them to a man. During the banquet the unfortunate Welshmen had laid aside their bows and arrows, and were totally unable to defend themselves.

Not content with having committed this atrocity, De Breos, as soon as the last chieftain was slain, hastened away with all possible speed to the home of Seisyllt—the ruins of which are still to be seen in the Llanover estate—and completely destroyed it by fire. At the same time he rushed in and murdered Seisyllt's son Cadwaladr, and seizing the young chieftain's mother, carried her off as a prisoner to his fortress.

Celtic revenge, if slow in coming, came suddenly and certainly. The sons of the slain marched to Abergavenny Castle, scaled the walls, took possession of the fortress, and razed it to the ground. De Breos, the object of their hatred, was absent, but the Welsh followed him to Monmouthshire, where he was wounded, but not slain. Ultimately De Breos fled to France, where, it is said, he spent the last years of his life in begging bread from door to door.

The wife of De Breos was Maud de Valeri, daughter of Fitz-Walter, Earl of Hereford. This strong-minded, strong-armed woman was a reputed witch, who for many years had been regarded as a student of occult mysteries, and

one who did at unholy hours practise magic
arts to the annoyance of her neighbours. It
was said that, totally unaided, she built the
castle of Hay, in Brecknockshire, in a single
night. The story goes that, while occupied in
carrying stones with which to build the castle,
a pebble fell from her apron into her shoe.
This troubled the witch so much that she
passionately threw it away to the opposite side
of the Wye. This "pebble," which was nine
feet long, is still to be seen in Llowes Churchyard, Radnorshire, where it is pointed out as a
memorial of the witchcraft and physical power
of Maud, known in folklore and nursery story
as "Mol Walbee."

This extraordinary woman lived to meet a
terrible fate.

In the feuds between King John and her
husband, Maud of Hay presented the Queen of
England with four hundred white kine, each
of which had beautiful red ears. This was
meant as a kind of peace-offering, because
De Breos had failed to make good his pay-
ments for Munster and Limerick, which had
been bequeathed to him by his brother. King
John wanted hostages in the persons of her
children, but she refused, declaring that she
would not trust her family to a man who had
so cruelly murdered his own nephew. For
this King John would not forgive her. Maud

s

and her children were taken prisoners, and
the king refused to release her or absolve her
husband from his debts. The reputed witch
then offered a ransom of forty thousand marks,
but "broke her bargain" more than once.
This was done so that her husband might
have a chance of escaping to France, and Maud
thought the king would then relent towards
her.

But John never forgave her for having called
him a murderer.

Maud was imprisoned with her children at
Bristol, and afterwards taken under strong
escort to Windsor.

The story goes that, soon after her arrival
at Windsor, Maud and her family were imprisoned in a few small rooms, around which
a tower was gradually built. In that tomb
Mol Walbee, the witch, known in better days
as Maud de Valeri, and her family were slowly
starved, and buried alive near the spot where
Windsor Castle now stands.

It is interesting here to take glimpses of the
social condition of the Welsh in the twelfth
century, and to hear what pleasant, self-satisfied
Giraldus Cambrensis has to say on the subject. After referring to the warlike habits of
the Welsh, and their animating spirit, which,
in his opinion, was nationality rather than
patriotism, in the form of clanship and family

ambition, Giraldus sarcastically adds that his countrymen loved their brothers far better when they were dead than when they were living; and he proceeds to say :—"As the southern part of Wales, near Cardiganshire, and especially Pembrokeshire, is pleasanter on account of its plains and sea-coasts, so North Wales is better defended by nature, is more productive of men distinguished for bodily strength, and more fertile in the nature of its soil. For, as the mountains of Eryri (Snowdon) could supply pasturage for all the herds of cattle in Wales, if collected together, so could the Isle of Mona (Anglesea) provide a requisite quantity of corn for all the inhabitants,—on which account there is an old British proverb, 'Mona is the mother of Wales.' It is to be observed that the British language is more delicate and richer in North Wales, that country being less intermingled with foreigners. The people of Cornwall and the Armoricans speak a language similar to that of the Britons. It is intelligible to the Welsh in many instances—nay, almost in all. No one of this nation ever begs, for the houses of all are common to all, and they consider liberality and hospitality amongst the first virtues. Those who arrive in the morning are entertained till evening by the conversation of young women and the music of the harp. In the evening, when no more guests are expected, the usual meal is prepared according to the number and dignity of the persons assembled and the wealth of the family who entertains. While the family is engaged in waiting on the guests the host and hostess stand up, paying unremitting attention to everything, and take no food till all the company are satisfied. The women, after the manner of the Parthians, cover their heads with a large white veil, folded together in the form of a crown. Both sexes exceed any other nation in attention to their teeth, which they render like ivory. These people being of a sharp and acute intellect, and gifted with a rich and powerful understanding, excel in whatever studies they pursue. Their musical instruments charm and delight the ear with their sweetness. In their rhymed songs and set speeches they are so subtle and ingenious that they produce in the native tongue ornaments of wonderful and exquisite inventions, both in the words and sentences; hence arise those poets whom they call bards. The Welsh esteem noble birth and generous descent above all things, and are therefore more desirous of marrying into good than rich families. Even the common people retain their genealogy, and cannot only readily recount the names of their grandfathers and great-grandfathers, but even refer back to the sixth or seventh generation. The greater part of their land is laid down to pasturage, little is cultivated,

a very small quantity is ornamented with
flowers, and a still smaller sown. They seldom
yoke less than four oxen to their ploughs. The
boats which they employ in fishing or in crossing the rivers are made of twigs, not oblong,
nor pointed, but almost round, or rather tri-
angular, covered both without and within with
raw hides. The fishermen, according to the
custom of the country, in going to and from the
rivers, carry their boats on their shoulders.

"In ancient times, and about two hundred
years before the overthrow of Britain, the Welsh
were instructed and confirmed in the faith by
Faganus and Damianus, sent into the island, at
the request of King Lucius, by Pope Eleutherius,
and from that period when Germanus of Auxerre
and Lupus of Troyes came over on account of
the corruption which had crept into the island
by the invasion of the Saxons, but particularly
with a view of expelling the Pelagian heresy,
nothing heretical or contrary to the true faith
was to be found among the natives. But it is
said that some parts of the ancient doctrines
are still retained. They give the first piece
broken off from every loaf of bread to the poor.
They sit down to dinner by three in a company,
in honour of the Trinity. . . . Happy and fortunate would this nation be, nay, completely
blessed, if it had good prelates and pastors, and
but one prince, and that prince a good one."

CHAPTER XXIV

LLEWELYN THE GREAT

HILE the laws affecting the succession in Wales prevented any one with a physical or mental defect ascending the throne or inheriting lands, and counted him as "one dead," his direct heir, if unafflicted, could legally succeed the unfortunate possessor of any blemish.

Thus the ancient annals of Wales record the fact that when Davydd, the son of Owain Gwynedd, had reigned "for above Twenty-Four Years; and one would think, that so long a Possession would secure him in his Throne, that it could not be very easie to pull him down. But possession is not always the surest Card, which proved very true in Prince *David's* case at this time; for *Llewelyn*, the son of *Iorwerth Drwyndwn* (Edward with the broken nose), who was the eldest son of *Owen Gwynedh*, Prince of *North-Wales*, being now arrived to Years of maturity, and having Sense enough to understand what a just Title and Claim he had to the Principality of *North-Wales*, of which his Uncle *David* had so unjustly kept him out ; he thought it high time to endeavour to recover what was lawfully his own, which, however, he was well persuaded his uncle *David* would never easily part with. And therefore, being well assured that the justness of the Title would never mount him up to the Throne, without he had an Army at his heels to help him on ; he called together all his Friends and Relations by his Mother's side . . . he came into *North-Wales* proclaiming how . . . though his Father *Iorwerth* had been incapable of taking upon him the Government, by reason of some Infirmity ; yet there was no reason that his Father's Weakness should exclude him out ; and therefore, being now sensible of what he was not capable to understand in his youth, he laid claim to the Principality, which was justly his own. But there was no great need of conjuring to understand his Claim, nor of much Rhetorick to persuade the People to own him for their Prince ; whose Affection was cooled, and almost worn off from *David*, ever since he had dealt so unnaturally with his Brothers, whom after he had deprived of their Estates, he banished out of the Country. And therefore, before *Llewelyn* could expect to have any sure footing, the whole Country of *North-Wales* was at his devotion, excepting only

Three Castles, which *David*, by the help of the *English*, in whom by reason of his Affinity with the late King Henry, he depended much upon, kept to himself. And thus David, being deprived of almost all that he formerly possessed ; we shall reckon him no more among the Princes of *North-Wales*, but restore the Principality to the true Heir *Llewelyn ap Iorwerth*."

When Iorwerth, the son of Owain Gwynedd, and father of the celebrated prince who now appears as claimant to the throne of North Wales, was prevented succeeding owing to his physical defect, he became the object of his brother Davydd's jealousy. Accordingly he took sanctuary at Pennant Melangell, in Montgomeryshire, where he died.

In Pennant's "Tour," vol. iii. p. 175, it is stated that in the parish church of Melangell there was a rude effigy of a man holding a shield against his breast, and bearing the broken fragment of a sword in his hand, and this memorial was supposed to represent the unfortunate Iorwerth.

Llewelyn, Iorwerth's son, is described as having been a fine, high-spirited, and handsome youth, whose popularity and the justice of his claim gained for him, in A.D. 1194, the throne of North Wales. In the course of his long reign three English kings successively wielded the sceptre. They were Richard I., John, and Henry III.

When young Llewelyn ascended the throne he made a resolution to reintroduce and carry out the constitutional organisation of Roderic the Great, or Rhodri Mawr.

With reference to Rhodri's government, the following passage, translated from Caradoc's "Chronicle," appears in the "Myvyrian Archæology," ii. p. 481 :—"Rhodri the Great instituted a new system of government in Wales, as far as his jurisdiction extended, and it was as follows :—

"Ceredigion he gave to Cadell, his eldest son ; his court to be at Dinevor. North Wales he gave to his Anarawd ; his court to be at Aberffraw, in Anglesea. Powys he gave to his Mervyn ; his court to be at Mathraval. The eldest of these he enjoined to pay a tribute to the King of London ; and to the eldest son the other two were each of them to pay tribute also. These were called the three diademed princes, because they, contrary to all that preceded them, wore frontlets about their crowns, like the kings of other countries ; whereas, before that time, the kings and princes of the Welsh nation wore only golden chains. Rhodri settled sovereignty on the eldest of the three supreme diademed princes ; with a request and commandment that they should defend and protect Cambria, and its people, against assaults of enemies, and against all anarchy and disorder."

According to the Iolo MSS., the tributes to which reference is here made were:—"A tribute in gold, from Aberffraw, amounting to £20; a tribute in honey, from Dinevor, amounting to four tons; and a tribute in oatmeal, from Powis Wynfa, amounting to four tons; but, in default of honey from Dinevor, or of oatmeal from Powis, a commutation, amounting to £20, from each of these provinces."

Llywarch ap Llewelyn, known as *Prydydd y Môch*, or the "Poet of the Pigs!" thus sings of Llewelyn ap Iorwerth, afterwards known as the "Great"—

"Who from invaders will our waters guard?
Llywelyn,—he will guard the boundary wave;
The lion in the breach, ruler of Gwynedd,
The land is his to Powys' distant bounds."

This young prince appears to have asserted his rights early, and in truly warlike fashion, for the "Poet of the Pigs" again sings—

"In battle's whirlwind, 'mid the clash of arms,
The hero-youth, when ten years old, attack'd
Davydd, his uncle, who, like Cæsar, was
A blood-stain'd chief, gen'rous, without a fault,
But fierce as pointed flames are in their wrath,
. . . . . . Llywelyn brave
From him of Aberconway got his right,
He was our prince before the fights befell."

In April A.D. 1197, just three years after the accession of Llewelyn the Great, Rhys ap

Gruffydd, the sometimes turbulent and irascible Lord of Dinevor, died, and was buried in the cathedral of St. David's. Of this ever-restless and passionate prince, several curious elegies appear. One runs thus—

> "O glory of warfare, and shield of the army,
> Defence of your country, and honour of arms!
> Virtue of Hercules bear in your bosom,
> Wedded to sternness like to Achilles."

The poet then continues, describing the hero as one who possessed the "modesty of Nestor, the daring of Tydeus, the strength of Samson, the sobriety of Hector, the swiftness of Euryalus, the beauty of Paris, the eloquence of Ulysses, the wisdom of Solomon, the impetuosity of Ajax!"

Another bard enthusiastically refers to him as "the only anchor, hope, and stay of all South Wales, seeing that he had brought it out of thraldom, and the bondage of strangers, and given it liberty; and many times defended it manfully in the field, daunting the pride and the courage of its cruel enemies, whom he either chased out of the land or compelled to live in it quietly. Woe to that unkind destiny which spoiled the miserable country of her defence and shield! who as he was sprung from noble, nay, from princely blood, so did he surpass all others in virtues, and in qualities of the mind!

He was the overthrower of the mighty and the setter-up of the weak; the destroyer of castles; the scatterer of troops; the dispenser of his foes, *amongst whom he appeared as a wild boar or a lion, who, for very rage, lashed the ground with his tail!*"

The above amusing description, though by no means flattering, was faithful, especially as regards the prince's passionate disposition.

A quiet and quaint Chronicler thus writes:—"This year likewise dyed the valiant *Rhys*, Prince of *South Wales*, the only Stay and Defence of that part of Wales; for it was he that got them their Liberty, and secured it to them. He often very readily exposed his own Life for the defence of theirs and their Country; generally he got the better of his enemies, and at last either brought them entirely under his Subjection, or forced them to quit their Country. He was no less illustrious for his virtuous endowments, than for his Valour and Extraction; so that it was with good reason that the *British Bards* and others wrote so honourably of him, and so mightily deplored his Death."

During the concluding years of the reign of Richard the First, Llewelyn's life was comparatively uneventful, but in 1201 a treaty of peace was concluded between unfortunate Iorwerth's victorious son and the Earl of Essex. Warrington's "History," pp. 353–403, contains the articles of the treaty, the first and foremost of which was, that the King of North Wales "swore to maintain perpetual fidelity to King John in the fulness of feudal ideas."

In 1202 Llewelyn the Great convened an assembly of all the chieftains in Wales, who, with one exception, took the oaths of allegiance as requested.

The exception was Gwenwynwyn, Lord of Higher Powys, whose pet scheme was to extend Wales to its original limits, and therefore he would not pay homage, upon which the Convention agreed that the recusant should be compelled to perform his duty or forfeit his territory. There was one dissentient to the compulsory vote of the Convention, and he, Elise by name, for having courageously spoken his mind, had his landed property and possessions immediately confiscated.

Llewelyn the Great took an army down to Powys-land, but owing to the influence of friends, the refractory Gwenwynwyn made submission in due form, and thus avoided bloodshed.

In 1208 a curious circumstance occurred.

Gwenwynwyn, Prince of Powys, went to Shrewsbury to confer with the lords in council, and being there, was requested to take the oath of fealty to King John. He refused, and was cast into prison, where they kept him until he complied and gave hostages for his obedience. A copy of the treaty between King John and the Prince of Powys appears in Rymer's *Fœdera*, where the names of twenty hostages are recorded. On the eve of the Feast of St. Denis, at Shrewsbury, the Prince of Powys swore, "touching the sacred Gospels," to faithfully serve King John both in person and land for ever; on all matters of laws he was to submit himself to the royal court, and he was to appear before the English monarch whenever that potentate summoned him.

Meanwhile, true to the old Welsh love of pillage, Llewelyn the Great construed the visit of the Prince of Powys to Shrewsbury as an act of disloyalty to him as King of North Wales, and forthwith seized the prince's castles and territories. When the Prince of Powys returned home, he was obliged to replenish his armoury, restock his estates, and wholly refurnish his residences.

It may here be remarked that in 1204 King John gave his daughter, Princess Joan, in marriage, with a dower consisting of the lordship of Ellesmere, Shropshire, in the Marches of Wales, to Llewelyn, and on hearing of his son-in-law's outrage against Gwenwynwyn he called him severely to account. Whereupon the King of North Wales made reparation to the Prince of Powys, and then received his royal father-in-law's full pardon.

According to Roger of Wendover, in 1209 that which "had never been heard of in times past" occurred. The Welsh, although it was greatly burdensome to the rich and poor alike, went to Woodstock and did homage to King John. Soon afterwards the Welsh and the lords of the Marches commenced new hostilities.

When attempting the subjugation of the Welsh, Ranulph, Earl of Chester, was beset by them in Rhuddlan Castle, and relieved by Roger de Lacy, Lord of Halton. Of this relief a curious story is told.

From the days of Hugh Lupus the monks of St. Werburgh, Chester, held their annual fair on the feast-day of that saint. This gathering went by the name of the Abbot's Fair. Just when the business of the fair was at its best, Roger de Lacy, Constable of Chester, who is described as a "ryght valiaunt manne," rushed into the market square, and explained that Ranulph, the earl of the city, was sorely harassed by the Welsh "mountaineers," and help was immediately needed. A request of that description, coming from no less a person than the Constable of Chester, was equal to a command, and forthwith around the English standard a motley crowd of drunken musicians and fiddlers assembled. They were augmented by the "rag-tag and bob-tail" of the fair, and followed by these, De Lacy set forth to the aid of his beleaguered earl. It is said that the Welsh, seeing the approach of a large and hideous host, and hearing terrible discords of fiddles and flutes, sackbuts, and other discordant instruments, concluded that the English Constable was accompanied by lunatics and madmen. Thereupon the Welsh raised the siege, and left Rhuddlan as quickly as possible.

Earl Ranulph, with Roger de Lacy, returned to Chester at the head of the victorious minstrels, and at once chartered the holding of the Abbot's Fair for ever. Numerous privileges and immunities were granted to the citizens, and to the " brave " De Lacy, and his heirs perpetually, the licensing of and custody over the wonderful "Minstrels of Cheshire " were accorded. This prerogative was exercised by his descendants until the middle of the eighteenth century. The English for a long time " gloried over " the " bloodless fight of the fiddlers," to which the Welsh gave a far less agreeable name.

Soon after this, Llewelyn the Great commenced fierce hostilities against the Earl of Chester, for which King John marched into Wales, to chastise his undutiful son-in-law. But the king reckoned without his host. He had not long been in Wales before he was only too glad to get out of it. At the command of Llewelyn, the country people took all their cattle and effects into the impassable recesses around Snowdon, and thus cut off all the enemy's supplies.

King John promptly retreated, but in a few months later, he returned with stronger forces, before which the Welsh quailed, and Llewelyn's vassal princes failed him.

Left utterly alone, the King of North Wales was forced into unwilling submission, and Joan his queen, who is called by some of the quaint old Chroniclers, " a prudent sly woman ! "— mediated successfully on his behalf. Llewelyn was taken into the presence of the king, who granted him pardon and peace, on certain hard conditions. King John demanded forty horses and twenty thousand cattle towards the expenses of the war, and cede to the crown of England for ever the inland parts of his dominions.

For a time Llewelyn was completely despondent.

But relief came from an unexpected source.

In 1212, Pope Innocent III. absolved Llewelyn from his allegiance to King John, and "strongly commanded the King of North Wales, under penalty of excommunication, to molest and annoy the King of England, who proved himself to be an open enemy to the Church of God." At least, so it is recorded in Powell's Caradoc, p. 234.

The Welsh immediately taking advantage of the Pope's permission, made raids upon the

border countries. Under the direction of
Llewelyn, the Welsh princes, chieftains, and
people marched forth, and promptly carried
their king's plans into execution with the
resolution and savage ferocity of the age.

Before the death of King John, Llewelyn
the Great nearly approached the realisation of
his great and fondly cherished idea—United
Wales.

Proceeding with his great national enterprise,
he made a glorious and successful expedition
throughout Wales. As a stroke of good policy,
he induced Reginald de Bruce, an influential
baron of South Wales, to marry his daughter,
and having reduced Carmarthenshire and Cardiganshire to subjection, he returned home.

Llewelyn was then able to satisfy his ambition
by winning and bearing the title for which he
had fought so long and resolutely, and, at last,
he found himself King of All Wales.

This dignity was short-lived.

After the accession of Henry III. he was
again forced to submission, and during the
remainder of his life he pursued the phantom
of supreme sway, the substance of which he
once held, but too soon withdrew his grasp.

To the end of his existence this true-hearted
Welshman — who unaided was able to unify
Wales—had the interests and independence of
his country at heart. He maintained the honour

and dignity of his name and nation, even
when his mind was perplexed, and his actions
formidably impeded by feudal obligations. To
the last, the bards of his age, who revered and
idolised him, lovingly sang his praises in thrill-
ing tones of music, and lauded his victories in
glowing flowers of rhetoric.

In the "Cambro-Briton," Vol. I., p. 470,
the following ode by Davydd Benfras is to be
found. It was probably composed in commemoration of the defeat of the English army, under
the personal command of Henry III, in the
frontier of Wales in A.D. 1228. The translation is attributed to the young bard Maurice
Roberts of Llanrhudol :—

> "O may the Muse her Vigour bring,
> While I Llywelyn's praises sing— . . .
>> Ne'er was such a warrior seen,
>> With heart so brave, and gallant mien :
> From a regal race descended,
> Bravely he the land defended.
>> Kings have learnt his power to dread,
>> Kings have felt his arm and fled.
> Loegria's king with conquest flushed,
> Boldly to the battle rushed ;
>> Then was heard the warlike shout,
>> Signal of the approaching rout.
> Great Llywelyn raged around,
> Bravest chieftains pressed the ground ;
>> None his valour could withstand,
>> None could stem his furious hand :
> Like a whirlwind o'er the deep,
> See him through their Squadrons sweep, . . .

> Far is heard Llywelyn's name,
> Resounded by the trump of fame, . . .
> Ere upon his honoured tomb,
> Herbs shall rise and flowers shall bloom,
> May the Redeemer intercede,
> And unto God for mercy plead ; . . .
> Then may Llywelyn, warrior brave,
> In glory live beyond the grave."

In the ancient chronicles Llewelyn the Great is described as a "Prince of great Courage, and Audacity, and no less Prudence in contriving, than Boldness in executing, any martial Adventure ; he was a great Support to the *Welsh*, and no less a Plague to the *English* ; he made very considerable Conquests upon the Borders, and extended the Frontiers of *Wales* much beyond their former Limits."

The domestic life of Llewelyn was not happy.

Dissensions arose between this monarch and his son Gruffydd, of whom it is said, "This latter having kept himself in possession of the Cantref of *Merionyth*, contrary to the Consent and well-liking of his Father, the Prince, therefore, having now no great matter of moment abroad, was resolved to curb the Insolency of his Son, and therefore sent to him to command his appearance, and to wish him to deliver up the Cantref quietly, lest he should be forced to take it violently out of his hands. Gruffydh was not in the least dismayed at his threatenings, but being resolved to keep what at present

he enjoyed, would neither go to his Father, nor
deliver up the Cantref to him. The Prince
being enraged that he should be so slighted by
his Son, made a vehement Protestation that he
would be severely revenged both of him and all
his accomplices. . . . and was resolved to drive
his Son out of the Country."

Subsequently Gruffydd was cast into prison,
and the chroniclers state that when a temporary
peace was concluded between the English and
the Welsh, " Prince Llywelyn let his son
Gruffydd at liberty, whom for his disobedient
and restless Humour, he had been detained in
close Prison for the space of Six Years."

Llewelyn's wife, the Princess Joan, who at
the most critical periods had exhibited the
strongest proofs of her sincere affection and
unswerving fidelity to her husband, became the
subject of a wicked and unfounded jealousy,
which cost the life of a distinguished English
prisoner, William de Breos.

In North Wales, near Aber, known in early
British history as " Aber Gwyn Gregin," or the
" stream of the white shells," there is a field
called " Cae Gwilym Ddu "—" Black William's
Field "—in connection with which the following
story is told :—William de Breos by chance of
war fell into the hands of Llewelyn the Great,
who, tormented by the " green-eyed monster,"
cruelly misconstrued the Englishman's courtesy

to the Princess Joan, who had always been devoted to her husband. After de Breos had been ransomed, Llewelyn vindictively sought revenge. He invited the unwary Englishman to a banquet during Easter in April 1230, and, when heated with wine, the Welsh prince reproached his guest for having endeavoured to break the seventh commandment. Llewelyn then ordered de Breos to be ignominiously dragged from his presence, and hung on a neighbouring hill. The place is called to this day, from the tree on which de Breos was hung, "Gwern-y-Grogfa," or the "Alder of Execution." Tradition states that Llewelyn's domestic bard, accidentally meeting with the princess, who was ignorant of the fate of de Breos, accosted her thus—

> "Diccyn doccyn, gwraig Llewelyn,
> Beth a roit am weled Gwilym?"

To which the princess promptly replied—

> "Cymru, Lloeger, a Llewelyn,
> Rown i gyd am weled Gwilym."

Translated, the rhymes run as follows:—

> "Tell me, wife of Llewelyn,
> What would you give for a sight of William?"

The princess replied—

> "Wales, England, and Llewelyn,
> I would give them all to see William."

Thereupon the malicious bard took her to see the lifeless body of William de Breos hanging on an alder tree.

The very charming village of Aber, about two miles and a half from Llanfairfechan, stands at the opening of a beautiful and deep glen, bounded by Maes y Gaer, and Blaen y Garu. At the entrance to the glen, and quite close to the village, a large mound, about sixty feet in diameter, is to be seen. This was the site of one of Llewelyn's castles of which some foundations and remains are still to be seen. Beyond it is the great mountain called Carnedd Llewelyn. At the foot of it is the extinct volcano known as Llyn Dulin, or the Black Lake, the steep crater-like appearance of which testifies to the nature of its origin. Around the lake may still be seen blocks of pumice stone, and masses of sulphureous pyrites. Not far from Aber, in one of the wildest valleys in Wales, is the celebrated Arrow Stone, Carreg-y-Saethau, upon which the Welsh chieftains of old sharpened their battle-axes, spears, and arrows, while swearing allegiance to their king and death to their enemies.

It is said that Llewelyn sorely repented of his unjust suspicions against his devoted and innocent wife, who died in the spring of 1237. Her death is recorded in the following way :— " Joan, King John's Daughter, and Princess of *Wales*, departed this Life, and was buried according to her own desire, upon the Sea shore, at a place called Lhanfaes (Llanvaes) in the Isle of *Anglesea;* where the Prince, in memory of her, afterwards founded a religious House, for the Order of Mendicant Friars."

Her monument is still extant.

In 1240, after a reign of forty-six years, Llewelyn the Great died, and was buried by his own wish, in the Abbey of Conway, where his body remained until Edward the First, wishing to build his new town, moved all the monks of that religious institution to the monastery of Maenan.

CHAPTER XXV

A BURDEN OF SORROW

THERETO the pious men conveyed the coffin of their royal founder and patron. This memorial is now preserved in Llanrwst Church, but the coffin, which is large and empty, is without a lid.

When Llewelyn the Great died, his eldest, but natural son, Gruffydd, claimed the right of succession, on the ground that, being the first-born, he was heir in chief, while Davydd, as the only legitimate son, asserted his rights as sole heir, with the additional dignity of being nephew to King Henry the Third of England.

Each claimant had his partisans, who immediately threw the whole of North Wales into a scene of fierce strife and confusion. At length the rivals agreed to hold a conference for the settlement of all disputes, and if possible to effect reconciliation and peace. The place, time, and conditions of the meeting were arranged, and Gruffydd, accompanied by the Bishop of Bangor and others, while on his way to the spot, was treacherously siezed by order of his brother, and promptly imprisoned at Criccieth. Whereupon Davydd, without opposition, ascended the throne.

Gruffydd, when in prison, appealed to Henry the Third, who interceded with his nephew, Davydd, but to no effect. The lawful son of Llewelyn the Great refused to release the prisoner, because, if Gruffydd were set free, " Wales would never be at peace." The prisoner then privately sent to tell the king, "that if by Force he would deliver him out of Prison; he would not only hold his Lands for ever from him, but also pay him the yearly Acknowledgement of Three Hundred Marks; offering to give both Oath, and to deliver up sufficient Pledges for the performance of it; and withal to assist the King with all his Power to bringing in the rest of the Welch to his subjection. Moreover, *Gruffydh ap* Madawc, Lord of *Bromfield*, positively assured the King that in case he would lead an Army into *Wales*, to revenge the Falsity and injurious Practices of *David*, he would give him all possible Aid and Assistance. . . . The king being chiefly allured with the Promises of the *Welch* in behalf of Gruffydh, levied a very

formidable Army to lead to *Wales;* strictly
commanding by Proclamation all the *English*
who owed him any Martial-Service, to repair
armed to *Gloucester* by the beginning of *August.*
This Rendezvous being accordingly performed,
the King came thither in person at the time
appointed, and, having regulated his Troops,
and put all Matters in convenient order, he
marched to *Shrewsbury*, where he remained
Fifteen Days to refresh his Army."

Lhuyd says that many noblemen, who yielded
because of their hatred to Davydd for betraying his brother, appeared at the council, and
were received with favour in peace by the king.

Amongst those present to meet Henry the
Third at Shrewsbury was Gruffydd's devoted
wife, who effectually pleaded her imprisoned
husband's cause. Having full powers to make
a treaty, she undertook that, for the liberation
of Gruffydd and his son Owain, six hundred
marks should be paid, and her husband would
abide the king's decision as to what share of
his father's possessions and honours he should
enjoy.

She also promised that her husband would pay
three hundred marks a year from whatever territory he would be allowed as vassal of the king,
one-third to be paid in money and the remainder
equally in cattle and horses. Half of this tribute
would be paid at Easter, and half at the feast of

St. Michael and All Angels. She further undertook that her husband should keep the peace towards Davydd, and bring to justice all rebels
against the king.

This brave-hearted princess, whose fortitude
never forsook her in the hour of direst need,
offered to give up her sons Davydd and Rhodri
as hostages for the observance of the treaty, on
the condition that if her husband died, one at
least of them should be released to succeed. She
took a solemn oath to fulfil and abide by her
agreement, and to see that Gruffydd did the
same. The following persons were prepared to
see the treaty faithfully kept :—" *Ralph*, Lord
Mortimer of Wigmore (who married Gwladys
Dhu, or the Brunette, daughter of Llewelyn the
Great and Princess Joan), *Walter Clifford*,
Roger de Monte Alto, Steward of *Chester ;*
Maelgon ap Maelgon, *Meredith ap Rolpert*,
Lord of *Cydewen*, *Gruffydh ap Madawc* of
Bromfield ; Howel and *Meredith*, the Sons of
Conan ap Owen Gwynedh, and *Gruffydh ap
Gwenwynwyn*, Lord of *Powys*. These Noblemen
prevailed so far with King *Henry*, that a league
was concluded between him and *Senena* the Wife of
Gruffydh. For the performance of these Articles,
the aforesaid Noblemen offered to be Securities,
and bound themselves by their several Writings."

Although Davydd found the English against
him, he still proudly refused to liberate his

brother ; but, according to the "Annales of St.
David's," in a few weeks the Welsh prince began
to dread the powers he defied, and to quail
before popular opinion, which was strongly in
favour of his imprisoned brother.

Henry the Third sent a command to Davydd
to appear before him at Diserth, and to bring
with him his brother Gruffydd with his son
Owain, and all who were in prison with them.

Davydd obeyed, but privately reminded the
king of his relationship to him, and the invalidity
of his brother's claim, whereupon Henry, says
Llunyd the historian, " knowing him (Gruffydd)
to be a man of great courage, would in no wise
grant him liberty."

Gruffydd, accompanied by his wife, children,
and friends, went to London in the autumn of
1241 ; but, although he received a noble a day for
his subsistence, he was imprisoned in the Tower,
and Henry resolutely refused to set him free.
There the unfortunate but heroic and courageous
son of Llewelyn the Great, and father of Llewelyn
ap Gruffydd, remained until death put an end
to his hopelessness on St. David's Day, 1244.
The story of his last moments runs thus :—" As
soon as *Gruffydh* found out King *Henry's* mind,
and that it was the least part of his design to set
him at liberty, having flatly denied the Bishop
of *Bangor* his request therein ; he began to set
his Brains a-working, and to devise a means

whereby he might escape out of the Tower.
Whereupon, having one night deceived his
keepers, he let himself down from the top of
the Building by a Line which he had composed
out of the Sheets and Hangings of the Room;
which being too weak to bear his weight, being
a heavy corpulent Person, he came headlong to
the ground; by the greatness of which Fall, he
was crushed to pieces, and so, presently expired.
King *Henry* being informed of this unhappy
Accident, severely punished the Officers for their
inexcusable Carelessness; and ordered that his
Son, who was kept Prisoner with him in the
Tower, should be more narrowly observed."

The records referring to this unfortunate
Prince's imprisonment in the Tower do not
mention young Llewelyn, who in time became
the grandest hero Wales ever possessed. When
in 1234 Llewelyn the Great released his son
Gruffydd from prison, where he had been incar-
cerated for six years, he gave him a moiety of
Lleyn as patrimony. A small portion of that
beautiful part of Wales would be acceptable as
Paradise to one who had spent long years in
prison; for the wild promontory of Lleyn is
one of the finest and boldest in Wales. On it
are the lofty conical hills called Carn Boduon
and Carn Madryn; under the little town of
Nevin stretches the lovely bay of Porthdynllaen;
on the northern coast are the three towering

peaks known as The Rivals, called by some
"Yr Ufel" or "Beacon Fire," enclosing the
romantic and historic spot called Nant Gwr-
theyrn or Vortigern's Valley; while at the extreme end of the promontory is Aberdaron,
divided from the celebrated and mysterious Island
of Bardsey by a furious race of tide, across which
the Druids of old, and saints of the early Christian Church, fled for seclusion and sanctuary.

Among the grand mountains and lovely
valleys of Lleyn, Gruffydd, the son of Llewelyn
the Great, found a temporary home, and there,
probably about 1235, Llewelyn was born.
When in 1241 his parents were sent to the
Tower, he either, as a child of six, accompanied
them, or perhaps remained with other relatives
and friends in Wales.

During his uncle Davydd's reign, and after
his father's death, Llewelyn appears to have
lived in retirement at Maesmynan, one of the
possessions of Gruffydd. These included Dyfryn
Clwyd, Rhos, and Rhyvoniog, in the counties
of Flint and Denbighshire. English historians
state that Owain, who accompanied Gruffydd to
the Tower, stole away privately from "the
luxuries of Henry's court;" but it is more likely
he escaped from the Tower and afterwards
returned to Gwynedd.

The miserable and confused condition of Wales
at the death of Gruffydd passes description.

Henry the Third again attacked the Principality, and this time Davydd raised a rebellion against his uncle.

Wild warfare was carried on between the English and the Welsh, and when the latter suffered defeat, they fled to the mountains, wherefrom they showered darts and hurled huge rocks and boulders upon the enemy. In one of these terrible encounters Hubert Fitz-Matthew, though some Chroniclers say de Burgh, whom Henry had sent with three hundred horsemen, fell. The night before his death this Englishman had a dream, in which he imagined he was under a dreary mountain, wherefrom a huge rock was thrown, striking him off his horse, and afterwards he was robbed of all his armour and wearing apparel.

This premonitory dream came true the next day.

He was struck from his horse by a rock hurled from a mountain, and on the following day his soldiers found his mangled body reft of all his armour and garments.

Later on Davydd was driven back by his enemies into the fastnesses of Eryri, while the king of England and his forces assembled round Diganwy, called by the English Gannock Castle.

At this period the Welsh, bravely fighting for their country, feared neither cold, darkness, hunger, nor thirst in their indomitable defence against Henry. But the English suffered severely, as illustrated by Matthew Paris in his " History," wherein appears the following letter, written by an influential officer in the English army :—" The King with his Army is encamped at *Gannock*, and is busie in fortifying that place, sufficiently strong already, about which we lay in our Tents, in watching, fasting, praying, and freezing. We watch for fear of the *Welch*, who were used to come suddenly upon us in the night time : We fast for want of Provision, the Half-penny Loaf being now risen to Five Pence : We pray that we may speedily return safe and Scot-free home : And we freeze for want of Winter-garments, having but a thin Linnen Shirt to keep us from the Wind. There is a small Arm of the Sea under the Castle where we lye, which the Tide reached, by the Conveniency of which, many Ships bring us Provision and Victuals from *Ireland* and *Chester :* This Arm lies betwixt us and *Snowden*, where the *Welch* are encamped, and is in breadth, when the Tide is in, about a Bow-shot. Now it happened, that upon the *Monday* before *Michaelmas*-day, an *Irish* vessel came up to the Mouth of the Haven, with Provision to be sold to our Camp, which being negligently lookt to by the Mariners, was upon low ebb stranded on the other side of the Castle, near the *Welch*. The Enemy perceiving this, de-

scended from the Mountains, and laid siege to
the Ship, which was fast upon the dry Sands;
whereupon, we detached in Boats Three Hundred
Welch of the Borders of *Cheshire* and *Shropshire*, with some Archers and armed Men, to
rescue the Ship: But the *Welch*, upon the
approach of our Men, withdrew themselves to
their usual Retirements in the Rocks and
Woods, and were pursued for about two Miles
by our Men afoot, who slew a great number
of them. But in their return back, our
Soldiers being too covetous and greedy of
Plunder, among other sacrilegious and profane
Actions, spoiled the Abbey of *Aberconwey*,
and burnt all the Books and other choice
Utensils belonging to it. The *Welch* being
distracted at these irreligious Practices, got
together in great number, and in a desperate
manner setting upon the *English*, killing a
great number of them, and following the rest
to the Water-side, forced as many as could not
make their escape into the Boats, to commit
themselves to the mercy of the Waves. Those
they took Prisoners they thought to reserve
for exchange; but hearing how he put some
of their captive Nobility to death, they altered
their minds, and in a revengeful manner scat-
tered their dilacerated Carcasses along the surface of the Water. In this Conflict, we lost a
considerable number of our Men, and chiefly

those under the Command of *Richard* Earl of
Cornwal; as Sir *Alan Buscell*, Sir *Adam de
Maio*, Sir *Geoffry Estuemy*, and one *Raimond*
a *Gascoign*, with about a Hundred common
Soldiers. In the mean time Sir *Walter Bisset*
stoutly defended the Ship till Midnight, when
the Tide returned; whereupon the *Welch*, who
assailed us of all sides, were forced to withdraw, being much concerned that we had so
happily escaped their hands. The Cargo of
this Ship were Three Hundred Hogsheads of
Wine, with a plenty of other Provision for
the Army, which at that time it stood in very
great need of. But the next Morning, when
the Sea was returned, the *Welch* came merrily
down again to the Ship, thinking to surprise
our Men; but as Luck would have it, they
had at full Sea the Night before relinquished
the Ship, and returned safe to the Camp. The
Enemy missing of our Men set upon the Cargo
of the Ship, carryed away all the Wine and
other Provisions; and then when the Sea began
to flow, they put Fire to the Vessel, and returned to the rest of the Army. And thus
we lay incamped in great Misery and Distress
for want of Necessaries, exposed to great and
frequent Dangers, and in great fear of the
private Assaults and sudden Incursions of our
enemies. Oftentimes we set upon and assailed
the *Welch*, and in one Conflict we carried away

a Hundred Head of Cattel, which very triumphantly we conveyed to our Camp. For the
scarcity of Provision was then so great, that
there remained but one Hogshead of Wine in
the whole Army ; a Bushel of Corn being sold
for Twenty Shillings ; a fed Ox for Three or
Four Marks ; and a Hen for Eight Pence ; so
that there happened a very lamentable Mor-
tality both of Man and Horse, for want of
necessary Sustenance of Life."

In October 1245, the King gave the command
that his out-wearied forces were to return to
England, and according to the *Annales*, vast
numbers of unburied dead were left on
the sea shore and inland parts of Wales, "in
memory" of the "useless expedition."

When Henry the Third returned to London
he levied a war-tax of forty-shillings per shield,
which was long remembered as the "*Scutage*"
of Gannock.

In 1246, Davydd ap Llewelyn died at Aber,
under Penmaenmawr, and was buried at Aberconway.

With reference to this Prince's death the old
chronicles state :—" The only thing unpardonable in this Prince was his over Jealousie and
Severite against his brother *Gruffydh*, a Person
so well beloved by the *Welch*, that upon his
account their Affection was much cooled, and
in some entirely alienated from their Prince.

Indeed, thus much may be said for *David*, that *Gruffydh* was a valorous and aspiring Man, and if set at liberty, would bid fair to eject him out of his Principality."

At the death of Davydd, his sister Gwladys was direct heiress to the Crown of Gwynedd; but, having married Sir Ralph Mortimer, her husband claimed the succession in the right of his wife.

The Welsh were wholly opposed to Mortimer, and unanimously elected Llewelyn and Owain ap Gruffydd as successors to Davydd the son of Llewelyn ap Jorwerth.

It may here be mentioned that Gwladys "Ddu" was married twice, first in 1225 to Reginald de Breos, Lord of Brecknock and Abergavenny, and secondly in 1240 to Sir Ralph Mortimer, Lord of Melinydd.

Gwladys, Princess of Wales and Lady Mortimer, died at Windsor in 1251.

CHAPTER XXVI

"LLEWELYN OUR LAST HELM."

EARLY, if not affectionate, memories of a grandfather, whose great and lofty ideals were national independence, constitutional liberty, and freedom of conscience in happily United Wales, filled and fed the mind of young Llewelyn ap Gruffydd with the ardour of a heroism that remained unquenched from his accession to the day of his death.

Heart-rending knowledge of a heroic father's vicissitudes and dreary terms of imprisonment, followed by a fruitless attempt at escape, and a tragic death, embittered the young prince's thoughts, while the only gleams of sunshine in the dawn of a distinguished career were tender recollections of, and reverence for, a brave and good mother's wifely intercession, and noble devotion to her children, her home, and her country.

In the quiet seclusion of his little patrimony

near Caerwys, in Flintshire, Llewelyn must have watched the events of his uncle's reign with keen interest.

He saw before him a reigning and childless prince, who failed to rule his people—a wearied man sorely stricken in body and mind, and overwhelmed by miseries—a leader, who, in the lingering autumnal campaign of 1245, received little but reproaches and taunts from his followers—a servile but wavering vassal of the English king, and a jealous and relentless chieftain, to whom Matthew Paris has attached the severe appellation of " perjured fratricide."

He recognised in his aunt, the lawful heiress to the throne of Gwynedd, a lady who—according to Lewis Glyn Cothi, the celebrated bard— although married successively to two English noblemen, was thoroughly patriotic, a lover of Wales and the Welsh, an ardent patroness of the poets and harpists of the Principality, and what was more, a fluent speaker of the grand old vernacular. But her marriage to an English- man was an insuperable barrier to her claim to the crown of Gwynedd.

In the words of an old chronicler—

" The *Welch* Nobility, being assembled to- gether for the electing and nominating a *Suc- cessor*, thought it by no means advisable to admit a Stranger to the Crown though his Title was never so lawful ; and especially an

Englishman, by whose Obligations to the Crown of *England* they must of necessity expect to become Subjects, or rather Slaves to the *English* Government. Wherefore they unanimously agreed to set up Llewelyn and Owen Goch, the Sons of Gruffydd. . . . Brother to Prince David, who, being sent for, and appearing before the Assembly, all the Nobles and Barons then present, did them Homage, and received them for their Sovereigns."

The first year of Llewelyn's reign was in few ways encouraging.

Matthew Paris says—"Agriculture, trade, and pastoral occupation alike, having ceased, they were being consumed through want; and bowed down unwillingly beneath the behests of the English, their ancient proud nobility withered away, and the harps of their bards rang only with notes of woe."

Yet there was some reason for gratitude.

The body of the young prince's father, Gruffydd, was recovered from the King of England by the Abbots of Ystrad Flûr and Conway. In the latter place it received "a very pompous and honourable Enterment."

In a year or two after the accession of Llewelyn and Owain, Henry the Third renewed hostilities against the Welsh, and in person invaded North Wales with formidable forces. Thereupon strong pressure was brought to bear

against the two young princes, who were alarmed
or led into a treaty of peace with the English
king. It is probable that Owain persuaded
Llewelyn into temporary submission to Henry
the Third, who received their own homage and
the promised obedience of their respective
heirs.

Not content with this, the English monarch
wiled his victims into complete resignation "for
ever" of the four Cantrevs of Rhos, Rhyvoniog,
Dyffryn Clwyd, and Englefield, which were
bestowed on the king's son Edward, the right
to navigate the Conway, and the lordship of
Mold, and all belonging to it.

Henry then proceeded to make a grant of
Welsh possessions to the princes under the
following conditions :—"That Llewelyn should
serve Henry in Wales or the Marches, with one
thousand foot, and twenty-four horse, or with
five hundred foot only, elsewhere, and that he
should hold the Principality under the English
crown ; but he was, on the other hand, to receive
the homage of the Welsh nobles !"

Nine years of comparative peace succeeded
this unfair treaty.

During that time Llewelyn was not only able,
as some historians say, "to cultivate the arts of
peace," but to study the intricacies of state-craft,
while his brother Owain commenced his intrigues
and taught the same to David.

Meanwhile, Prince Edward in 1254 received from his father the lordships already mentioned, together with the earldom of Chester, the castles of Dyserth, Rhuddlan, and Diganwy ; the lordships of Montgomery, Caermyrddin, Cardigan and Builth, until, as Matthew Paris says, the young prince was a "most shorn king."

Edward promptly took possession of his Welsh castles, and garrisoned them with ruffians, whose cruelties were beyond description.   Matthew Paris declares that Prince Edward, in one of his progresses through North Wales, commanded his attendants to "cut off the ear, and pull out one eye of an inoffensive Welsh youth !"   The members of his various households in the castles of Wales were renowned for their atrocities, equalling, if not surpassing, those of cruel King John.

At the same time, the estates of the Welsh chieftains and nobility were seized without opportunity for appeal, while the owners were themselves mercilessly punished without cause.

These events, and renewed oppression of the Welsh by the English, roused the fiercest ire of the princes and people alike, and, unfortunately, to accentuate troubles, domestic dissension recommenced.   The national and besetting sin of the Welsh tempted Owain ap Gruffydd to rise up in arms against Llewelyn.   Owain easily persuaded his younger brother David to aid him in intrigues which brought about an open rupture in 1255.

Henceforth Llewelyn reigned alone and supreme over North Wales, and gradually won all the people to his side.

Wales was true as steel to its chosen leader, and bravely rallied around him, when he marched forth against his rebellious brothers.

Llewelyn's power over his people was more than a match against the wild and irregular insurgents, and the prince, in a sanguinary contest at Bryn Derwyn, was triumphant. In a single hour, Owain and David surrendered, after which they were imprisoned, their estates were confiscated, and the elder brother was sent to Dolbadarn Castle near the lake of Llanberis.

The solitary tower of that ancient castle and fortress, which once formed the portal of the grim Pass of Llanberis, still remains as a memorial of the daring turbulence of the oppressed Cymry, who restlessly fretted against terrible odds, where—

> " High in the air the rock its summit shrouds
> In brooding tempests, and in rolling clouds ;
> Loud storms around, and mists eternal rise,
> Beat its bleak brow and intercept the skies."

The deep clear waters of the lake bore the reflex of mountain shadows, dark as the clouds of anguish which, in the days of Llewelyn, hung over the sorrow-stricken Principality.

After the capture of Owain and David, the
English, according to the ancient chronicles,
"seeing the *Welch* at this rate oppress and
destroy one another, thought they had full
liberty to deal with them as they pleased;
and thereupon began to exercise all manner of
Wrong and Injustice against them; insomuch
that the next year, all the Lords of *Wales* came
in a body to Prince *Llewelyn,* and declared their
Grievances, how unmercifully Prince *Edward*
(whom his father had sent into *Wales*) and
others of the nobility of *England* dealt with
them, how without any colour of Justice they
seized upon their estates without any room for
Appeal; whereas if themselves offended in the
least, they were punished to the utmost extremity. In fine, they solemnly declared, that
they preferred to dye honourably in the Field
before to be so unmercifully enslaved to the
Will and Pleasure of Strangers. Prince *Llewelyn*
was not a Stranger to all this; and now having
happily discovered the Bent and Inclination of
his subjects, was resolved to prosecute, if possible, the Expulsion of the *English,* and to be
revenged upon them for their most cruel,
and almost inhuman Practices towards the
Welch."

Collecting his forces, he recovered " in the
space of one Week " all the inland parts of North
Wales, whence he marched and regained the

mountains of Merionydd and the lands of Cardigan.

In 1256 he entered into Powys against Gruffydd ap Gwenwynwyn, who was subject to England, and, having vanquished that prince, successfully opposed Rhys Vychan, the " apostate chief," who immediately appealed for aid to Henry III. The English army landed at Carmarthen in "Whitsun week," but were defied by the Welsh at Dinefwr, after which "the *English* decamped before the Castle, and put themselves in posture of Battel, which the *Welch* perceiving, they made all haste to answer and oppose them. Whereupon there ensued a very terrible Engagement, which lasted a very long while ; this being for number of Men the greatest Battel that had been fought between the *English* and the *Welch*. But the Victory favoured the *Welch*, the *English-mon* being at length forced to fly, having lost above Two Thousand Men, besides several Barons and Knights, who were taken Prisoners."

Llewelyn returning victoriously to North Wales, laid waste the domains of English settlers and Welsh rebels, and then pressed homeward to receive bitter complaints against the oppressive conduct of Geoffrey de Langley, Prince Edward's lieutenant, to whom Henry III. had ceded Llewelyn's paternal estates.

Later on Prince Edward made a "state pro-

gress " to Chester, whence he proceeded on a visit
to the estates and castles he had robbed from
the Welsh, and, wherever he went, his vassals
did homage.

This royal visit roused in the Welsh the burning sense of wrong and merciless tyranny, and
goaded Llewelyn and his adherents almost to
desperation.

For Wales and the Welsh the cup of bitterness
and gall was filled to overflowing.

The heroes of national independence now knew
that there was nothing left for them but voice-
less submission, or open and immediate revolt.

The ancient *Annales* referring to this period
state that the Welsh, "Insulted and spoiled
of their liberties and their honours as they
were, and inflamed with zeal for the right as
ardent as that of the Maccabees, they chose
rather to die honourably in doing battle for freedom, than thus to be trodden down by vile
aliens ; so they presented themselves before
Llewelyn ap Gruffydd, that noble youth, and
with tears, and groans, and great lamentation,
told him what bondage and tribulation they
endured."

Thus the Welsh of the anti-English party
appealed to Llewelyn, who determined at once
to avenge the wrongs of which they complained.

About the end of 1256 the Welsh, under
Llewelyn, who was now designated as "Prince

of Wales and Lord of Snowdon," openly revolted, and in less than a week overran the whole district of Perveddwlad.

In spite of the strength of the enemy, and the fierce minions of the English Prince, Llewelyn became master of the land, and bore down all opposition, even so far as the very gates of Chester.

Prince Edward, unprepared for this unexpected and vigorous attack, at once appealed to his uncle, the King of the Romans, for supplies of men and money ; but even these were helpless before Llewelyn's mighty forces, consisting, says Llwyd in his " Historie of Cambria," p. 321, of "ten thousand armed men, every one ready to die in the field in defence of his country."

Once more treason was at work against Llewelyn.

Gruffydd ap Madog, lord of Dinas Brân, who, according to the chroniclers, was a " Person of notorious Reputation for Injustice and Oppression," basely forsook the *Welch*, and leagued with England against Wales, whose prince had driven him from his possessions, after which, as a fugitive, he joined the English barons in Montgomery.

By this time all the chieftains in South Wales flocked around Llewelyn, in whom they recognised a faithful patriot and supporter of national independence.

Thus Llewelyn's attention was again directed to the south.

There, Nicholas, lord of Kemeys; Patrick, lord of Kidwelli and Carew; and Stephen de Bauzan— had made a raid upon the celebrated Abbey of Ty Gwyn, where they "did great despite to God and all the saints; for they beat the monks, and robbed the convents, and carried off all the horses, and the spoils of the abbey and the church, and in the cemetery they wickedly slew one of the servitors of the convent."

Llewelyn then led a large army against the offenders.

In May, 1257, De Bauzan and his adherents marched forth from Carmarthen to lay waste the land of Ystrad Tywi, and reached Llandeilo Vawr. There the Cardigan Welsh met and assailed them with showers of dart and arrows, accompanied by hoarse shouts and wild cries, which struck terror into the hearts of the English, many of whom with their "guide," the treacherous Rhys ap Rhys Mechyl, fled to the Castle of Dynevwr. The remainder of the English, stung to the quick by what they called unarmed "bush-fighters," endeavoured to press on to Cardigan.

But the brave and stalwart men of Ystrad Tywi showered their missiles from every available rock, and, as the baggage-encumbered English, sweltering under their armour, in which they trusted, says Matthew of Westminster, "more than in their God," wended their way through dank morasses, dense woods, and marshy lowlands, they saw nothing before them but hopelessness and disaster.

At last the arrow-hail of the men of Ystrad Tywi had effect, and, after a short conflict, three thousand of the English forces fell, De Bauzan being among the slain.

On his return home Llewelyn met Prince Edward, whom he compelled to make a swift retreat with great dishonour. Some of the historians are of opinion that this personal repulse of Prince Edward was the cause of the fierce animosity with which the Welsh were afterwards pursued, to the ultimate triumph of the English. Already Edward had imposed English jurisdiction on those lordships which were immediately under his control, and many severe measures roused the Welsh to extreme indignation against their oppressors.

Once more Llewelyn, with three thousand infantry and one thousand horse, invaded the English frontier near Chester, and so beset Edward that the latter obtained aid from Ireland. Llewelyn sent out only a few ships, but the little Welsh fleet was so successful that the Irish squadron was defeated.

The next event of importance was the proposed entry of Henry III. into the heart of North Wales.

Llewelyn, collecting the wives and children, the flocks and herds, and all the movable property and provisions of his adherents, retired to the strongholds of Snowdon. But before his departure he ordered all bridges and mills to be destroyed, all fords to be obstructed, and all the meadows to be ploughed up.

Henry, baffled by this policy, returned to Chester.

Subsequently Llewelyn made offers of peace to the English, but the very suggestion was rejected with bitter indignation.

From that time forth Llewelyn became the object of Prince Edward's deeply-rooted enmity, and hostilities between the English and the Welsh were carried on with fierce vigour.

In 1258 "all the Nobility of *Wales* convened together, and took their mutual Oaths to defend their Country to Death, against the oppressing Invasions of the *English*, and not to relinquish and forsake one another, upon pain of Perjury."

This was followed by fresh campaigns, in which the Welsh were generally successful.

Anxious for the preservation of peace, Llewelyn, about 1259, made new overtures to Henry III., but they were refused, and all the Welsh Prince could obtain was extension of truce to a third year.

Exasperated at the failure of his peaceful

desires and intentions, the Prince of Wales renewed hostilities. He ravaged the territory of his cousin, Sir Roger Mortimer, son to Gwladys Ddu. When Llewelyn besieged the castle of Maelienydd, in Radnorshire, during the absence of Sir Roger Mortimer, an interesting episode occurred. In the ancient Chronicles it is stated that, having taken the governor, with his wife and children, prisoners, "the Castle was demolished by the Prince's Order. *Sir Roger Mortimer* hearing of this, with a great Body of Lords and Knights came to *Melienyth*, where Prince *Llewelyn* met him; but *Sir Roger*, not daring to hazard a Battel, planted himself within the Ruins, and finding he could do no good, desired leave of the Prince to retire peaceably. The Prince, upon the account of Relation and near Consanguinity betwixt them, and withal because he would not be so mean-spirited as to fall upon an Enemy who had no power to resist him, let him safely depart with his Forces, and then passing on himself to *Brecknock* at the request of the People of that Country, who swore fidelity unto him; so passed on and returned to *North Wales*."

By this time Llewelyn's sovereignty of Wales was acknowledged throughout the Principality, with the exception of Dinevwr.

In 1261 Llewelyn entered into an alliance

with Simon de Montford, Earl of Leicester, whose rebellion in England led to three great results. First, after it there were no more inroads of foreign invaders; second, it marked the end of papal interference in England; and third, from this time forward a Parliament representing the whole nation, to which the king's ministers should be responsible, was the ideal at which Simon de Montford aimed.

De Montford had been sent with formidable forces to invade the Principality, instead of which he openly took the part of Llewelyn, whom he aided in every way. This indomitable Englishman led his army successfully against Sir Roger Mortimer and the Lords Marchers, and captured Prince Edward, who was then imprisoned for a time in Hereford Castle.

Llewelyn being then considered a confederate of Montford, induced the renewed resentment of Henry III., and the displeasure of the Church; but a brief interval of peace ensued, and the Prince of Wales and Lord of Snowdon enjoyed comparative repose.

Simon de Montford at this time was obliged to seek refuge with Llewelyn, who promised him protection on condition that the Earl of Leicester would acknowledge the independence of Wales, and surrender the castles of Hawarden, Mold, and Montgomery, with the lordships of Whittington and Ellesmere.

These concessions were granted, and, at the
same time, De Montford added the offer of his
daughter Eleanor's hand in marriage.

The betrothal of Eleanor to Llewelyn, Prince
of Wales, was followed by further hostilities,
and the defeat and death of Simon de Montford at Evesham in 1265.

About the same time, Llewelyn's brother
David was released from prison, and according
to the chroniclers, signalised his release by "un-
gratefully" forsaking his country "and with all
his might sided with his enemies the English."

In 1267 a treaty of peace terminated the prolonged and severe hostilities between Llewelyn
and Henry III., and for the succeeding five
years the heroic Welsh prince and patriot enjoyed a season of comparative serenity.

During the treacherous calm of the next few
years, Llewelyn had opportunity and time to
contemplate the future of his country.

In his castle at Aber, where the royal standard
of Wales fluttered in the breeze, and the fearless
eagles of Eryri swooped down from the sun-
kissed heights to the shadowy valleys under
Snowdon, Llewelyn's thoughts were filled with
noble aspirations and desires for the emancipa-
tion and welfare of his country.

He must have had many a grand and all-
absorbing, but illusive reverie, there among the
lonely mountains and romantic glens of his

native land, whither the last of the Britons had been driven by Saxons and Normans, only to be still further oppressed by the earlier Angevin kings, sometimes called the Plantagenets.

In those brief and brilliant day-dreams Llewelyn saw Wales under his command, boldly and bravely shaking off the English yoke, and, in the near future, gaining freedom from galling and merciless thraldom against which his people had fought without avail.

From the departure of the Romans to the final conquest of Wales by Edward the First—a period of more than eight hundred years—the Welsh, as the last of the primitive British races, had resolutely opposed the invaders of their native land.　But slowly, though surely, they lost their rightful territory.　While the centuries rolled away, it truly came to pass as Taliesin sang—

> " Their Lord they will praise,
> Their speech they will keep,
> Their land will they lose,
> Except wild Walia."

The latter they steadily defended until the superior power of England completely stifled the proud national spirit of the Welsh, who would die fighting for freedom rather than live to brook insolence, tyranny, and cruel bondage.

Under the iron heel of fierce oppression,

ancient British laws, customs, and observances were ruthlessly crushed into the dust.

Fair domains were wrested from their rightful owners, and given to strangers and aliens; goodly forests, and rich pastures were seized by the minions of the Plantagenets, who took possession of the stately castles and strongholds of Wales, and filled them with retainers by whom the Welsh language was regarded as a crack-jaw jargon, or uncouth medley of consonants.

Overwhelming power, and a cruelly cold determination, formed the basis of English rule and legal infliction in the Principality.

Song and tradition regulated the laws and customs of Wales, and Nature had endowed the people of western Britain with rare gifts of eloquence, and stately dignity of demeanour. It is greatly to their credit, that although the confusion of conflict almost ceaselessly filled the land, peaceable English and foreign travellers were not only allowed to pass unmolested through the mountainous districts, but were most hospitably entertained by all classes.

Yet, as Henry the Second found, the humble wearers of wolf or goat-skins, and the torque-wearing chieftains who shared the "rude splendours" of the Courts of Dyserth, Dwyganwy and Aber, could be as proud as himself, and meet politeness with courtesy, or sarcasm with scorn.

In spirit, the last of the Britons and original possessors of the soil, felt that the English should not aggressively enter and wholly absorb Wales, and, having been driven to the western verge of the island, they desired to be left unmolested and in peace. Failing that, when interfered with, they were prepared to defend every rood of their country, and each law of their land.

It was but natural that the flame of Welsh liberty, which during the reign of Davydd the son of Llewelyn the Great, had flickered down almost to a spark, revived again, and was fanned to a fierce flame when Llewelyn ap Gruffydd appeared as a hero ready to sustain the honour of his land.

In him the Welsh recognised a spirited prince and Pendragon, who was to set them free from galling bonds and merciless thralls of the enemy; to gain for them national independence, religious liberty—all the privileges of right and redress of wrong, under the unfurled and royal standard of United Wales.

During the truce between Henry the Third and the Welsh, Llewelyn might have secured the grand realisation of his noblest ideals. The whole Principality was almost completely under his control, and he had, at least, brief respite from the animosity of his foreign enemies. But when the restless tide of time approached, which, if " taken at the flood," would probably have led to future prosperity, the golden opportunity was lost, and henceforth Wales and the Welsh passed slowly into contact with the first shadow of the dire eclipse that wholly obliterated National Independence.

Blame for this neglect, must ever rest upon the age and its circumstances.

In vain Llewelyn endeavoured to quell the jealousies and conflicting interests of his subjects; vainly he tried to utilise the season of tranquillity by avoiding those perilous dissensions, some of which, however, hopelessly involved his name.

At this crisis, the patriot prince's humane and generous disposition and desire for peace, doubtless allured him to forget that strong forces were still secretly and actively at work in the temporary calm, resembling those halcyon days which invariably prelude storms.

In 1274, the brooding tempest burst, and with it came a renewal of the fierce rivalry that personally began between Edward and Llewelyn in Gwynedd, and ended in the final tragedy on the banks of the Irvon.

When, in November 1272, Henry the Third died, his son, Prince Edward, was in the Holy Land, and did not return to England until 1274, in the August of which year the new king's coronation took place.

To quote the words of the chronicler:—
" Prince *Llewelyn* was summoned to attend
at his Coronation, but he flatly refused to
appear, unless upon sure Terms of Safe Conduct, for having offended several of the *English*
Nobility, he could not in safety pass thro' their
country, without the danger of exposing his
Person to the inveterate Malice and acceptable
revenge of some of them. And therefore, without the King's Brother, the Earl of *Glocester*,
and *Robert Burnell*, Lord Chief Justice of *England*, were delivered up as Pledges of his safe
Conduct, he would not come up to do his Homage and Fealty at his Coronation according to
the Writ directed to him . . . . However,
Prince *Llewelyn*, to shew that it was not out
of any stubbornness or disrespect to the King
of England, that he refused to come, sent up
his Reasons by the Abbots of *Ystratflur* and
Conwey to *Robert Kilwarby*, Archbishop of
Canterbury, and the rest of the Bishops then
sitting in Convocation in the *New-Temple* at
London, which were to this effect :—

" 'To the most Reverend Fathers in God, *Robert*
Archbishop of *Canterbury*, and Metropolitan of
all *England*, the Archbishop of *York*, and the
rest of the Bishops in Convocation ; *Lhewelyn*
Prince of *Wales* and Lord of *Snowden* sendeth
Greeting.

" ' We would have your Lordships to under-

stand, that whereas formerly most terrible and
incessant Wars were continually managed betwixt *Henry* King of *England* and our self; the
same were at last composed, and all matters
of Differences were adjusted by the means of
his Excellency Cardinal *Ottobonus* the Pope's
Legate, who, having drawn the Articles and
Conditions of the Peace agreed upon, they were
signed and swore to, not only by the King,
but also the Prince his Son, now King of
England. Among these Articles were comprehended that we and our Successors should
hold of the King and his Successor the Principality of *Wales,* so that all the *Welch* Lords,
one Baron excepted, should hold their Baronies
and Estates in *Capite* of us, and should pay
their Homage and Fealty for the same to us;
we in like manner doing Homage to the King
of *England* and his Successors. And besides
that the King and his Successors should never
offer to receive and entertain any of our
Enemies, nor any such of our own Subjects as
were lawfully banished and excluded our Dominions of *Wales,* nor by any means defend
and uphold such against us. Contrary to which
Articles, King *Edward* has forcibly seized upon
the Estates of certain Barons of *Wales,* of which
they and their Ancestors have been immemor-
ably possessed of, and detains a Barony, which
by the form of Peace should have been delivered

to us; and moreover, has hitherto entertained *David ap Gruffydh* our Brother, and *Gruffydh ap Gwenwynwyn*, with several others of our Enemies who are Out-laws and Fugitives of our Country. And tho' we have often exhibited our Grievances and Complaints against them, for destroying and pillaging our Country, yet we could never obtain of the King any relief or redress for the several Wrongs and Injuries we received at their hands; but on the contrary, they still persist to commit wastes and other outrages in our Dominions. And for all this, he summons us to do him Homage at a place which is altogether dangerous to our Person, and where our inveterate Enemies, and which is worse, our own unnatural Subjects, bear the greatest sway and respect with the King. And tho' we have alleged several Reasons to the King and his Council, why the place by him assigned, is not safe and indifferent for us to come, and desire him to appoint another, whereto we might with more safety resort, or else that he would send Commissioners to receive our Oath and Homage, till he could more opportunely receive them in Person; yet he would not assent to our just and reasonable Request, nor be satisfied with the Reasons we exhibited for our non-appearance. Therefore we desire your Lordships earnestly to weigh the dismal effects that will happen to the

Subjects both of *England* and *Wales* upon
the breach of the Articles of Peace; and that
you would be pleased to inform the King of
the sad Consequence of another War, which can
no way be prevented, but by using us according
to the Conditions of the former Peace, which
for our part we will in no measure transgress.
But if the King will not hearken to your
Council, we hope that you will hold us ex-
cused, if the Nation be disquieted and troubled
thereupon, which as much as in us lieth we
endeavour to prevent.'"

The historian then continues—"King *Edward*
would admit of no excuse, nor hearken to any
manner of Reason in the case, but was unmercifully enraged, and conceived an unpardonable
displeasure against Prince *Llewelyn*, which yet
he thought convenient to conceal and dissemble
for a time. Indeed, he never could abide
Llewelyn, since the time that he was vanquished
and put to flight by him at the Marches, so
that the chief cause of King *Edward's* anger
originally proceeded from a point of *Honor*
which this refusal of Homage served sufficiently
to increase."

King Edward, who desired to carry out his
great design of uniting the whole kingdom under
one crown, immediately began with Wales.

His first and unchivalrous precaution was to
seize and hold as prisoner, Prince Llewelyn's

promised bride, who was considered the most beautiful lady in the land.

After the battle of Evesham, Eleanor de Mout-ford and her brother Amaury became refugees in the Court of France. While in France, the widowed Countess of Leicester placed her daughter in the convent of Montargis, and when, in the words of the Chronicler, application was made for Llewelyn's future wife, her mother "sent over for *Wales* her daughter the Lady *Eleanor* (whom Llewelyn extremely loved) with her brother *Aemerike*, to be married to the Prince, according to the Agreement made in her Father *Earl Montfort's* time."

Edward, aided by the treachery of a knight in Eleanor's train, intercepted the fleet of four French ships of state in which the bride set sail for Wales, and captured them off the Scilly Islands, early in 1276. The king, as Eleanor's feudal superior, promptly laid claim to her guardianship, and maliciously detained her in his custody for two years, during which time she was a lady-in-waiting to the queen. Her brother Amaury was imprisoned in the Castles of Corfe and Sherburn, and did not regain his liberty until the Pope resolutely interfered in 1282.

The captivity of Eleanor roused Llewelyn's fierce indignation. His first desire was to take up arms against the English king, but, for a time, affection conquered. At length he offered a large sum for the ransom of his bride, but Edward refused to accept the offer unless the Welsh prince complied with certain arbitrary demands which he firmly resisted.

Llewelyn's love for Eleanor was ardent and sincere, but even that would be sacrificed rather than the liberty of Wales should be jeopardised.

Once more there was no alternative but to take up arms, and Llewelyn again had to learn the bitter lesson of faithlessness and ingratitude.

Llewelyn's own people were against him.

David and Rhodri, who for treason with Owain against Llewelyn had lost their lands, were glad to seize an opportunity for revenge. They went immediately over to the enemy, and fought inveterately to procure the downfall of national liberties.

Rhys ap Meredith of South Wales threw in all his strength against Llewelyn, and with strong forces augmented King Edward's army. The English, accompanied by the disaffected Welsh, marched across the Dee into Flintshire, and by wary arts of warcraft, managed to get possession of Anglesea.

Llewelyn, whose supplies were thus cut off, retreated once more to Snowdon, and the complete prostration of the Welsh was accomplished without a blow being struck.

In the grand but lonely fastnesses of Snowdon Llewelyn, with his brave and resolute followers, waited for an auspicious opportunity to descend against the English.

Fierce and revengeful feelings, and the bitterness of national resentment, filled the hearts of the Welsh in those early summer days of 1277, when, from the ranges of Snowdon, they watched Edward's army opening a military road through the dense and spreading forests below them, and saw the enemy's hosts lurking like hungry panthers on the warpath.

It must have been a sad and depressing scene. The goodly plains of Aber and Penmaenmawr bore traces of the sword, where from the furrows of the ploughshare, the young green ears of corn should have been unfurling their banners.

In the meadow-lands of Lleyn the unmown pastures were rank with overgrowth, and to mock the lark's song of freedom the raven croaked ominously.

Among the pathless tracks of Eryri eagles congregated, prophesying carnage, while down through the dark ravines foxes heralded treachery.

Llewelyn glancing downward from Snowdon, yearned for power to vanquish his enemies, while Owain ap Gruffydd, peering skyward from his prison in Dolbadarn, by Llanberis, hoped he had fully expiated the crime of treason, and would soon gain freedom.

Soon for all the sons of ill-fated Gruffydd ap
Llewelyn freedom would come, but not borne
by Liberty in her car of Triumph.   No: for
them and Wales already the death-wail and
omens of dissolution were heard wandering
along the dreary marches of Rhuddlan, while
the English flag floated over the ancient stronghold; and Edward, the king, oppressor, and
conqueror, making merry with his hosts on the
Deeside, knighted Davydd ap Gruffydd as a
reward "for his probity and faithfulness!"
Besides which, the king gave to him in marriage
the widowed Countess of Derby, whose dowry
was the castle of Denbigh and a thousand
"Pounds in Lands."

Thus the long summer days passed away,
bringing little immediate advantage to Edward,
and less to Llewelyn.

But the wary English monarch knew that
though victory was certain, there would be
considerable risk attending a battle, so he resolved to starve Llewelyn and his forces rather
than fight with them.

Penned in among their mountains, the Welsh
held out while September changed the emerald
bravery of the woodlands to brilliant tints of
golden, scarlet, and burnished copper; but when
chill October, clad in russet, wandered down
through the desolate valleys of Gwynedd, and
silver mists hung heavily around the crags of

cloud-encircled Snowdon, the brave hearts of
the Welsh began to quail.

Cold and unfriendly was the rain that swept
the mountain-sides, and sent the last of the
Britons shivering into caves and hollows of
shelter; colder still were the gnawing pangs
of hunger that the warmth of log-fires failed
to assuage, and the bracing winds only intensi-
fied; more piercing than all were the bitter
thoughts filling the souls of Llewelyn's men
with an agony of quenched heroism.

Edward the king, holding court at Rhuddlan,
calmly waited the result of his scheme, which
truly worked as he desired.

Impelled partly by the famishing and suffer-
ing condition of his army, and finding himself
without hope or chance of relief—at the same
time being eager to obtain his bride—Llewelyn
capitulated, and the Welsh prince unwillingly
submitted to the English king's arbitrary and
humiliating terms of peace.

On the Eve of St. Martin, Edward, who was
then at Rhuddlan, and Llewelyn, who had
descended to Aberconway, ratified the treaty
as agreed upon by William of Southampton,
Robert Tibetot, and Anthony Bek on the
English side, and by Tewdwr ap Ednyved and
Gronw ap Heylyn on behalf of the Welsh.

To quote the words of the old historian:—
" Prince *Llewelyn* . . . finding his own Sub-

jects to forsake him, but more especially being desirous to recover his espouse the Lady *Eleanor*, thought it likewise advisable to submit, and therefore sued to King *Edward* for a Peace, who granted it, but upon very severe Conditions upon *Llewelyn's* side."

This agreement, consisting of ten articles, ran as follows :—" 1. That the Prince should set at liberty all manner of prisoners, that upon the King's Account were detained in Custody. 2. That for the King's favour and good will, he should pay 50,000 Marks, to be received at the King's pleasure. 3. That these four Cantreds or Hundreds, viz., *Cantref Ros*, where the King's Castle of *Teganwy* stands ; *Ryfonioc*, where *Denbigh ; Tegengl*, where *Ruthlan ; Dyffryn Clwyd*, where *Rhutbyn* stands, should remain in the King's hands. 4. That the Lords Marchers should quietly enjoy all the Lands they had conquered within *Wales*, excepting the Isle of *Anglesey*, which was wholly granted to the Prince. 5. That in consideration of this Island, the Prince should pay 5000 Marks in hand, with the reserve of a 1000 Marks yearly to begin at *Michaelmas ;* and in case the Prince died without Issue, the whole Island should return to the King. 6. That the Prince should come every year to *England* to pay his Homage to the King for all his Lands. 7. That all the Barons of *Wales*, excepting five in *Snowden*, should hold their Lands and Estates of the King, and no other. 8. That the Title of Prince should remain only for his Life, and not descend to his Successors, and after his Death, the five Lords of *Snowden* should hold their Lands only from the King. 9. That for the performance of these Articles, the Prince should deliver up for Hostages ten Persons of the best Quality in the Country, without imprisoning, disinheriting, and any time of redemption determined. And farther, that the King should chuse Twenty persons within *North Wales*, who, besides the Prince, should take their Oaths for the due performance of these Articles, and in case the Prince should swerve and recede from them, and upon admonition thereof not repent, they should forsake him, and become his Enemies. 10. The Prince was obliged to suffer his Brethren quietly to enjoy their Lands in *Wales*, whereof *David* (as already seen) for his Service was dubbed Knight by the King, and had the Earl of *Derby's* Widow given him in Matrimony, and with her as a Portion, the Castle of *Denbigh*, in *North Wales*, besides 1000 Pounds in Lands. His other Brother *Roderic* was lately escaped out of Prison into *England*, and the younger called *Owen*, was upon his Composition delivered out of Prison."

The same authority quaintly continues :—" It seems very probable that Prince *Llewelyn* submitted to these intolerable Conditions, more upon

the account of his Amours, and to regain the
Lady *Eleanora* out of the King of *England's*
hand, than that he was apprehensive of any
considerable Danger he might receive by the
English Troops. For it is hardly conceivable
that a Prince of such notorious conduct and
Valour, would so easily accept of such hard
Terms, and, in a measure deliver up his Principality, when there was no necessity so to do,
without resisting an Enemy whom he had frequently overcome, and forced to retire back with
greater inequality than the *English* had at present
over him. But the force of love worked Wonders,
and, in this case, proved irresistible, which to
obtain, *Llewelyn* did not think hard to forfeit
his proper right to his inveterate Enemies, and
for ever to exclude his Posterity from succceding
in their lawful inheritance."

In accordance with the terms of this treaty,
Llewelyn went to London to do homage to the
King. On this occasion he was attended by a
retinue of distinguished princes, chieftains, and
patriots, whose language and manners provoked
the mirth and derision of the English. Part of
Llewelyn's *suite* lodged at Islington, where a
sufficient supply of milk could not be obtained
for them, and they were sneered at because the
wine, beer, and bread of that neighbourhood did
not, as the English historians say, " suit their
constitutions." In the Mostyn MS. it is recorded

that, owing to the offensive behaviour of the
people who congregated around them, they made
a resolution "never to visit Islington again,
except as conquerors," for which they were
dubbed as "irascible, dyspeptic barbarians."

After this, Llewelyn returned to his home
among the mountains, wherefrom he was hastily
summoned by Edward to Worcester, where his
bride was promised to him on certain conditions.
One of these was "that the said prince should
never at all keep in his land any man contrary
to the King's will, nor show favour to any;
whence it might happen that the prince would
find himself deprived of all his faithful servants."
Llewelyn agreed to this demand "through such
fear as might happen to a steadfast man."

This promise was extorted "before mass" on
the eve of Llewelyn's marriage, which was
solemnised in the presence of King Edward
and Queen Eleanor at Worcester, on October
the 13th, 1278, "all the Nobility and Persons
of Quality in *England* honouring the Wedding
with their presence." Immediately after the
ceremony, and "not without great exultation of
heart," Llewelyn took his wife, the beautiful
Eleanor, in great haste to his court and home
at Aber, near Conway, where he generally
resided in the autumn.

The next two peaceful and happy years of
Llewelyn's life appear like a day of glorious

sunshine after a season of gloom and storm. The joy of having won Eleanor caused the Welsh prince to forget for the time the high affairs of State, the unruly passions of the nobles, and the overbearing ambition of the king.

In their home at Aber, and other royal residences, Llewelyn and Eleanor passed the hours in social pleasures, which must have been a welcome relief after long years of waiting on the one hand, and captivity called "easy," but yet unwelcome.

There, surrounded by loyal bards and faithful friends, the prince and his bride listened while national songs were heard in the hall, and olden stories were told in the "ladye's bower." During this period Eleanor's influence over her husband was very potent, and would probably have so continued had Simon de Montford's daughter lived a few years longer.

Eleanor endeavoured to maintain peace between Llewelyn and Edward, with whom she kept up correspondence. According to the records of this period, the fair writer is described as "Eleanor, Princess of Wales and Lady of Snowdon." In one of the letters to the King of England, which is dated "October 10th, 1279 A.D.," the princess asks her royal kinsman to allow the things bequeathed to her by her mother to be placed in the king's exchequer.

At the same time, since Edward would not permit one Nicholas de Whatham to "prosecute" the Countess of Leicester's will, Eleanor hoped the king would be good enough to inform her when and where she was to receive the share left to her. Thus the Countess of Leicester's last requests should be observed.

In a letter dated "July 8th, 1280 A.D.," the princess desires to hear good news of the king, and expresses her intention of doing anything in furtherance of his wishes. She also begs him not to believe any reports of disaffection on her part or Llewelyn's, after which she reminds her kinsman of the honours received "at Worcester." On October 18th of the same year, Eleanor made a very earnest appeal on behalf of her brother, who still was kept in prison. Having heard that at the next Parliament Amaury's case was to be "inquired into," the Princess of Wales begged the king to treat his kinsman with the clemency extended to aliens. The sisterly pleading was of no avail then, and Amaury de Montford was not released until 1281.

Llewelyn's domestic happiness was short-lived, for, in the summer of 1280—some records place the date as 1281—the beautiful Princess of Wales and Lady of Snowdon died in giving birth to a daughter, who for many years survived her father. For a time the heroic prince could not be consoled, but, when at last his grief had somewhat subsided, old animosities revived, and the Welsh again took up arms against the English. The immediate cause of the renewal of hostilities is thus described :— "This specious Amity, and the Peace lately concluded between them, did not last long, the *English* Governors in the Marches and in-land Counties of *Wales*, presuming upon the Prince's submission to the King, grievously oppressed the Inhabitants of the Country with new and unheard - of exactions, and, with intolerable partiality, openly encouraged the *English* to defraud and oppress the *Welch*. These insupportable practices moved the *Welch* to go in a Body to *David*, Lord of *Denbigh*, to endeavour a reconciliation between him and his Brother the Prince, that they both being at Unity might easily deliver themselves and their Country from the unmerciful Tyranny of the *English*. *David* was not ignorant of the miseries of his Country-men, and therefore gladly submitted to be reconciled to his Brother, with promise never to side again with the King of *England*, but to become his utter Enemy."

Once more the national spirit of the Welsh was roused to action.

David's reconciliation with his brother had a powerful effect upon his countrymen, some of whom had called him a traitor, who, for English honours and money, told the secrets of Wales to-the king. Others charged him with duplicity, and having merely played the spy in the English court, while his heart remained true to his brother. A few believed that the revival of Davydd's patriotism was the result of wounded pride at finding himself, a sovereign prince, treated as a common liegeman of the English king; in addition to which, the prospect of succeeding as heir to Llewelyn—who only had a daughter—tempted the Welsh prince to return to his own again.

History is silent as to the real cause of the reconciliation between the brothers; but, judged by the variations of human nature, Davydd's motives are easily understood.

As of old in the world, popularity and power evoked rivalry, jealousy, and bitter animosity, and when, by the voice of the nation, Llewelyn became the leader of the people, Owain chafed against circumstances that thrust him from the throne.

Hoping by force to be reinstated as ruling prince, he induced his younger and inexperienced brother to aid him in revolting against Llewelyn. Hereditary tendencies to fierce rivalry and jealousy, added to domestic dissensions, which for ages had been the besetting sin of Welsh Nationalism, were briskly at work, and the result was high treason against the elected and reigning prince, succeeded by the usual penalty.

Fine and imprisonment taught both Owain and Davydd a dearly-purchased experience. When too late, the brothers felt that perhaps their want of unity with Llewelyn in the bygone years had resulted in dire calamity and impending doom, and, at almost the ninth hour, natural affection, combined with a last glimmer of patriotism, returned.

. In the case of Davydd, fierce passion prompted him to fight against his native land and liberties, and to oppose Llewelyn in his struggle for Welsh independence. But when his beloved country was in direst need, Davydd, evidently urged by remorse, wholly forgot the past in the injuries of the present, and, the old heroism reviving, urged him onward, through severe hardships and fearful perils, to a terribly tragic death.

Many fierce and furious battles followed the reconciliation and reunion of the brothers, who now knew that the last hope of Wales was perfect unity.

Late at night on Palm Sunday, March 22nd, 1282, Davydd, with a band of trusty followers, suddenly attacked Hawarden Castle, put the garrison, among whom was Fulk Trigald, to the sword, and surprised the Governor and Justiciary, Roger Clifford, who was at the time in bed. Clifford endeavoured to defend himself, but in the attempt he was wounded and taken prisoner. Davydd's success in this attack was so marked that hundreds of Welshmen took up arms and flocked to his standard, and from that time the Principality put forth its whole and united strength to the utmost, for the hour of direst need was approaching.

Llewelyn and Davydd took the strongholds of Flint and Rhuddlan, and obtained some slight advantages over the English in the Marches.

But even when Wales moved, England stealthily advanced, and, as usual, the greater power was wary. Yet immediate measures were taken for the complete subjection of Wales.

Taxes were levied in England and Ireland, and large forces were led by Edward into North Wales, where at first the English suffered partial defeat, but afterwards triumphed.

Edward regained Rhuddlan, and by-and-by John Peckham, Archbishop of Canterbury, endeavoured to mediate between the English and the Welsh. This learned prelate's overtures included careful exhortations and covert threats, together with gentle admonitions and ominous menaces.

In the ancient records it is stated :—"To these partly Admonitions and partly threatenings of the Archbishop, Prince *Llewelyn* returned an Answer : That he humbly thanked his Grace for the Pains and Trouble he undertook in his and his Subjects' behalf ; and more particularly, because he would venture to come to *Wales,*

contrary to the pleasure and good liking of the
King. And as for concluding a Peace with him,
he would not have his Grace be ignorant, that
with all readiness he was willing to submit to
it, upon condition that the King would duly and
sincerely observe the same. And though he
would be glad of his longer continuance in
Wales, yet he hoped that no Obstructions would
happen of his side, why a Peace (which of all
things he most desired) might not be forthwith
concluded, and rather by his Grace's procuring
than any other's; so that there would be no
farther need of acquainting the Pope with his
Obstinacy, nor moving the King of *England* to
use any force against him. And though the
Kingdom of *England* be under the immediate
Protection of the See of *Rome*, yet, when his
Holiness comes to understand of the great and
unsufferable Wrongs done to him by the *English;*
how the Articles of Peace were broken, Churches
and all other religious Houses in *Wales* were
burned down and destroyed, and religious Persons unchristianly murthered, he hoped he would
rather pity and lament his Condition, than with
addition of Punishment increase and augment
his Sorrow. Neither shall the Kingdom of *England* be any wise disquieted and molested by his
means, in case the Peace be religiously observed
towards him and his Subjects. But who they
are, that delight themselves with War and Blood-

shed, manifestly appears by their Actions and
Behaviour; the *Welch* being glad to live quietly
upon their own, if they might be permitted by
the *English*, who coming to the Country, utterly
destroy whatever comes in their way, without
regard either to Sex, Age, or religious places.
But he was extreme sorry that any one should
be slain, having paid his Ransom; the Author of
which unworthy Action he did not pretend to
maintain; but would inflict upon him his con-
dign Punishment, in case he could be got out of
the Woods and Deserts, where as an Outlaw, he
lives undiscovered. But as to commencing a
War in a Season inconvenient, he protested he
knew nothing of that till now; yet those that
did so, do solemnly attest that to be the only
measure they had to save themselves, and that
they had no other security for their Lives and
Fortunes than to keep themselves in Arms.
Concerning his Sins and Trespasses against
God, with the assistance of his grace, he would
endeavour to repent of; neither should the
War be willingly continued by him, in case
he might save himself harmless; but before he
would be unjustly dispossessed of his legal Pro-
priety, he thought it but reasonable, by all possible measures to defend himself. And he was
very willing, upon due Examination of the Trespasses committed, to make Satisfaction and
Retribution of all Wrongs committed by him

and his Subjects ; so that the *English* would observe the same of their side ; and likewise was ready to conclude a Peace, which he thought was impossible to be established, as long as the *English* had no regard to Articles, and still oppress his People with new and unwarrantable Exactions. Therefore seeing his Subjects were unchristianly abused by the King's Officers, and all his Country most tyrannically harassed, he saw no reason why the *English*, upon any fault of his side, should threaten to bring a formidable Army to his Country, nor the Church pretend to censure him ; seeing also, he was very willing upon the aforesaid Conditions, to submit to a Peace. And lastly, he desired his Grace, that he would not give the more credit to his Enemies, because they were near his Person, and could deliver their Complaints frequently, and by word of mouth ; for they who made no conscience of oppressing, would not in all probability, stick to defame, and make false Accusations ; and therefore his Grace would make a better estimation of the whole matter, by examining their Actions rather than believing their Words."

When Edward received these propositions from Llewelyn, he refused to treat with the Welsh prince on equal terms.

The Archbishop again intervening made four new propositions, three of a public and one of a private nature. The private proposal was that

Llewelyn should surrender Snowdon for an English county and a thousand a year, while Davydd was to make the Holy Land his home "during His Majesty's pleasure!" Moreover, Llewelyn's daughter should be provided for "according to her birth and quality," and, if the prince ever married again, the county and annuity should "remain to his posterity" in the male line "for ever."

The bearer of these terms of complete exile was John Wallensis, otherwise known as John of Wales and Bishop of St. David's.

The public articles sent by the English to the Welsh were brief, and to the point, and ran thus—

"I. The King will have no Treaty of the four Cantreds, and other Lands which he has bestowed upon his Nobles; nor of the Isle of Anglesey.

"II. In case the Tenants of the four Cantreds submit themselves, the King purposeth to deal kindly and honourably with them; which we are sufficiently satisfied of, and will, what in us lies, endeavour to further.

"III. We will do the like touching Prince Llewelyn, concerning whom we can return no other Answer, than that he must barely submit himself to the King, without hopes of any other Conditions."

Llewelyn promptly forwarded to the king the National reply of the Welsh, expressed in the following words :—

"1. Though the King would not consent to treat of the four Cantreds, nor of the Isle of *Anglesey;* yet unless these be comprehended in the Treaty, the Prince's Council will not conclude a Peace; by reason that these Cantreds have, ever since the time of *Camber*, the Son of *Brutus*, properly and legally belonged to the Princes of *Wales;* besides the Confirmation, which the present Prince obtained by the Consent of the King and his Father, at the Treaty before Cardinal *Ottobonus*, the Pope's Legate, whose Letters Patents do still appear. And more, the Justice of the thing itself is plainly evident, that it is more reasonable for our Heirs to hold the said Cantreds for Money and other Services due to the King, than that Strangers enjoy the same, who will forcibly abuse and oppress the People.

"2. All the Tenants of the Cantreds of *Wales* do unanimously declare, that they dare not submit themselves to the King's Pleasure; by reason that he never from the beginning took care to observe either Covenant, Oath, or any other Grant to the Prince and his People; and because his Subjects have no regard to Religion, but most cruelly and unchristianly tyrannise over Churches and religious Persons; and then, for that we do not understand ourselves any way obliged thereunto, seeing we be the Prince's Tenants, who is willing to pay the King all usual and accustomed Services.

z

" 3. As to what is required, that the Prince simply commit himself to the King's Will, should we all declare, that for the aforesaid Reasons, none of us dare come, neither will we permit our Prince to come to him upon those Conditions.

" 4. That some of the *English* Nobility will endeavour to procure a provision of a Thousand Pounds a Year in *England*; we would let them know, that we can accept of no such Pension; because it is procured for no other end, than that the Prince being disinherited, themselves may obtain his Lands in *Wales*.

" 5. The Prince cannot in honesty resign his paternal Inheritance, which has for many Ages been enjoyed by his Predecessours, and accept of other Lands among the *English*, of whose Customs and Language he is ignorant; and upon that score, may at length be fraudulently deprived of all, by his malicious and inveterate Enemies.

" 6. Seeing the King intends to deprive him of his antient Inheritance in *Wales*, where the Land is more barren and untilled; it is not very probable that he will bestow upon him a more fruitful and arable Estate in *England*.

" 7. As to the Clause, that the Prince should give the King a perpetual Possession of *Snowden;* we only affirm, that seeing *Snowden* essentially belongs to the Principality of *Wales*, which the Prince and his Predecessours have enjoyed since *Brute*, the Prince's Council will not permit him to renounce it, and accept another Estate in *England*, to which he has not equal Right.

"8. The People of *Snowden* declare, That though the Prince should give the King possession of it, they would never own and pay Submission to Strangers; for in so doing, they would bring upon themselves the same Misery that the People of the Four Cantreds have for a long time groaned under; being most rudely handled and unjustly oppressed by the King's Officers; as wofully appears by their several Grievances.

"9. As for *David*, the Prince's Brother, we see no reason, why against his Will he should be compell'd to take a Journey to the *Holy-Land;* which if he happens to undertake hereafter upon the account of Religion, it is no cause that his Issue should be disinherited, but rather encouraged."

Edward was at Rhuddlan when the Welsh rejected his proposals, and his first act was to send part of his army by sea to Anglesea, where the English had little opposition, and gave less mercy to the surprised and almost helpless natives. The king's troops then crossed the Menai Straits by means of a bridge of boats, and landed at Moel-y-Don, near Bangor.

The ancient chronicles contain the following quaint description of this encounter. "The Bridg being finished, which was so broad as that Three Score Men might pass abreast, *William Latimer*, with a Strong Party of the best experienced Soldiers, and *Sir Lucas Thany*, Commander of the *Gascoigns* and *Spaniards*, whereof a great number served the King, passed over, but could discover no sign, or any the least intimation of an Enemy. But as soon as the Tide began to appear, and the Sea had overflown beside the Bridg, down come the *Welch* fiercely out of the Mountains, and setting upon the disheartened *English* killed or drowned their whole number, excepting *Latimer*, who, by the swimming of his Horse, got safe to the Bridg. In this Action, several worthy Soldiers of the *English* side were lost; among whom were *Sir Lucas Thany*, *Robert Clifford*, *Sir Walter Lyndsey*, two Brothers of *Robert Burnet*, Bishop of *Bath*, with many others; in all to the number of Thirteen Knights, Seventeen young Gentlemen, and Two Hundred common Soldiers. A little after, or as some say, afore, another Engagement passed between the *English* and the *Welch*, wherein the former lost Fourteen Colours, the Lords Audley and Clifford being slain, and the King himself forced to retreat for safety to the Castle of *Hope*."

In this celebrated battle of the bridge, the English lost fifteen knights, thirty-two Esquires, and about a thousand private soldiers, who, in the early and dreary days of November, perished in the seething and fog-enveloped waves of Menai.

Encouraged by this victory, and relying upon the retreat of the English as winter approached, Llewelyn felt that the hour of triumph was at hand.

Once more the bards, sanguine and expectant of success, tuned their harps and sang inspiring songs, and commemorated the defeat of the English at Moel-y-Don as the eve of that important period when, according to Welsh prophecies, "The Prince of Wales in London should be crowned."

National enthusiasm and native superstition, aided by the grand pæans of the bards, renewed the strength, and revived the flagging energies of the Welsh in their last struggle for independence.

But the "fatal die" was cast.

While the English king raised fresh levies for the purpose of renewing his attacks upon the Principality, the Earl of Gloucester endeavoured to reduce South Wales.

In a fierce encounter near Llandeilo, Vawr Dinevwr was defeated, and the people of the South fought their last battle for freedom.

Leaving Davydd to defend the passes of Snowdon, Llewelyn with a small army marched to Aberystwyth and Cardigan, where he gained some slight advantage over Rhys ap Meredydd the renegade, after which he passed into Radnorshire to defend the Wye with the forces of South Wales.

Having posted a small band of men at Pont Orewyn, on the south side of the Wye, near Mochryd, about three miles from Builth, Llewelyn waited in the neighbouring woods for the arrival of some of the chieftains who had promised to meet him there.

Some authorities state that Llewelyn waited in his hunting-lodge, or small fortalice, overhanging the Wye, in the woods near the Rocks of Aberedw, below Builth.

While there, Llewelyn observed the English unexpectedly approaching, and in order to rejoin his forces without detection as to the route, tradition states that the prince sent for Madog Goch Min Mawr, the red-haired blacksmith, and commanded him to reverse the shoes of his own horse and those of his companions. Snow had fallen, and the marks of the horses' hoofs would easily baffle the enemy.

Meanwhile the English army crossed the Wye at Cafan Twm Bach, and intercepted the route between Llewelyn and his forces.

The Welsh prince and his few sturdy and

faithful followers galloped to Builth Castle. There they hoped to remain in secure concealment for the time; but were sternly refused admission by the Lords of Builth, who dreaded the enemy, and thereby obtained the sobriquet of *Bradwyr Bualt*, or the Traitors of Builth. Llewelyn soon afterwards discovered that Madog Goch Min Mawr, the treacherous blacksmith, had given information with reference to the prince's *ruse*, and the English started in full pursuit.

Hoping yet to rejoin his forces, Llewelyn rode swiftly northward along the banks of the Irvon and crossed the river at Pontycoed, near Llanynus Church, where he left his small party of followers. Then, unarmed and accompanied only by a single esquire, Llewelyn entered a deep and secluded dingle beside the river. While there he heard the men left by him at Pontycoed shouting, and when told by his esquire that they were guarding the bridge, Llewelyn, who implicitly trusted in the faithfulness and bravery of his escort, said he " would not stir from thence though the whole power of England was on the other side of the river."

Presently the English attacked the intrepid defenders of the bridge, overpowered them, and rapidly surrounded the dingle in which Llewelyn had taken refuge.

Foiled in his purpose, Llewelyn saw there was no chance left to him but to take flight.

Unarmed and unattended, the last prince of
the ancient British race, inspired by the spirit
of his forefathers, made a daring venture to
escape and rejoin his troops. Boldly emerging
from the dingle, Llewelyn paused but a moment
to glance around, when a single and unexpected
adversary assailed him, and instantly plunged
his spear into the body of the defenceless prince.

The adversary was Adam de Francton, an
English soldier, who, it is stated, did not know
the rank of his victim. But if the story of the
red-haired blacksmith and the Lords of Builth
be true, Francton evidently knew that only
the prince and one faithful attendant occupied
the dingle, and if not quite sure of his man, he
would not allow him to escape.

Immediately afterwards the two armies met,
and fought desperately, the brave-hearted Welsh
all the time eagerly expecting their beloved
prince, who came not. The conflict was short,
but fierce and terrible, resulting in heavy losses
on both sides.

The English momentary loss was gain, and
the triumph of the oppressor over the sons of
freedom.

But out there, in the frosts of winter, and the
snow, two thousand heroes fell in the last great
struggle for Welsh independence.

Meanwhile, at the top of the dingle, while the
wind sighed drearily through the snow encum-

bered branches of the hoary trees, Llewelyn suffered the throes of mortal agony.

It was a sadly impressive scene.

Slowly, as the precious life ebbed away, the religious fervency of the prince prompted him to desire spiritual consolation.

In the dim twilight of death he beheld a white friar hastening along the highway, and faintly expressed the wish to be shriven.

It is probable that the devout man was either coming from, or returning to, the Cistercian Abbey of Cwm-Hir, in the Clwyedog Valley, wherefrom many a holy friar had gone forth to succour the sick and wounded after the recent battle.

Having given the prince a cooling draught of water from the well close by, the friar was about to perform the last sacred duties of religion, when Adam de Francton returned to the dingle.

Looking closely at the dying man, de Francton recognised the prince, and, heedless of the friar's holy admonitions, or the mortal agony of his victim, the ruthless English soldier immediately cut off Llewelyn's head, before death had brought unconsciousness.

In the unpolished words of the ancient Chronicler, "The Battle being over, *Francton* returned to plunder his dead; but perceiving him to be the Prince of *Wales*, he thought himself to have obtained a sufficient Prize, and thereupon presently chopt off his Head, and sent it to King *Edward*, at *Conwey*, who very joyfully caused it to be placed upon the highest Pinacle of the Tower of *London*. And thus fell this worthy Prince, the greatest, though the last of the *British* Blood, betrayed most basely by the Lords of *Buelht*, and being dead, most unworthily dealt with by the King of *England*; who, contrary to all Precedents, treated a lawful Prince like a Traytor, and exposed his crowned Head to the derision of the multitude." In a letter from Roger Lestrange to King Edward I., his death took place on the 11th of December, 1282.

Edmund Mortimer, as leader of the English, received the contents of Prince Llewelyn's pocket, which included some State documents and a private seal; but the gory head was taken to King Edward I., who, in savage glee, sent it to London.

There the brave and patriotic prince's head was received with barbarous shouting and loud clamour of the populace, and discordant noises of various instruments, after which, says Matthew of Westminster, it was crowned with ivy, and placed in the city pillory, where it remained for a day, to be scoffed and mocked at by coarse jesters and their ribald companions. Next morning it was borne on the point of a lance through Cheapside, and, in the evening, it was set up over the gateway of the Tower of London. And of this, Knyghton says:—" The prophecy which foretold he should ride crowned through Cheap, which made him think that he should be King of England, was fulfilled."

Thus perished Llewelyn ap Gruffydd, the last native Prince of Wales, on the 11th of December, 1282, after a reign of twenty-eight years, and with him vanished the already waning shadow of the ancient British Empire and its independence.

In the words of Warrington, the English historian, it was, "An empire which, through various changes of fortune, had opposed the arms of imperial Rome, and for more than eight hundred years had resisted the utmost efforts of the Saxon and Norman princes. The fall of nations, distinguished only by misfortunes, or only illustrious for conquests, may raise for a moment a sigh of pity, or the transient effusion of applause. But a people like the Welsh, satisfied with their mountains, who had been forced into a long and unequal contest in defence of their native rights, with few other resources than their valour, and a fond attachment to their liberties, though falling in the ruins of their country, will have a claim on the esteem, and excite the admiration of the world, so long as manly sentiment and freedom shall remain."

Whatever benefits may have resulted since the Principality ceased to be recognised as an independent power, the patriotic hearts of the Welsh

people must always experience pangs of pain,
and the profound grief of deep regret that are
inseparable from any sympathetic thought and
careful reflection upon the life and death of
Prince Llewelyn.

His few faults and occasional waverings sink
into complete insignificance under the grand
heroism, the resolute and undaunted courage,
and the indomitable perseverance with which he
defended national honour, privilege, and liberty,
afterwards facing a cruel doom and tragic death
rather than desert his country's cause.

Inspired by the noble and grand example of
the greatest hero Wales ever produced, may the
Welsh of to-day and succeeding generations
wholly forget all political, religious, and social
differences in paying their highest tributes to the
sublime and immortal memory of Llewelyn Ein
Llyw Olaf!—"Llewelyn, our last helm!"

According to Rymer, Llewelyn's body was for
some time denied Christian burial, "because that
he had been excommunicated by the Church."
Tradition only points out Cefn-y-Bedd, the
"Ridge of the Grave," near Builth, in the heart
of Mid Wales, where the Prince was slain, as his
resting place.

Subsequently Maude de Longspée, the wife
of John Gifford of Bromfield, "who was licenced
to hunt wolves in Hertfordshire," a distant
relative of Llewelyn, interceded, and the body

was buried in the Cistercian Abbey of Cwm-Hir.

Florence of Worcester, referring to the death of Prince Llewelyn, says :—"As for the body of the Prince, his mangled trunk, it was interred in the Abbey of Cwm-Hir, belonging to the monks of the Cistercian Order." This version is also recorded in the "*Historia Anglicana*" of Bartholomew Cotton. But the historians are silent as to what became of Llewelyn's body between the date of his death and that of his supposed interment in the Abbey Church of Cwm-Hir. Perhaps the old tradition is of some weight, and the Prince's body found a *temporary* resting-place at Cefu-y-Bedd, wherefrom it was removed to the Abbey of Cwm-Hir. It was also suggested by Mr Stephen W. Williams, in his Historical Address on "the Abbey of Cwm-Hir" before the Honourable Society of Cymmrodorion, London, May 15, 1895, "that the body was carried into Builth, and there preserved awaiting the King's decision and the Archbishop's as to its ultimate disposal." The same authority stated, "Documentary evidence is therefore clearly in favour of Llewelyn being buried at Cwm-Hir, and that very shortly after his death at Cefu-y-Bedd."

Dr. Isambard Owen, who in December 1894 attended the representative London meeting, "To discuss the advisibility of erecting a

national memorial to Llewelyn, the last independent Prince of Wales," stated that "in
the course of an interview with Lord Bute
they had discussed the question of site, and
though a certain amount of discretion was necessary, still, some definite proposition should be
put before the country. Lord Bute thought it
probable that Llewelyn's body would be found
in a well-constructed stone vault in the middle
of the chancel, or between the two pillars of
the nave, or in the centre of the nave. All
the graves would have to be opened reverently,
and after inspection immediately closed. The
body of the prince would be distinguished by
the fact that it was decapitated. His lordship
concluded by suggesting that a memorial might
be erected at the Abbey of Cwm-Hir or at the
Abbey of Conway, which the prince thought to
make the Westminster Abbey of Wales. Dr.
Owen proceeded to say that he considered Lord
Bute's proposal a very rational one. Edward
I.'s grave at Westminster was carefully maintained, while that of his Welsh rival was
neglected, unrecognised, and unhonoured. The
first step that should be taken was to discover
the spot where the body was laid, and to erect
a suitable monument there. The finding of
the grave would be a point of historical interest
and importance, and he had no doubt that
the Cymmrodorion Society would do the work.

He thought that a memorial should, in the first instance, be placed on or near the grave. of Prince Llewelyn."

Enshrined in the pathetic songs, melodies, and traditions of Wales, the name of Llewelyn ap Gruffydd will live for ever, and through all the long centuries to come, patriotic Welshmen and women, making pilgrimages to the scenes of their beloved hero's life and struggles, will feel deeply touched.

North and South alike share the honour of having spots sacred to his memory.

There are Caerwys in Flintshire, where the boy-prince grieved over his ill-starred father's fate; ruined Aber, where Llewelyn and his beautiful wife Eleanor spent part of their short, but supremely happy wedded life; Snowdonia, where the prince, after his sore bereavement, suffered privation with his people; Aberedw in Breconshire, where he waited his doom; Cwm Llewelyn near Builth, where he was wounded and died; Cefn-y-Bedd, where, according to tradition he was buried, or more likely his body received temporary attention; and the Cistercian Abbey of Cwm-Hir, which it is supposed was his final resting-place.

Soon after the tragic death of Llewelyn, his infant daughter was taken prisoner, and sent with her nurse into England, by order of the king.

According to some authorities, she received the name of Catherine Lackland, and was married to Malcolm, Earl of Fife.

Other records state that she was brought up in England with her cousin Gwladys, the daughter of Davydd ap Gruffydd, and afterwards both princesses lived together for many years in the convent of Sempringham. Piers Langtoft, in his rhyming chronicles, under date 1337, says—

"More than a year before he met his shame,
A daughter was him born, Wencilian her name,
In her cradle young to England she came;
Through counsel of the king was brought to Sempringham;
And there was she in four and fifty year,
Nourished with wynne, nun and secular.
Nor have we new lattles, dead is Wencilian,
Llewelyn's daughter of Wales, that on England ran.
Her death was much mentioned, for she was full courteous,
Amongst the ladies gentle they tell of her loss,
The seventh day of June, Whitsun even the time,
Died that lady between midern and prime."

Davydd ap Gruffydd did not long survive his heroic brother.

Hearing of Llewelyn's defeat, as a last refuge he garrisoned and strengthened his fortress of Bere, which being in the midst of a morass, appeared to be impregnable, but, the Earl of Warwick, entering the defiles of Snowdon, routed the Welsh, took Davydd's stronghold, and put the prince with his followers to flight.

From May until Midsummer 1283, Davydd lurked in the woods, but was then captured through the treachery of Einion ap Evan. The Welsh prince was sent in fetters to Rhuddlan, where he was kept a close prisoner while waiting for trial.

His wife, two sons, and seven daughters, who had shared his privations, were also taken prisoners, and held in bondage at Rhuddlan.

A special Parliament was convened by the king at Shrewsbury, where, on September the 30th, that solemn assembly passed sentence of "death to the traitor."

The Welsh prince was doomed to undergo that barbarous punishment, which until recent times, still remained upon the English statute book as the penalty of high treason. He was sentenced "to be drawn to the gallows as a traitor to the king who had made him a knight; to be hanged as the murderer of the gentlemen taken in the castle of Hawarden; to have his bowels burnt because he had profaned by assassination the solemnity of Christ's passion; and to have his quarters dispersed through the country because he had in different places compassed the death of his lord the king."

To the everlasting disgrace of the warrior King of England, the unfortunate prince suffered the extreme penalty of the law on or about October the 7th, 1283, after which the dis-

membered parts of his body were publicly
exposed at Bristol, Northampton, York and
Winchester. The *Annales Menevenses* substi-
tute Shrewsbury and Lincoln for Northampton
and York.

Davydd's head was grimly placed on the
" highest ' Pinacle of the Tower of London,"
where in the autumn sunlight, still was kept
the bleached skull of " Llewelyn Ein Llyw Olaf."

Thus perished Prince Davydd, the first on
record to suffer that terrible form of punishment for high treason, which the stern and
pitiless Edward the First, who was unable to
discern the difference between patriotism and
insurrection—cruelly inflicted upon Scotland's
hero, Sir William Wallace, in A.D. 1305.

After Davydd's death, the king, says the
ancient Chronicler, " for the easier keeping the
Welch in due subjection, built Two Strong
Castles in *North Wales*, the one at *Conwey*,
and the other at *Caernarvon*. There was none
that now stood out besides *Rhys Fychan* of
Ystratywy; and he finding *David* was gone,
and himself likely to do nothing to purpose,
fairly yielded himself up to the Earl of *Hereford*, who, by the King's Orders, committed
him Prisoner to the Tower of London ; and so
all the Country of *Wales* became ever since
subject to the Crown of *England*."

CHAPTER XXVII

OWAIN GLYNDWR

AFTER the death of Llewelyn, the last Prince of Wales, and through the whole of the fourteenth century, petty insurrections continually recurred in many parts of Wales, and so strict was the English law against "traitors" that a great number of distinguished Welshmen sought refuge from the woes of their unhappy country in France.

Many of these flocked around the standard of Edward the Third in his wars with France, when the Black Prince led the first division of the English army to the field of Crecy, where the Welsh and Cornish men, with long, sharp knives, slew great numbers of the French, and valiantly aided the king's sturdy archers.

Here is found another story with reference to the first adoption of the leek as a Welsh national emblem.

In the Iolo MSS. it is stated that at Crecy

"the Welsh acquired great fame for their brave achievements in support of Edward the Black Prince. It was at this time that Captain Cadwgan Voel called to the Welsh, desiring them to put leeks in their helmets, the battle there being in a field of leeks; and when they looked about they were all Welshmen in that locality except 130, and it was from this circumstance that the Welsh took to wearing leeks."

Among the Welshmen in France at this period was Yvain de Galles, a descendant of the princes of Gwynedd. He fought in the French ranks at Poitiers in 1356, and served in the war in Spain between Pedro the Cruel and Henry of Trastamare for the crown of Castile. In 1372 this same Yvain entered into an alliance with Charles the Fifth of France, who granted him a loan of three hundred franks of gold, with the assistance of which he hoped to regain possession of Wales! But the assassination of Yvain by a Frenchman, in 1378, put an end to his vain and ambitious dreams.

Iolo tells us that in "1378, Owen, the son of Elidir, came to Wales from France, where he had espoused the cause of the French king, against Edward the Black Prince;—thus betraying England. This Owen built a very fair house at Llantwit Major; but his wounded conscience pained him so much for betraying Prince Edward in France, that, in penance, he abstained from all means of sustenance, until he died from want; and as they bore his body to the grave, two hounds, passing by, seized and tore him to pieces, leaving no two bones together. He wrote, in Welsh, an account of his deeds; and, at his death, the lord paramount took possession of his wealth; and very rich was he in gold and silver."

There were several Welsh military leaders who had "companies" at this time, and these included Edouart Yvain, probably a son of the redoubtable Yvain de Galles; Jehan Win, Yvain Greffin, and gay Robin ap Ledin.

Welsh deserters from the armies of Edward the Third appear as renowned captains of cosmo-politan banditti and freebooters, one of whom was the famous and much dreaded Chevalier Rufin. About this time the Lords Marchers of Wales frequently had their vigilance tried to the utmost by the presence of Welsh emissaries whom the French king sent to stir up rebellion in the land of the Cymry.

In 1399, Wales became the scene of the be-trayal and capture of Richard II. by Percy Earl of Northumberland. The king, on his return from Ireland, having been induced, under pre-tence of a promised and favourable interview with Bolingbroke, was met by the Earl of North-umberland, near the rock of Penmaen Rhos, near Llandulas, by Abergele, where the unfortunate

monarch was surrounded by the usurper's men-
at-arms and taken to Flint Castle.

The exact spot where Richard II. was captured
has been identified by means of the following
extract from the valuable MS. of the Harleian
Collection :—

> "Apres se volt partir
> De Cernuay le roi et seu venir
> A rotelant.
> Leane passa, qui fu moult large et grant ;
> Puis chevancha liij miles avant,
> Tant que la roche, au le conte au pendant
> Estoit tapis. . . ."
> " Montu le roi."

" Afterwards the king wished to depart from
Conway, to proceed to Rhuddlan, a place on the
way very large and grand. Then proceeding
forward four miles by a circuit, as far as the
rock, where the Count at that time was concealed, the king ascended it."

While at Flint Castle, Richard the Second's
favourite greyhound, *Math*, instead of fondling
his royal master in the usual way, transferred
his attentions to Henry of Lancaster, who asked
the meaning of the dog's caresses.

"Cousin," replied Richard Plantagenet, " it
means much for you, but little for me."

" Why so ? " asked Henry.

" I understand by it," said the unfortunate
monarch, " that *Math* pays his court to you as

King of England, which you will soon be, for I shall be deposed, as the fond creature perceives. Keep him, cousin, by your side, for lo ! he leaveth me, and will henceforth ever follow you."

From Flint Castle Richard was taken to Pontefract, where he was compelled to abdicate, soon after which he died—some say by voluntary starvation, but according to others, he was murdered by Sir Piers Exton.

While Welsh refugees in France forgot their native land, and the last of the ancient Britons saw the sons of their princes degenerating into untitled subjects of the English king, a child was born, who in manhood proved that the national spirit of Wales, though sleeping, was not dead, while one indomitable hero lived to strike blow after blow for right and justice.

Owain ap Gruffydd Vychan, popularly known as Owain Glyndwr, was born on the 28th of May, 1354, and, according to Hollinshed, "strange wonders happened" at his nativity, when the horses in his father's stables stood deeper than their knees in blood."

The superstitions clinging to Glendwr's name have been immortalised by Shakespeare, who causes the Welsh hero to say of his own birth—

> .   .   .   .   .   .   "At my nativity
> The front of heaven was full of fiery shapes,
> Of burning cressets ; and at my birth,
> The frame and huge foundation of the earth

Shak'd like a coward. . . .
The heavens were all on fire, the earth did tremble.
.   .   .   .   Give me leave
To tell for once again,—that of my birth
The front of heaven was full of fiery shapes ;
The goats ran from the mountains, and the herds
Were strangely clamorous to the frighted fields.
These signs have mark'd me extraordinary,
And in the course of my life do show
I am not in the roll of common men,
Where he is living,—clipped in with the sea
That chides the banks of England, Scotland, Wales,—
Which calls me pupil, or hath read to me ?
And bring him out that is but woman's son
Can trace me in the tedious ways of art
And hold me pace in deep experiments."

On his father's side Owain Glyndwr, being descended from the Princes of Powys, was of noble birth, though not of large patrimony. In his youth he was sent to study the law in London, where ultimately he gained distinction as an " outer barrister," but he does not appear to have practised much in his profession.

While pondering the prosaic intricacies of the law, or wandering thoughtfully among the shadows of the various Inns of Court, young Owain felt greatly influenced by the chivalrous spirit of the age ; but for a while his perseverance and high mental qualities kept him in subjection, and he continued his studies until he was called to the bar.

Although eminently a literary man, as his

subsequent life reveals, Owain presently appears
to have grown tired of dry detail and prosy
brief, and to have been lured by the attractions
of the world from the quietude of his books. It
is probable, too, that he was much impressed by
what had been said about the omens of his birth,
and, if not well read in astrology, he had sufficient knowledge of star-lore, or perhaps was
advised by some man of magic, to cast aside
the saturnine coif of the lawyer, for the
helmet of the soldier, and the fiery sword of
Mars.

Fortune favoured him as a soldier even more
than in his efforts as a lawyer, and he had not
long taken up the profession of arms before he
attracted the attention of Richard the Second,
who appointed him as his Scutiger or Shield-
bearer. In that capacity he attended the English monarch during his martial expeditions into
France and Ireland, and he was also engaged in
the domestic wars of the Roses. Afterwards he
became a fearless and active partisan in the
cause of the ill-fated king, who rewarded him
with the Order of Knighthood. Owain remained with Richard the Second during his
imprisonment in Flint Castle; but when that
monarch was removed to Pontefract the Welsh
hero returned to his own home, where, for a
time, he devoted himself to social pleasure and
unbounded hospitalities.

But his enjoyment was short-lived.

Scarcely a year had passed when a dispute arose between Owain Glyndwr and Reginald, Lord Grey de Ruthyn.

According to the ancient records :—" Betwixt this *Owen* and *Reginald*, Lord *Gray* of *Rhuthyn*, there happened no small Difference touching a Common lying between the Lordship of *Rhuthyn* whereof *Reginald* was Owner, and the Lordship of *Glyndowrdwy*, in the possession of *Owen*, whence he borrowed the name of *Glyndwr*. During the reign of *Richard* the Second, *Owen* as being a Courtier, and in no mean esteem with the king, did overpower *Reginald*, who was neither so well befriended at Court, nor beloved in the Country as *Owen* was."

When Henry of Lancaster usurped and ascended the throne, Lord Grey seizing the opportunity of retaliating upon Glyndwr, forcibly took possession of the land in question. Thereupon Glyndwr, as the rightful owner, made "Complaint in Parliament" against Grey, "for thus divesting him of his Right. No redress being found, the Bishop of St. *Asaph* wished the Lords to take care that by thus slighting his Complaint they did not irritate and provoke the *Welch* to an Insurrection, to which some of the Lords replied, ' *That they did not fear those rascally bare-footed People.*'"

Thus was Glyndwr's suit haughtily dismissed,

and, instead of redress, he at once received much contempt and many injuries.

Lord Grey's revenge was still incomplete.

In the first year of Henry the Fourth's reign, the king issued writs commanding the attendance of his subjects on a military enterprise to Scotland. Lord Grey de Ruthin was deputed to deliver a writ to Glyndwr, but kept the document, and when the troops were assembling he handed it back to the king as though Owain had refused to obey the royal command. Soon after this Grey, encouraged by Henry, seized Glyndwr's territory, confiscated it, and the owner thereof was proclaimed to be a traitor.

Wronged and robbed by Henry the Fourth and his malicious minion, and proscribed as a traitor, Glyndwr resorted to the sword, and almost "in the twinkling of an eye," the old British spirit of animosity, which had been suppressed but not quenched by Edward the Third, burst forth into a fierce flame, which was rekindled at Ruthin, and expired among the mountains of Breconshire.

Glyndwr made no secret of his intentions.

Boldly and openly he avowed himself as a defender of law and liberty, and, on the 20th of September 1400, he was proclaimed Prince of Wales.

Immediately afterwards he found numberless supporters. Some were urged by inveterate

hatred against Grey and other Lords Marchers;
others were politically opposed to Henry as an
usurper; but the great majority of his followers
hailed Glyndwr as the *Mab-y-Darogan*, the
"heir of the prophecy," who was to finally
liberate Wales from the yoke of the oppressor.

History repeated itself.

Once again a King of England found it
necessary, with all his forces, to invade the
Principality, and once more a Welsh chieftain
—who, if not actually a prince, was of royal
and legal descent—held Snowdonia against the
English, and compelled Henry the Fourth to
an ignominious retreat.

Bitterly resentful at his defeat, the king issued
a proclamation offering pardon to all "rebels"
who would immediately make oaths of allegiance
at Chester. And in the Parliament of January
1401, "Ordinances" were passed whereby the
Welsh were prohibited from purchasing lands
in the towns of the Marches, or representing
any constituency in Parliament, or holding any
corporate office or position of trust. All English-
men married to Welsh women, and *vice versa*,
were deprived of their goods and chattels, with
the addition that the men were to be disen-
franchised, and rendered ineligible to hold any
kind of office in Wales or the Marches. Meetings for counsel, save by licence of the lord of
the place and in the presence of himself or his

representatives, were forbidden to the Welsh; and no food or ammunition might be imported into Wales without the king's permission. And, perhaps, worse than all, the Welsh were not allowed to educate or apprentice their children to any kind of work "in any borough or town of the realm."

Powell, the historian, describes these statutes as being "unreasonable and unconscionable laws, such as no prince among the heathens ever offered to his subjects." He further says such regulations tended to keep the Welsh in "perpetual thraldom and misery," and adds, "Let any indifferent man judge and consider whether the extremity of law, when justice itself is mere injury and cruelty, be not a cause and matter sufficient to withdraw any people from civility to barbarism."

These severe and extreme measures caused many exiles from the Principality to return home and take up arms with Owain Glyndwr.

Wales in the lator half of the fourteenth and early part of the fifteenth centuries had seen many changes. The tragic fate of Llewelyn ap Gruffydd had for a time stunned his countrymen, whose swords may be said to have almost rusted, or only used on one or two occasions, as, for instance, when Sir Gruffydd Llwyd of Carnarvonshire invoked a trivial insurrection in 1360, for which he was promptly sent to the scaffold.

The Welsh *proletaire* sank into dumb submission to inevitable fate; the artisans migrated
right into England; and the sons of the better
classes were sent to Oxford, Cambridge, and
London, where they received education equal
to any English gentleman. The result was that
when Glyndwr revolted against Henry the
Fourth, his ranks were augmented by learned
Welsh scholars from the English universities,
by artisans who had settled in England, and
knew something about right and liberty, and
around these the bards congregated, while the
lower classes believed that the *Mab-y-Darogan*
had really come.

Young Wales that flocked to the standard of
Owain Glyndwr comprised the pick of educated
youths and talented men in their early manhood.
A grave complaint was lodged in Parliament
that the Welsh scholars of Oxford and Cambridge had gone over to the " traitor and rebel,"
while working men " by stealth " took weapons
and armour across the Marches.

Edward the Third had to fight against well-
educated and royal leaders of a much-oppressed
people, who owed their heroism to the prompt-
ings of British song and story, and were largely
indebted to bardic regulations and Druidical
lore for stern discipline and sublime fortitude
in facing death rather than disgrace or defeat.
And in stress of war, or in defence of private

liberties, they would rather be found guilty of a crime than a meanness.

Henry the Fourth found himself face to face wtih a highly learned, intelligent gentleman, lawyer, soldier, and patriot, whose followers included young men of culture, of noble birth and bearing. Shakespeare's estimate of Glyndwr is forcibly illustrated in that hero's retort at Bangor to Hotspur, who said—

> "Let me not understand you, then ;
> Speak it in Welsh."

To which Glyndwr replied—

> "I can speak English, lord, as well as you ;
> For I was train'd up in the English court ;
> Where, being but young, I framed to the harp
> Many an English ditty, lovely well,
> And gave the tongue an helpful ornament—
> A virtue that was never seen in you,"

and then daringly promised him he should "have Trent turn'd" to suit his fancy.

Again, when Hotspur complained—

> . . . "Sometimes he angers me
> With telling me of the moldwarp and the ant,
> Of the dreamer Merlin and his prophecies,
> And of a dragon, and a finless fish,
> A clip-wing'd griffin, and a moulten raven,
> A couching lion and a ramping cat,
> And such a deal of skimble-skamble stuff
> As puts me from my faith. . . ."

Mortimer replied—

"In faith, he is a worthy gentleman,
 Exceedingly well read, and profeited
 In strange concealments; valiant as a lion,
 And wondrous affable, and as bountiful
 As mines of India. . . ."

Early in 1401 the renowned Henry Percy, surnamed Hotspur, justiciary of Chester, watched the "rebellion" and reported accordingly. At first the insurgents were described as being of little account, but later on Hotspur was less hopeful, and complained that the "stubborn obstinacy" of the "rebels" had exceeded expectation.

Owain made Plinlimmon his headquarters and rallying point whereto or from his adherents of the North and South could easily come or go. Soon afterwards Glyndwr led Young Wales forward to smart and active service. The towns of Montgomery and Welshpool were sacked and burnt; the estates of the Lords Marchers were ravaged; the Abbey of Cwm-Hir was plundered; the Castle of Maelienydd was destroyed; all the horrors of fire and sword made havoc in Radnor, and then Cardiganshire was assailed. Whereupon the Flemings of Rhos and the Welsh partisans of Henry the Fourth in Cardigan rose up in arms and managed to encompass Glyndwr and his men at

Mynydd Hyddgant, where the so-called "rebels" made a desperate resistance.

The situation was exceedingly perilous, and Glyndwr, in a fervent address, told his small army that they must either die of famine or immediately cut through the enemy, while if death was to be their doom, it was best to meet it armed fully for defence. He commanded them to charge the enemy and give no quarter, which they did with such fiery impetuosity that the Welsh and Flemings of Cardigan retreated, and Glyndwr rescued his army.

This brave exploit caused Henry to re-enter Wales, but though he remained there until the autumn, he only burnt the Abbey of Ystrad Flûr, *Strata Florida*, and proclaimed Owain as "a rebel."

Glyndwr was triumphant.

His popularity increased, and those who fondly clung to the superstitions of the age saw in the comet of 1402 a presage of future good fortune for the brave chieftain whose star was still in the ascendant.

Early in that year Lord Grey, the author of all this discord, prepared to attack his old enemy, but as soon as he opened the campaign, Glyndwr boldly marched to Ruthin Castle, and by clever strategy "bearded the lion in his den" and took him prisoner. In the words of the Chronicler, Glyndwr would not allow Grey

to have his liberty "under Ten Thousand marks
for his Ransom, whereof Six Thousand to be
paid upon the Feast of *St. Martyn* in the 4th
Year of *Henry* the Fourth, and to deliver up his
eldest Son with some other Persons of Quality
as Hostages for the remainder; the king at the
humble score of *Reginald*, seeing no other way
for his enlargement, gave way thereto, authoris-
ing Sir *William de Roos*, Sir *Richard de Grey*,
Sir *William de Willoughby*, Sir *William le
Zouche*, Sir *Hugh Huls*, as also *John Harvey*,
William Vans, *John Lee*, *John Langford*,
Thomas Payne, and *John Elnestow*, to treat
with *Owen* and his Council, and to conclude in
what way they should conceive most expedient
and necessary to be done for his redemption.
Whereupon they, consenting to give the sum
demanded by *Glyndwr* for his deliverance, the
King gave License to *Robert Braybroke*, Bishop
of *London*, as also to Sir *Gerard Braybroke* the
Father, and Sir *Gerard* the Son, then Feoffees of
divers Lordships for this *Reginald*, to sell the
Mannor of *Hertelegh* in the County of *Kent*,
towards the raising of that Money."

The King also "was pleased to grant that
whereas it was enacted that such Persons who
were owners of Lands in *Ireland* and did not
there reside, should for such their neglect, forfeit
two parts of the Profits of them to the King;
that notwithstanding this Act, he should forfeit

nothing for non-residence there, during the term of six years next ensuing."

The most curious conclusion to this compact with Owain was that Lord Grey agreed to marry Glyndwyr's daughter Jane. Probably Grey, who had "grievously felt" Owain's power, thought "discretion the better part of valour," after which no further hostilities are recorded between the Lord of Ruthin and his redoubtable father-in-law.

In May 1402, Henry of Monmouth ravaged Owain's domains at Sycarth, and boasted in his despatches that he had captured one of Owain's "great gentlemen," whom he put to death rather than descend to take five hundred pounds ransom.

Meanwhile, in true border fashion the warfare continued, while Owain's power greatly increased.

A curious story is told of this period.

Glyndwr's cousin, Hywel Sele, of Nannau, was a zealous partisan of King Henry. This engendered bitter animosity between the relatives, who were, as the world says, with "daggers drawn."

Local tradition stated that the Abbot of Cymmer desired to reconcile the cousins, and for that purpose arranged a meeting. Matters went well until Glyndwr suggested that as Hywel was such a renowned archer, he should try his bow upon a red deer.

Hywel, appearing greatly flattered, drew his bow, but, instead of aiming it at the deer, he treacherously directed it against Owain.

But, unknown to his adversary, Glyndwr wore concealed armour, and the would-be assassin was foiled.

Owain's attendants seized Hywel Sele, and threw him into the hollow of an ancient oak, where he was left to perish, and there, forty years later, his bleached skeleton was found.

Another version, giving a more humane colouring to the story, describes an altercation between the cousins, in which Hywel was slain, and his body was secretly concealed in the oak.

For forty years the fate of the unfortunate Lord of Nannau was a mystery, but, at the expiration of that time, one of Glyndwr's friends, who witnessed the fray, revealed the truth to Hywel's family. From that time until the early part of the present century, the oak which had concealed the body of poor Hywel Sele remained standing in Nannau Park. Then the hoary tree fell, owing to its extreme old age. This celebrated oak was known as *Ceubren yr Ellyll*, or the Hobgoblin's Hollow Tree.

In the summer of 1402, Owain gained a victory over Sir Edmund Mortimer, the uncle and guardian of young Henry, Earl of March, who was the rightful successor of Richard II. Glyndwr imprisoned Mortimer, and about the same period unsuccessfully besieged Carnarvon, destroyed the cathedrals of Bangor and St. Asaph, and ravaged the territory of the Lords Marchers.

Late in the August, or early in September, King Henry went in person with a large army into Wales, but, says the old Chronicler, "by reason of extraordinary excess of weather, which some attributed to the magic of *Glyndwr*, he was glad to return safe."

Hollinshed says—"The King, to chastise the presumptuous attempts of the Welshmen, went with a great power of men into Wales, to pursue the Welsh captain Owen Glendwer, but, in effect, he lost his labour; for Owen conveyed himself out of the way into his known lurking places, and (as was thought) through art magic, he caused such foul weather of winds, tempest, rain, snow, and hail, to be raised for the annoyance of the King's army, that the like had not been heard of."

Meanwhile, Owain went ravaging through South Wales, particularly in the Vale of Glamorgan, where the young men hailed his presence with great enthusiasm. According to the various records, Glyndwr paid several "rebellious" visits to South Wales.

In the Iolo MSS. it is stated that "in the year of Christ 1400, Owen Glyndwr came to Glamorgan, and won the Castle of Cardiff, and many more : he also demolished the Castles of Penlline, Landough, Flemingston, Dunraven of

the Butlers, Tal-y-van, Llanblethian, Llanquian,
Malefant, and that of Penmark; and burnt
many of the villages and churches about them.
He burnt, also, the villages of Llanfrynach and
Aberthin; and many houses in Llantwit Major,
and other places, the men of which would not
join him. But many of the country people
collected round him with one accord; and they
demolished castles and houses innumerable;
laid waste, and quite fenceless, the lands, and
gave them in common to all. They took away
from the powerful and rich, and distributed the
plunder among the weak and poor. Many of
the higher order and chieftains were obliged
to flee to England, under the protection and
support of the king. A bloody battle took
place on Bryn-Owen Mountain (now called The
Stallingdown) near Cowbridge, between Owen
and his men, and the king's men, but the
latter were put to flight after eighteen hours'
hard fighting; during which the blood was up
to the horses' fetterlocks, at Pant-y-wennol, that
separates both ends of the mountains."

From the same MSS. the following story
is taken:— "When Owen Glyndwr travelled
about the country, in the guise of a strange
gentleman, attended by one faithful friend, in
the habit of a Servant, and both being unarmed (for no armed person was secure at
that time), and going about to ascertain the

disposition of the inhabitants, he went to the
castle of Sir Lawrence Berkerolles, and requested
in French a night's reception for himself and
servant, which was readily granted, attended by
a hearty welcome, the best of everything in
the castle being laid before him ; and so pleased
was Sir Lawrence with his friend, that he earnestly pressed him to remain with him for some
days, observing that he soon expected to see
Owen Glyndwr there ; for that he had dis-
patched all his tenants and servants, with many
other confidential friends, under an oath of
fidelity, through all parts of the country, to
seize Owen, who, he was told, had come to
that district of the principality ; and that he
was himself sworn to give honourable rewards
to his men who should bring Owen Glyndwr
there, either alive or dead. "It would be very
well, indeed," said Owen, "to secure that man,
were any persons able to do so." Having remained at Sir Lawrence's castle for four days
and three nights, Owen thought it would be
wise to go his way ; therefore, giving his hand
to Sir Lawrence, he addressed him thus: 'Owen
Glyndwr, as a sincere friend, having neither
hatred, treachery, nor deception in his heart,
gives his hand to Sir Lawrence Berkerolles,
and thanks him for the kindness and gentle-
manly reception which he and his friend (in
the guise of a servant) experienced from him

at his castle; and desires to assure him on oath, hand in hand, and hand on heart, that it will never enter his mind to avenge the intentions of Sir Lawrence towards him; and that he will not, as far as he may, allow such desires to exist in his own knowledge and memory, nor in the minds of any of his relations and adherents,' and then he and his servant departed; but Sir Lawrence Berkerolles was struck dumb with astonishment, and never afterwards recovered his speech; no word thenceforth having ever escaped his lips."

Another story told by Iolo, is that of " Cadogan of the Battle-Axe." It runs thus :—" Cadogan of the Battle-Axe lived at Glyn Rhontha (near Aberdare) during the time of Owen Glyndwr's war, and was one of that chieftain's captains over the men of that vale. When Cadogan went to battle, he used to perambulate Glyn Rhontha, whetting his battle-axe, as he proceeded along; from which circumstances Owen would call out to Cadogan,— 'Cadogan! whet thy battle-axe;' and the moment that Cadogan was heard to do so, all living persons both male and female, in Glyn Rhontha, collected about him in military order; and from that day to this, the battle-shout of the men of Glyn Rhontha has been, 'Cadogan! whet thy battle-axe,' and, at the word, they all assemble as an army."

Cardiff suffered badly under the hands of Owain Glyndwr, who besieged the town, whereupon the inhabitants petitioned the king for help. The Earl of Devon and the Courtenays were commissioned to press men for the purpose, and "proceed forthwith by sea to rescue the castle of Cardiff, then in great peril."

But help came too late.

Owain took the town and utterly destroyed it, though he spared the "suburb of Crokerton," known afterwards as Crockherbtown, because of the Friars Minors who had always espoused the cause of Richard the Second, and who also favoured the revolt of Glyndwr against Henry the Fourth.

Cardiff Castle was made the depositary of all the wealth and valuable goods of the inhabitants in the town and neighbourhood, and thereto the Friars Minors had taken their religious vessels, books, and papers. When Owain took the castle and to a great extent destroyed it, the Friars Minors petitioned him for their possessions. But it was too late, and Glyndwr, who had left their convent in the Crockerton untouched said, "Why did you put your goods in the castle? If you had kept them in your convent they would have been secured and protected."

Owain Glyndwr attacked Llandaff, destroyed the bishop's palace and the archdeacon's residence, after which the cathedral was much damaged. Penmark and Coity Castles were besieged, and the corporate towns of Wick and Broughton lost their charters for having "welcomed the rebel."

So effectually was the whole Principality scoured by Glyndwr, that the panic-stricken people quailed when his name was mentioned. Constables and governors surrendered their fortresses and castles without a stroke; cathedrals and abbeys were robbed of their richest treasures, costly vestments, and magnificent altar-pieces; monasteries and convents were plundered and destroyed; towns and houses were sacked and burnt, and wherever the chieftain appeared, people found it better to accord him a welcome than to oppose his force with arms.

In 1402 the Percies, represented by Hotspur, who were endeavouring to dethrone Henry the Fourth, made overtures to Glyndwr, in the hope of gaining his aid and the release of Edmund Mortimer. The ratification of the alliance between Hotspur, Mortimer, and Glyndwr forms the subject of the celebrated scene at Bangor immortalised by Shakespeare. One of the stipulations of this treaty was, "That if, through God's providence, it should appear in course of time unto these lords that they are the very persons of whom the prophet speaks as

those who should divide and share the realm
of Great Britain between them ; then they,
and each of them, shall labour to the very
extremity of their power to bring it effectually
to pass."

Halle says the three distinguished leaguers
" unwisely " had been made to believe " by the
deviation, not the divination, of that mawmet
Merlin," that Henry the king was the "mole
cursed of God's mouth," and in order to fulfil
the prophecy, Glyndwr assumed the cognomen
of the Dragon, Percy took the Lion, and
Mortimer the Wolf.

Soon afterwards Glyndwr obtained the permission of his countrymen to assume the title of
Prince of Wales. For this purpose a Parliament
assembled at Machynlleth, in Montgomeryshire,
and there his title was formally recognised.

At this Parliament Davydd Gam made himself conspicuous. In the old chronicles it is
recorded that " David *Gam,* so called by reason
he had but one Eye, the Son of *Llewelyn ap
Howel Vaughan* of *Brecknock,* . . . was a great
stickler for the Duke of *Lancaster,* and for that
reason became mortal enemy to Glyndwr, who
having his Education, as is said before, at one
of the Inns of Court, got to be preferred to the
service of King *Richard* the Second, who, as
Walsingham says, made him his *Scutifer* or
Shield-bearer. . . . Glyndwr . . . summoned a

Parliament to meet at *Machynlleth*, whither the Nobility and Gentry of *Wales* appeared, and among the rest, Sir *David Gam*, but then not upon the same design with the rest, having an intention in this meeting to murder *Glyndwr*. But the Plot being discovered, and Sir *David* secured, he had liked to undergo present execution, had not *Glyndwr's* best Friends, and the greatest Upholders of his Cause, pleaded in his behalf, by whose intercession he was prevailed with to grant Sir *David* . . . his life." But not his liberty, it appears, for he was imprisoned among the mountains at Glyndyvrdwy, the ruins of which still are to be seen. Subsequently Glyndwr burnt Davydd's house and confiscated his property. Davydd remained in prison until 1412, and his subsequent career is thus described in a chronicle of Wales :—

" When King *Henry* the Fifth went with an Army to *France* against the *French* King, Sir *David Gam* brought into his service a numerous Party of Stout and Valorous *Welch*-Men, who upon all occasions expressed their Courage and Resolution. In the Battel of *Agincourt*, News being brought to the King that the *French* Army was advancing towards him, and that they were exceeding numerous, he detached Captain *Gam* to observe their motion, and review their number. The Captain having narrowly eyed the *French*, found them twice to exceed the *English*, but not

being in the least daunted at such a multitude,
he returned to the King, who inquiring of him
what the Number of the *French* might be, he
made answer, *An't please you, my Liege, they are
enough to be killed, enough to run away, and
enough to be taken Prisoners.* King *Henry* was
well pleased, and much encouraged with this
resolute and undaunted answer of Sir *David's*,
whose Tongue did not express more Valour than
his hands performed. For in the heat of Battel,
the King's Person being in danger, Sir *David*
charged the Enemy with that eagerness and
masculine Bravery, that they were glad to give
ground, and so secured the King, tho' with the
loss of much Blood, and also his Life, himself and
his Son-in-Law *Roger Vaughan*, and his Kinsman *Walter Llwyd* of *Brecknock*, having received
their mortal Wounds in that encounter. When
the King heard of their Condition, how they
were past all hopes of recovery, he came to them,
and in recompence of their good Services,
Knighted them all three in the Field, where they
soon after died ; and so ended the Life, but not
the Fame, of the signally Valiant Sir *David
Gam.*"

Not long after Glyndwr was proclaimed Prince
of Wales, Hotspur collected his forces, and
hastened to the Welsh borders, while Northumberland stayed behind to wait for an army of
Scots who were to join the enterprise. Hotspur

had raised the men of Chester, who were devoted
to the cause of the rightful heir to the Crown,
and marched on towards Shrewsbury, where the
battle was lost before Glyndwr, who was stationed at Oswestry, could bring his army into
the field. Hotspur was slain, and the rebel army
was completely routed, leaving Henry the Fourth's
troops victorious.

As soon as the English army quitted their
position, Glyndwr marched forth through the
country. Again towns were destroyed and castles
pillaged, while, as usual, the Lords Marchers were
vehemently assailed.

Henry's financial position was now very im-
poverished, and all the English monarch could
do was to restrict himself to defensive measures,
while Glyndwr ravaged the country, and ultimately entered into an alliance with Charles VI.
of France, who was glad to proceed against the
Lancastrian "usurper."

Doctor Gruffydd Yonge and Sir John Hanmer
were sent as Glyndwr's representatives to the
French monarch, and the treaty was signed at Paris
by James de Bourbon, and Count de la March, on
behalf of Charles. The alliance does not appear
to have been of much service, though the French
forces reached Carnarvon more than once. In a
letter of Reynolde de Bayldon, an officer of
Conway Castle, addressed to Sir Roger de Bresey,
the Constable of Chester, which appears in Ellis'

Original Letters, 1404, it is stated that "The
Frenshmen were makyn al the ordinance that
thae mae or can for to assaele the towne of
Carnaruan, in ale the haste that thae mae, knowin
wel that the towne is more febil nowe then hyt
was the laste tyme that thae wer beforehyt,
forasmuche as a hepe o the beste that wer in
Carnaruan that tyme bene-got betaghte sethin;
and as hyt seemethe to me hyt wer nedeful than
thae had helpe in haste tyme." This letter was
"Wrytyn in grete haste at Conwaye, the xxvj.
daye of Feuerzer, 1404."

Early in 1405, Owain attacked Harlech and
Conway Castles, and in March of that year Lady
Constance Spenser, keeper of Caerphilly Castle,
contrived the escape of the young Earl of
March and his brother from Windsor Castle,
where they were imprisoned by Henry IV.; but
before the youths reached Wales they were recaptured.

On March 11th the great battle of Grosmont
was fought, when more than a thousand brave
men were slain, most of them being Glamorganshire "rebels," as young Prince Henry the victor
informed his father.

Glyndwr once more made a strong effort
against the English, and on March the 15th he
led his forces to Mynydd-y-Pwll Melyn, in
Breconshire, where he was defeated. Fifteen
hundred men were killed or taken prisoners,

and Owain had to lament the captivity of his
son Gruffydd, and the death of his brother
Tudor.

The battle was fatal to the hopes of Owain
Glyndwr.

His followers, disheartened by defeat, disaster,
and the rumoured death of their leader, abandoned the cause which had held them as in a
spell for many years.

Glyndwr, who took up the sword in defence
of right and liberty, and whose heroic and
venturesome life was full of dramatic interest,
at last found himself deserted except by a few
faithful friends. And they ministered to his
necessities when their hero was forced for a time
to seek shelter in caverns and desolate places.

This is the saddest part of Owain's strangely
stirring history.

Left comparatively alone to lament over the
waning spirit and energy of the Welsh, whose
fifteenth century Parliament was but an empty
show, Glyndwr must have felt that, if any blame
could be attached to his character as a military
leader, its weakness was most marked after the
battle of Shrewsbury, when Henry's troops were
in a flagged condition, and the Welsh army was
strong enough to have gained a signal victory.
The heroic Welshman's military skill was generally of too desultory a nature to admit of
powerful strokes when most necessary, but at

other times was bold, forceful, and perhaps too
impetuous for the occasion.

To call Glyndwr a traitor, is to libel the
most distinguished and energetic Welshman of
his time, and one, who, to Richard the Second
of England, had been a faithful friend and
devoted adherent, alike abroad and at home.
When the ill-fated king, and last of the Plantagenets, who was seized by Henry Bolingbroke, found his few attendants faithless, and
even his dog *Math* a deserter, Glyndwr remained, only leaving that unfortunate monarch
on his being hurried to his dark doom at
Pontefract.

For many years this heroic Welshman endeavoured to establish national liberties and
rights that were continually set aside, and in
no way protected. His power over the people
whose cause he so ardently advocated, was
forcibly illustrated fifteen years after his death.
When a request was made for the enforced
forfeiture of his lands, it was gravely stated in
the House of Commons that if the distinguished
Welshman, called by Shakespeare "the great
magician," succeeded in his "rebellion," the
English language would have perished for ever
in Wales.

Some historians describe Glyndwr as being
an outcast and fugitive of the most miserable
kind after his defeat in 1405, and during the

2 C

remainder of his life, but it is certain that
although he was obliged to retreat for some
months, he appeared again in the same year
to meet the French at Tenby, and the allied
forces besieged Carmarthen. Thence they went
to Worcester and took up their position on
Wobury Hill, wherefrom they menaced the
English, with whom they had a few smart
skirmishes, but nothing more.

In 1406 the French abandoned Wales.

From that year, Glyndwr's influence gradually
declined, and among his last adherents were the
ever brave men and heroes of Ystrad Tywi,
Carmarthenshire, who for long generations had
been firm and zealous supporters of Welsh
nationalism.

The remaining portion of Owain Glyndwr's
life was spent in comparative security, surrounded by his family and those friends who
still remained faithful to him.

On September 20th, 1415, this celebrated
fifteenth century leader of the people, and last
hero of Welsh independence, died in Herefordshire.

According to the MSS. of the Harleian Collection, Glyndwr's body, which was entire and of
" goodly stature," was discovered at Monington
in that shire, during the restoration of the
church in 1680. But his resting-place remains
unmarked and unrecognised.

Centuries have rolled away since Owain Glyndwr's enlightened patriotism roused all Wales to noble enthusiasm, but his name will live for ever, and his most enduring memorial is in the hearts of his countrymen.

He has borne the reputation of being a rebel, an outlaw, and last of all, the leader of desperadoes whose brigandage, though annoying to the English, was not dangerous.

Yet, in spite of all, Owain Glyndwr stands forth as one of the most remarkable sons of " Wild Walia."

It is easy, in the eve of the nineteenth century, for privileged citizens while enjoying great political, social, and religious advantages, to regard the enthusiasm and national spirit of their forefathers as wild excitability, and their patriotism as love of lawlessness, or selfish ambition.

Were it not for those old-time heroes and toilers, who, in promoting the general interests of their fellowmen, fell victims to the chances of war, the axe of the executioner, or the still more pitiful and tragic doom of long imprisonment and slow death, the people of to-day would still be existing under mediæval conditions.

The building of the goodly ship of British unity, which is the pride of our own, and the envy of all other nations, was commenced in

the long-ago, amid much vicissitude, and self
sacrifice, and well we know—

> " What Workmen wrought its ribs of steel,
>   Who made each mast, and sail, and rope,
>   What anvils rang, what hammers beat,
>   In what a forge, and what a heat
>   Were shaped the anchors of its hope ! "

CHAPTER XXVIII

THE ROSE OF MONA

RHYS AP TEWDWR and his brother William were executed at Chester in 1412, for having taken part in the "rebellion" of Owain Glyndwr against Henry the Fourth, and when these two heroes died for their country's cause, had any seer dared to prophesy that their descendants, the mighty Tudors, were to occupy the throne of England, his fate would have been that of a malefactor.

In 1227, just fifteen years after the execution of Rhys, his grandson Owen appears in Henry the Fifth's court, of which he was considered to be one of the most accomplished men, whose handsome and captivating face and figure gained for him the strange appellation—at least for a man—of the "Rose of Mona," or Anglesea, known also as Mam Cymru, or the Mother of Wales.

Owen, the son of Meredith ap Tewdwr, was

born at Pen Mynydd, where Owain Gwynedd triumphed over the Irish and Normans, and where many a Welsh hero fought and fell in the great struggles of old.

This young Welshman appears to have gone to court early, and there quickly gained royal favours from the English monarch and his queen.

Halle, the quaint old Chronicler, describes him as "a goodlie gentylman and a beautifulle personne, garniged (garnished) with manye good-lye gifts bothe of nature and of grace, callyde Owen Teuther."

In those more peaceful days the Welsh were renowned dancers, and the gay Owen was an adept in that art, which he used to advantage in the court, and thereby attracted the attention of the bewitching and beautiful Katherine of France, wife, and afterwards widow, of "Harry of England."

The story goes that once when Katherine, the widowed queen, invited Owen to dance in her presence, he chanced, quite accidentally, to stumble and fall into the royal lady's lap. Whereupon, as might be expected, there was much tittering and whispering among the fair ladies of the court.

Owen, equal to the occasion, and with nonchalant grace, made courteous apologies to her Majesty, who, says "Cambria Depicta," "Very

pleasantly jesting with him, said that so far
from offending her, it would only increase the
pleasure of herself and company if he would
repeat the same false step or mistake."

Whether Owen ever made a similar mistake
is not known, but, a little later, Welsh accents
of love, and French eloquence in response, which
had charmed the heart of Harry of England,
were mingled in silvery unison, until by and by,
the Belle of France and the Rose of Mona became one.

Perhaps, as the pretty novelettes of to-day
have it, there was a "delightful affinity of soul"
between the queen and her second husband, for
had not Katherine's father, Charles the Sixth,
assisted the great Owain Glyndwr against
England.

The Franco-Welsh marriage was distasteful to
the English courtiers.

To make matters worse, plain and homely
John ap Meredith, and Hywel ap Llewelyn,
came to see what their cousin Owen's dancing
had done for him.

Men of "goodlie stature and personage" were
they, but unlearned in English, and wholly
unacquainted with the ease of court life and
manners.

The sprightly and animated queen addressed
them in English and several other languages,
but, as they could not reply, she merrily ex-

claimed that they were "the goodliest looking dumb creatures that she ever beheld."

This conduct so greatly vexed the royal family that the "obscure gentleman" of Wales, named Owen Tudor, was requested to furnish proofs of his respectability.

Katherine promptly sent commissioners "of her own choosing" down to Pen Mynydd to glean information, and, bribed by the queen, these worthy gentlemen reported favourably. After that, the Duke of Gloucester, Protector of England, "out of veneration" for his brother, the late king, Henry the Fifth, did not further trouble his beautiful sister-in-law.

Owain and Katherine Tewdwr, afterwards corrupted to Tudor, had three sons and one daughter. The sons were Edmund, surnamed Hatfield, Jasper, and Owen, and the daughter Katherine. The beautiful widow of Henry the Fifth, and bride of Owen Tudor, died at Bermondsey on the 3rd of January 1437, at the early age of thirty-six, after nine years of happy wedded life with her Welsh husband.

Her death brought immediate trouble and disaster to Owen, whose children were instantly taken from his custody, and placed under the guardianship of the Abbess of Barking.

In after years Edmund was created Earl of Richmond, and married Margaret, granddaughter of John of Gaunt; Jasper became Earl of Pembroke and Duke of Bedford; while Owen, who was a monk of Westminster, and Katherine, his sister, died young.

Owen Tudor was then sent to prison at Newgate, where he remained some time; but at last, aided by his confessor and his servant, he made his escape. But, while endeavouring to gain an interview with his children, he was recaptured in Wallingford Castle, and was once more sent to Newgate.

Then came the Wars of the Roses.

By this time Owen Tudor appears to have been released, and joined the king, who, with his half-brothers Edmund and Jasper, donning the Red Rose of Lancaster, went forth to oppose the White Rose of York.

Owen, forgetting the old slights and injuries he had sustained, fought bravely for his stepson the king.

In 1460 Owen, as prisoner of war, was sent by the White Rose faction to Newport Castle, Monmouthshire.

Hearing of their countryman's imprisonment, friends of old in North Wales were determined to liberate the Rose of Mona, or to perish in the effort, and this was the last rescue in the cause of Welsh nationalism.

The people of North Wales wore the Red Rose, those of the South favoured the White.

Led by homely but heroic John ap Meredith,

aided by Hywel ap Llewelyn, one hundred gentlemen of Wales, many of them sons of Snowdon, rode rapidly all the weary way from the north to Monmouthshire.

Nothing daunted, they proceeded to Newport Castle, and were successful in their efforts for the release of Owen, which was quickly effected. But on their way from Newport, homeward, they were intercepted by some soldiers of the White Rose, more than double in number than the gallant Welshmen, who, in a daring attack, broke through the ranks, and proceeded on their journey.

It does not appear that Owen received any injury, but ponderous John ap Meredith was slightly wounded, and ever afterwards his friends called him the "Squire y Grath," Squire of the Scar.

Not long after his release, in 1460, Owen was knighted by his stepson, the king, who made him Ranger of the parks and forests of the lordships of Denbigh, the "woodwardship" of which was awarded to him by the Government as a "gift of the Crown."

Henry the Sixth is said to have done this because it was necessary to win Wales to his side.

In 1461 the celebrated battle of Mortimer's Cross, near Ludlow, was fought, in which the White Rose won, and the Red Rose lost. Jasper

Tudor, who at Queen Margaret's command led the forces against the rival army, escaped, but his father, heroic Owen, was taken prisoner, with Morgan ap Rhydderch, Davydd Lloyd, and other Welshmen to Hereford, and were there executed by order of the Earl of March, who was afterwards crowned as Edward IV.

Jasper Tudor, with his nephew, the young Earl Henry of Richmond, went to Pembroke, and, after placing the town in the custody of Sir John Scudamore, embarked at Tenby for Brittany.

Edmund Tudor married Margaret, granddaughter of John of Gaunt, the second son of Edward III., and their son, Henry, Earl of Richmond, who became King of England, was of royal lineage.

When the great Duke of Buckingham, and Morton, Bishop of Ely, with others, conspired to dethrone Richard the Third, and invite the grandson of Owen Tudor to accept the crown, a meeting was held at Brocon, where a large army of Welshmen assembled.

At this time Henry Tudor, Earl of Richmond, who is described as being below the middle stature, with fair complexion, grey eyes, and golden hair, was about thirty years of age, and lived in Vannes, Brittany, among the Brétons, descendants of those British emigrées to Armorica long centuries before.

The Bishop of Ely went to Vannes after the conference at Brecon, and persuaded Henry Tudor to accept the crown.

English history supplies the sequel.

In 1485 Henry Tudor, with his uncle Jasper, Earl of Pembroke, landed at Milford Haven, and proceeded to Carew Castle, where his country-men, the valiant and enthusiastic Welsh, met him.

To them it seemed that after long waiting, the real *Mab-y-Darogan*, the "heir of the pro-phecy," had come, and as such was welcomed by the poet Lord of Mathafran, who patriotically and eloquently reminded Henry Tudor of the old and often repeated story which promised the return of the line of Brutus to Britain.

First and foremost of the many who raptur-ously greeted Henry Tudor was Rhys ap Thomas, of Carew Castle, Newcastle, and Abermarlais.

There he stood, the illustrious representative of the ancient Welsh princes, and of Rhys ap Tewdwr, who fell at Hirwain, with thousands of Welshmen at his command, and a good will to use the sword for the grandson of the Rose of Mona.

A right valiant man was Rhys ap Thomas, who, in a letter dated "Carmarthen Castle, 1484," told Richard III. that "whoever ill affected to the State, should dare to land in those parts of Wales, where he had any employment under His

Majesty, must resolve with himself to make his entrance and irruption over his body."

To make good his word, tradition says that when Henry Tudor came to Carew Castle, Rhys ap Thomas stood under a bridge while the future King of England rode over it.

Rhys ap Thomas arranged to lead his Welshmen through Breconshire to Shrewsbury, while Henry Tudor took his Frenchmen through Cardigan to the same rendezvous.

Henry was accompanied by Richard Griffith, John Morgan, Arnold Butler, Sir George Talbot, the Earl of Shrewsbury, Sir William Stanley Lord of Bromfield, and others. In the "Memoir" of Rhys ap Thomas,—written in the reign of James I, and which afterwards appeared in the first volume of the *Cambrian Register*—it is stated that the French troops attending Henry Tudor "wanted both necessary furniture of arms and other munition, besides that they were very raw and ignorant in shooting, handling of their weapons, and discharging the ordinary duty of soldiers," and the Lord of Carew Castle had to furnish them " with all such things as he could spare, without the damage of his own particular, though in heart, he wished them back again in France, there being not one man of quality among them to endear future ages to make mention either of his name or service."

At Llwyn - Dafydd, Cardiganshire, Henry

Tudor was entertained by Davydd ap Ieuan; while Einion ap Davydd Llewelyn was the Earl's host at Wern Newydd in Llanarth. The army then proceeded via Brecon to Shrewsbury, and thence to Bosworth, where, on August the 21st, 1485, Richard the Third was slain, and the Earl of Richmond was proclaimed as King Henry the Seventh.

Rhys ap Thomas, the celebrated Welsh supporter of Henry Tudor, was directly descended from Urien Rheged of Arthur's days. He was born at Abermarlais Castle, Carmarthenshire, in 1451, and his father, like most intelligent men of that period, used to consult astrologers with reference to the aspects of the heavens upon all auspicious occasions.

When the astrologer said that the positions of the stars at the time of Rhy's birth were in their chief dignities, with Jupiter, in exaltation, Mercury in good aspect and fortified, and Saturn cadent, the father was highly gratified, and looked forward to his son's future with great expectation.

In view of this, Thomas ap Gruffydd of Abermarlais placed his infant son Rhys in the care of Dr. Lewis, a learned man of North Wales, and one who had travelled much, but studied more in the grand old University of Padua. Rhys remained with Dr. Lewis for some years, and then accompanied his father, who, owing to the turbulent state of the Principality, settled in Burgundy, and became a favourite of Philip the Good. Ultimately, after an affair of honour, Thomas ap Gruffydd found it necessary to return to Wales, where he was assassinated. Soon after his death, Morgan and Thomas, the sons of the lord of Abermarlais, fell in one of those unhappy domestic frays for which Wales was notorious.

Rhys while in Burgundy won golden opinions at Court and elsewhere, and was singularly celebrated for his skill in the equestrian and athletic exercises of the period. Philip the Good selected Rhys as a companion for his only son, and offered him the command of a troop of horse, but the young Welshman declined it on account of his inexperience. Rhys had rapidly risen from his position as a private soldier to the rank of Captain, and would have attained higher honours were it not for his father's flight and return to Wales. Rhys succeeded to his patrimony after the untimely death of his brothers, and his first act was, with the help of his advisers, to obtain a reconciliation with Henry ap Gwilym of Court Henry, Carmarthenshire, between whom and Thomas ap Gruffydd of Abermarlais deeply-rooted enmity had long existed. The attempt was successful, and Rhys soon afterwards married Eva, the daughter and co-heiress of his father's foe.

In the quaint old memoir already mentioned, it is stated that after his marriage Rhys ap Thomas devoted himself to his people, and patrimony, and "the gentry did continually flock to his house, as to some academy, for their civil nurture and education; by which means his house was so much frequented, and he so well attended, that, whenever he came, in respect of the greatness of his train, he bare shew rather of a prince than a private subject." At the same time the biographer adds, "his hospitality no way abated or diminished, shewing the middle way between base avarice and vicious prodigality."

Furthermore, says the same authority, "Because by conversation, familiarity is increased, and courtesy engendered," Rhys and his advisers, in imitation of the ancient law-makers, instituted certain festival days, to the end that men should assemble together, or entertain public sports; and places of meeting were appointed, and summer houses erected, where the women, with dancing and other allowable recreations, passed the time, and the men exercised all manly actions, as running, quoiting, leaping, wrestling, and the like; among whom this young Rhys ever made one, not refusing sometimes to decline his gravity, and to dance among his neighbours, but that was seldom, and then, too, with a decent and comely behaviour."

Thus Rhys ap Thomas—whose landed possessions were the most extensive in South Wales—
appears as a wise-minded social reformer at a
time when the *prolétaire* had greatly degenerated,
and trivial disputes were settled by means of
hand-to-hand encounters.

In addition to this, he was able at a moment's
command to secure the voluntary service of four
or five thousand horse, and that rendered him
one whom to claim as a friend, was of the greatest
advantage, while as a foe he would be exceedingly dangerous.

When first approached on the subject of de-
throning Richard the Third, Rhys was too loyal
to the reigning monarch to enter into any
schemes for his downfall. Besides which, had he
not promised in the Carmarthen letter to be
faithful to the King and State? But, when
Henry Tudor had gained the voice of the people,
and especially of the Welsh, Rhys felt that
private welfare should be subservient to the interests of the people. He then threw all his
energies into the popular cause, with the result
already described.

After the battle of Bosworth, Henry the
Seventh knighted his brave and faithful supporter, whose services had been so valuable.

Sir Rhys was also the recipient of many
honours.

He was appointed King's Justiciary and Chief

Governor in South Wales, Chamberlain of the shires of Carmarthen and Cardigan, Constable and Lieutenant of Brecon, and Seneschal of Builth.

In the exercise of his important duties, Sir Rhys was a peace-maker, and his biographer says that when obliged on rare occasions to have recourse to the extreme penalty of the law, he always pronounced sentence of death, *voce magis leniter severâ quam rabidâ.*

After two years of comparative quiet in Wales, Sir Rhys was called by the King to assist in suppressing the insurrection on behalf of Lambert Simnel, and to take part in the battle of Stoke, where the Welsh hero and social reformer was wounded.

Later on he appeared at the head of fifteen hundred horse at Blackheath, on June the 22nd, 1497, when the King led his army against Perkin Warbeck. In that battle he was thoroughly fearless and intrepid. Two horses which he had ridden fell under him, whereupon he mounted his favourite charger, "Llwyd y Bacsau," who had borne him through Bosworth, and, after charging against Lord Audley, the leader of the rebels, took him prisoner. For this, says his biographer, "the king gave him by way of reward the goods of the said lord, and withal, for his more honour, created him a banneret on the field, having then many wounds about him."

In 1506 the King bestowed upon him the lordship of Narberth, in Pembrokeshire, and the Order of the Garter. With reference to these honours, Fuller in his "Worthies" says, "The thrifty king, according to his cheap course of remuneration (rewarding churchmen with church preferment, and soldiers with honour), afterwards made him a knight of the order; and well might he give him a garter, by whose effectual help he had recovered a crown."

Sir Rhys was not an advocate for hereditary titles.

When Henry the Seventh offered him a peerage, he declined the honour, on the ground that he was satisfied with a simple knighthood, and if his descendants desired any higher dignity, they must exert themselves to obtain it.

To the end of his life Sir Rhys remained a loyal subject of the king, and, when Henry the Eighth ascended the throne, the faithful knight was confirmed in his appointments and honours. He accompanied the new monarch in his campaign in France, and fought valiantly in the battle of Therouenne, and the siege of Tournay, after which he returned to Wales, and lived chiefly at Carew Castle, where in 1527 he died at the age of seventy-six, and was buried in St. Peter's Church, Carmarthen.

It appears strange that the memory of this patriotic knight had not sufficient influence over

Henry the Eighth to prevent him executing the
grandson of Sir Rhys ap Thomas for assuming
the name of Fitzurien, which, say the historians,
the English king regarded as an indication of an
attempt to gain the sovereignty of Wales.

This ancient family is now represented by
Lord Dynevor, of Dynevor Castle, Llandilo,
Carmarthenshire.

During the lifetime of Sir Rhys ap Thomas
the relations between the Welsh and the English began to be more cordial, and of this period
the ancient chronicle states:—" King *Henry*
the Seventh being by his grandfather, *Owen
Tudor*, descended out of *Wales*, and having
sufficiently experienced the Affection of the
Welch towards him; first of those, who, upon
his first landing, opportunely joyned him, under
Sir *Rhys ap Thomas*, and then of those who,
under the command of Sir *William Stanley*,
Lord of *Bromfield*, *Yale* and *Chirkland*, aided
him in *Bosworth*-Field; could not in Honour
and Equity but bear some regard to the miserable state and condition of the *Welch* under the
English Government. And therefore this prudent Prince, finding the Calamities of the *Welch*
to be insupportable, and seeing what grievous
and unmerciful Laws were enacted against them
by his Predecessours, he took occasion to redress
and reform the same, and granted to the *Welch*
a Charter of Liberty and Immunity, whereby

they were released from the cruel Oppression which since their Subjection to the *English* Government they had most cruelly sustained. And seeing the Birth and Quality of his grandfather *Owen Tudor* was called in question, and that he was by many upbraided of being of a mean and ignoble Parentage; King *Henry* directed a Commission to the Abbot of *Lhan Egwest*, Dr. *Owen Pool*, Canon of *Hereford*, and *John King* Herald at Arms, to make inquisition concerning the Pedigree of the said *Owen;* who coming to *Wales* made a diligent enquiry into this matter; and, by the assistance of Sir *John Leyaf, Guttyn Owen, Bardh, Gruffyth ap Llewelyn ap Efan Fychan*, and others, in the consultation of the *British* Books of Pedegrees, they drew up an exact Genealogy of *Owen Tudor,* which, upon their return, they presented to the King."

The heading of the document runs thus :—

" *The return of a* Commission *sent into* Wales *by King* Henry *the Seventh, to search out the Pedigrees of* Owen Tudor.

" Henry the Seventh, King of *England*, &c.; Son of *Edmund* Earl of *Richmond* Son of *Owen ap Meredith*, and of Queen *Catherine* his Wife Daughter to *Charles* the Sixth King of *France*, &c."

The conclusion is signed in the following way :—

"*Abstracted out of the old Chronicles of* WALES *by Sir* JOHN LEIAF *Priest,* GUTTIN OWEN, GRUFFYDH AP LLEWELYN AP JERMY FYCHAN, MADAWC AP LLEWELYN AP HOWELL, ROBERT AP HOWELL AP THOMAS, JOHN KING, *with many others at the King's Majesty's Costs and Charges, The Abbot of* LLANGEWESTLE *and Dr.* OWEN POOL, *Canon of* HARF, *Overseers.*"

The old chronicle continues :—" King *Henry* the Seventh had already abrogated those unreasonable and intollerable Laws, which the former Kings of *England*, particularly *Henry* the Fourth, had made against the Welch ; and now, King Henry the Eighth, wishing to make a plenary Reformation of what his Father had wisely begun, thought it necessary towards the Good and Tranquillity of both Nations, to make the *Welch* subject to the same laws, and the same Government with the *English*. He understood that the usual Hostilities and Depredations were still continued and kept up by both sides upon the Borders ; and though his Father had eased the Yoak of the *Welch*, yet he perceived, that it did contribute but little towards the disannulling of that inveterate and implacable Envy and Animosity which raged in the Marches. Therefore to remedy this, otherwise unavoidable, Distemper, he concluded that it was the only effectual Method, to incorporate the *Welch* with the *English* ; that they being subject to the same Laws, might equally fear the Violation of them. And accordingly, in the Twenty-Seventh Year of his Reign, A.D. 1536, an Act of Parliament passed to that purpose, which together with another Act in the Thirty-Fifth of his Reign, made a plenary Incorporatian of the *Welch* with the *English*, which Union has had that blessed Effect, that it has dispelled all those unnatural differences which heretofore were so rife and irreconcilable."

Sir Rhys ap Thomas did not live long enough to see the final union of England and Wales, but his name remains as a link connecting the illustrious Welsh princes and heroic people of the past with their patriotic representatives of to-day, who are loyal and affectionate defenders of their liberty, conscience, and law.

INDEX

THE END